# The Big
# Revelation

# The Biochar
# Revolution

## Transforming Agriculture & Environment

### CONTRIBUTING AUTHORS

| | |
|---|---|
| Paul Anderson, PhD | Hugh McLaughlin, PhD |
| Albert Bates | Daniel Mulqueen |
| Karl Frogner, PhD | Robert Quirk |
| Peter Hirst | Ben Rose, BSc |
| Stephen Joseph, PhD | Karen Siepen |
| James Joyce, PhD | Christoph Steiner, PhD |
| Jonah Levine | Paul Taylor, PhD |
| Julie Major, PhD | Bob Wells |
| Jim Mason | Kelpie Wilson |

### CONTRIBUTING EDITORS

| | |
|---|---|
| Paul Taylor, PhD | John Lierman |
| Gary Levi | Ron Taylor |

## Edited by Paul Taylor PhD

FIRST EDITION 2010

Copyright 2010 Global Publishing Group

National Library of Australia
Cataloguing–in–Publishing entry:

Taylor, Paul, 1945–
The Biochar Revolution: Transforming Agriculture & Environment.

1st ed.
ISBN: 978 1. 921630 41 5 (pbk.)

1. Ashes as fertilizer.  2. Carbon sequestration. 3. Charcoal.
4. Soil amendments

631.4

GLOBAL
PUBLISHING
G R O U P

Published by Global Publishing Group
PO Box 517, Mt. Evelyn, Victoria 3796
email: info@globalpublishinggroup.com.au

For further information about orders:
Phone: +61 3 9736 1156
Email: info@GlobalPublishingGroup.com.au
Website: www.GlobalPublishingGroup.com.au

# ACKNOWLEDGEMENTS

I am grateful for the interest, support, patience, and effort expressed consistently—yet in unique ways—by each and every author, as we went though many revisions together. They are listed in the front of the book, with their bios in the back, under contributing authors.

I owe special thanks to Hugh McLaughlin and Paul Anderson for their belief, interest, advice and support in the book as a whole. Both read, and offered valuable editing suggestions on, diverse chapters. Hugh reviewed most of the final manuscript.

Gary Levi played a crucial role as chief editor and editorial advisor. He edited every chapter numerous times, and stayed with the project as it extended from 5 weeks to 5 months, working generously and meticulously to shape and organize the book. He was especially attuned to those new to biochar, helping us strike a balance between technical science, passionate advocacy, and readability. I also appreciate the editorial assistance of John Lierman.

The book would not exist without the faith and end-to-end support of my brother, Ron Taylor. He funded the publishing and editing of the book, contributed to assembling the manuscript, and set up the back-end websites to promote the book and our goal to raise awareness about biochar systems.

I thank Global Publishing Group and their staff for accommodating the extended timeline of the book.

I am also indebted to John Seed of the Rain Forest Information Center and to Artists Project Earth (APE). My interest in biochar focused on the backyard and small-farm scale, when John applied for and received a grant from APE. This initiated "Project 540: Low-emission, low cost biochar kilns for small farms and villages"—and involved me with Geoff Moxham in researching kiln design.

In the midst of our collaboration, Geoff suffered a fatal accident in his beloved rainforest near his home. Whenever I make or demonstrate small-scale biochar, I am following Geoff's enthusiastic, enlightened lead. His spirit has inspired this book, and I dedicate it to him (see page 348).

I am more than grateful for the unstinting support of my partner in life, Renate Kraus. She allowed me months of long days with limited distraction to focus on the book. In February 2010, seeing me immobilized by the heat and humidity of the tropical Australian summer, yet with a first deadline to finish the book by early May, she pushed me to reach out to potential authors. And behold—it worked!

The support and synchronicities for this book come from the magic of our relationship, the goodwill and enthusiasm of the biochar community, and the importance of biochar itself for the well-being of our planet.

Paul Taylor,
Mount Warning, NSW

# FREE BONUSES

www.TheBiocharRevolution.com

The book has a website, which is listed at the bottom of the left-hand pages throughout the book. Readers are encouraged to visit the website and use it as an additional resource.

The web version of the book will:

- Have images and charts in full color.
- Allow book-wide searches to quickly find material you seek.
- Have hyperlinks to instantly access reference material.

The website will also be updated to keep pace with this fast-moving field.

Access to the resource material on the website is restricted to owners of this book. All owners are encouraged to visit the site and register using the access code shown below.

You will need to enter this code the first time you access the material to register yourself as a book owner. After that you will need only your own user name and password.

Please enjoy this additional benefit as an owner of *The Biochar Revolution*.

**Enter This Code for your FREE Bonus**

Your access code: 716B4J

# www.TheBiocharRevolution.com

# Contents

# FOREWORD

Dr. Tim Flannery
Professor, Macquarie University
Sydney, Australia
Australian of the Year

I've often said that biochar may represent the single most important initiative for humanity's environmental future. This statement is consciously broad, and speaks to the simple truth that climate change is real and it's happening.

However, this statement may not be broad enough. Even if climate change could be arrested tomorrow, the world's population is growing faster than our capacity to feed it.

This book shows how, through small-scale individual steps through larger-scale approaches, biochar can play a key role in achieving more productive, sustainable, and environmentally beneficial agriculture. And justifies expanding my initial statement:

Biochar may represent the single most important initiative

for humanity's environmental *and agricultural* future.

Technically, biochar science is complex and evolving but its essence, as explained within these pages, is straightforward. If you heat almost any biological material to a certain temperature, and restrict or exclude oxygen, a process called pyrolysis occurs. The material changes form and you get two very useful end-products: charcoal and synthetic gas. The synthetic gas can be used in the same way as other fuels, including generating electricity.

The charcoal end-product has remarkable qualities and is the main focus of this work. When added to soil, the charcoal is called biochar. Biochar amends and improves the soil for the long term. Studies have proved that properly applied biochar improves crop yields.

At the same time, biochar in the soil sequesters carbon from the atmosphere for hundreds, perhaps thousands of years. This actively draws down atmospheric carbon and can help repair our global carbon debt.

This book articulates how producing and applying biochar can transform abundant, readily available biomass usually considered waste—the crop waste left rotting in the field after harvest, fallen limbs in a forest—into a renewable, environmentally friendly resource.

Here, we learn that these benefits are well within reach. The technologies for producing biochar already exist, and have been in use for centuries, dating back to the ancient Amazon basin. Those technologies have decidedly low-tech roots, and therefore may be globally adaptable.

For all of these reasons, biochar has profound potential. It can be a key part of the solution to the daunting, interlaced challenges we face, because above all other options offered to date, biochar represents a practical, scalable approach that can address those challenges *simultaneously*.

What about the title, *The Biochar Revolution?* The title is apt: it reflects that revolutionary change is needed—because we simply don't have time to wait for evolutionary change. In a very real sense, the predicate for the biochar solution is a biochar *revolution*.

On the other hand, despite the word "revolution," this is not a political or philosophical screed, aloof from garden and field. It is by design and execution a compendium of historical, scientific, and practical how-to information, flavored with inspiring personal histories, from a diverse community of contributors.

More pointedly, because biochar-making techniques are readily accessible to everyone, and the need is so pressing, this book shows concretely how all of us, in our own gardens and in our own communities, can contribute and help make a genuine difference *now*—"from the ground up"—without having to wait for our governments and institutions to fully mobilize. Those interested can try making their own biochar and by sharing their results, add valuable data to the worldwide knowledge base. Others can make an impact by participating in community biochar initiatives.

These messages in this book cannot be repeated enough. If it finds wide enough readership, and if enough people at the grass roots—literally and figuratively—take some of the small, easy steps outlined here, the cumulative power of the many will lever dramatic, sustainable, and *revolutionary* change for us all.

Tim Flannery
Sydney, Australia
September 2010

# PREFACE

Paul Taylor, Editor

Welcome to *The Biochar Revolution*.

In this ambitious book, we offer a compendium of material designed to inform and engage the spectrum of people interested in biochar. We embrace those who have never heard of it, as well as gardeners and farmers (small and large); ardent advocates pressing for global change; researchers and scientists working toward creative solutions; government agencies and decision makers in developed and developing countries seeking viable policy pathways; and entrepreneurs intrigued by new business opportunities from the ascending biochar phenomenon.

The book works "from the ground up." First are current global context, fundamental definitions, history, and science, much of it woven into personal stories. Those fundamentals are reiterated in context throughout the book to remind and refresh the reader. Next come more in-depth biochar science production, and practice. The last part of the book draws on and pulls together the previous material, offering large-canvas concepts on how biochar can profoundly impact the planet.

The "ground up" progression is also followed by starting with proactive individuals on up to households, communities, and utility-scale concepts. Small-scale, low-tech biochar production precedes large-scale, high-tech production.

## HOW THE BOOK IS ORGANIZED

The book consists of twenty chapters contributed by eighteen authors from various disciplines, organized into five parts.

### Part I   Ancient Origins, Modern Inspirations

This part contains five chapters, starting with an overview of the current and historical context for biochar and its benefits. The next four chapters offer inspiring and engaging personal stories from entrepreneurs, community builders, and farmers who discovered biochar and changed their lives.

### Part II   Understanding Biochar

Here are three chapters that help explain what biochar is, how it helps the soil, and how to characterize it before applying it to the soil. The last chapter contains step-by-step instructions for methods that can be applied at home to test properties of the biochar you make or purchase.

### Part III   Producing Biochar

Part III consists of five chapters on production that follow the previously noted progression from small-scale, low-tech, backyard production that can be done with recycled cans and drums, through modest-scale production methods applicable to the community garden or small farm, up to commercial scale.

A caveat on production: the authors provide outlines, concepts, or their own experience rather than instruction manuals. Use this as a basis to begin your own online research to find the most suitable, cleanest method for you. Take responsibility for your own safety and adherence to local codes.

## Part IV Testing, Conditioning, and Using Biochar

The three chapters in Part IV cover the important subjects of biochar testing, conditioning, and application to the soil. The last chapter offers insights on the methods for using biochar in mixtures and complexes—all relevant for your own experiments.

## Part V Changing the World

Part V consists of four chapters. It begins with a chapter explaining the limitations of the synthetic fertilizer-driven "green revolution" over the last 50 years, the dire need for a greener revolution, and how biochar can be integral to the solution.

Building on these themes, the other three chapters in Part V address specific applications of biochar that could produce material benefits ranging from widespread, small-scale, low-tech application in the developing world, through the potential for medium-scale application on millions of sugar cane farms worldwide, to large-scale biomass pyrolysis for simultaneously producing biochar and generating electricity.

## OUR EDITING APPROACH

In editing this work, we have attempted to preserve the authors' own voices and idioms. The authors contribute a variety of opinions and approaches, based on their experience and philosophies, in a field where the rules, methods, and science are still being defined.

The reader is encouraged to dive in and read the entire book, or to browse through chapters of interest before embarking on their own experiments. And even then, we encourage further exploration of the references given and internet research. We particularly encourage and invite visits to the book's website, www.TheBiocharRevolution.com. The website will provide useful supplemental information and updates.

## HELPING THE READER

We have used a variety of devices to help the reader:

- Each chapter begins with a brief overview of the topics you will learn about in that chapter. If you are a shotgun reader, this will help you navigate.

- Many chapters end with a bulleted list of key points to take away.

- The first time a technical word appears in a substantive portion of a chapter, it appears in **bold-face type**. This indicates that a brief definition can be found in the Glossary, except when the occasional word or phrase is bolded for emphasis rather than definition.

- For some bolded, technical words look for text boxes nearby called "Definitions for Non-Scientists."

- Some chapters contain text boxes of various other types: quotes (highlighting an interesting or key point of the author); asides (interesting, but not quite a part of the main text flow); technical boxes (more technical material for optional reading); instructions or "@Home Biochar" (helpful instructions for a particular procedure to be used in your own workshop or yard); additional reading; and tips.

- Occasional editorial comments are inserted [in square brackets].

Author and editor pictures and brief bios, most with email addresses, are located in the back of the book.

## BIOCHAR TERMINOLOGY

Because the following chapters have been written independently, it will be helpful to introduce some basic terminology. Pyrolysis of biomass to produce biochar is central to the subject of biochar, so here are some terms to get you started.

**Pyrolysis** refers to the breakdown of biomass when heated into solid charcoal, gases, and liquids.

**Biomass** refers to living or once living material. In this book it will usually mean plant material such as wood or crop wastes, although other biological materials, such as manure, can be pyrolyzed to produce biochar.

The solid residue from pyrolysis is given various names, depending on how it is produced, its components and qualities, and its intended use:

*Char* is a general term for the solid product arising from decomposition of any organic material, such as from forest fire.

*Charcoal* typically refers to carbon-rich material produced in traditional or modern charcoal kilns and generally intended as a fuel.

*Biochar* is a new term for charcoal that is intended for application to soils as a soil amendment and/or carbon sequestration.

*Black carbon* is a general term encompassing all carbon-rich solid residues from fire or heat, including char, soot, and graphite.

Sometimes an author will use the term char, black carbon, or charcoal even when the material is intended for soil (biochar) because the more general term suits the context (such as in discussing charcoal production methods for making biochar).

## STYLE AND UNITS OF MEASURE

The book is written in U.S. English. With five Australian authors, and with scientists' propensity to use the metric system, both metric and U.S. units occur in the text. In order to preserve reading flow, translations are made only occasionally. Since generally the quantities cited in the text are approximate, the following on-the-fly conversions can be kept in mind, or referred to (with more accurate conversion in parentheses):

1 inch = 2.5 cm (2.54)     1 foot = 30 cm (30.5)     1 mile = 1.5 km (1.6 km)

1 hectare (ha) = 2.5 acres  1 square meter = 10 sq ft (10.8)  = 1 sq yard (1.2)

1 US gal = 4 liters (3.78)    1 cu m = 35 cu ft = 1 cu yard (1.3)

1 kg = 2 pounds (lbs)  (2.2)

Generally, "ton" is used as a unit of measure for large weights (of biomass, etc.). All the following units of measure should be considered interchangeable for the approximate precision intended in this book:

1 tonne = 1 metric ton = 1,000 kg = approximately 1 long ton (UK) = 2240 lbs

In the United States and Canada, 1 ton = 1 short ton = 2,000 lbs

°C =°F  |  100 = 212 | 300 = 572 | 400 = 752 | 500 = 932 | 600 = 1112

## FINAL THOUGHTS

The book mirrors the nascent biochar movement: a diverse, steadily growing community of home gardeners, farmers, scientists, environmentalists, and entrepreneurs, all with different lenses. As in any large community, there is a measure of disagreement about terminology, about science, about results. In the biochar community much is new—or new again—evolving, and unsettled.

While much of the book's content may not be considered scientifically rigorous or exact, pains have been taken to preserve overall scientific integrity.

This book does have an ambitious reach. We have sought to offer a representative spectrum of contributions, and to make them sufficiently readable, so that readers with many backgrounds and intentions will find something, hopefully much, within these covers that will resonate—and that they can use now and over time.

Despite the myriad voices of those contributions, a single truth comes clear: there is ample room for all in this tent. No matter the lens, and no matter the motivation, the biochar community rows toward an overarching, greater good: healing the planet, and helping it sustain and feed us.

Paul Taylor, PhD
Mount Warning, Australia
September 2010

# Part I
## Ancient Origins, Modern Inspirations

"Carbon sequestration in soil also has significant potential. Biochar, produced in pyrolysis of residues from crops, forestry, and animal wastes, can be used to restore soil fertility while storing carbon for centuries to millennia. Biochar helps soil retain nutrients and fertilizers, reducing emissions of GHGs such as $N_2O$." —*James Hanson*

Chapter 1

# BIOCHAR
## Ancient Origins, Modern Solution

Paul Taylor, PhD

Biochar Consultant,
biocharbooks.org

**IN THIS CHAPTER YOU WILL LEARN:**

- How an intertwining host of problems—and harmful "solutions"—have compromised our planet.

- The instructive history of biochar as ancient technology, and how that technology can be adapted and used today.

- The interlinking soil-enhancing and environmental benefits of biochar.

"These problems–of our own making–are complex, proliferating, and alarming. But a surprisingly simple potential solution to a broad range of problems, a solution built on ancient knowledge, is within reach. In order to look forward to that solution, we must first look back to its origins."

# WHAT IS BIOCHAR?

When I say I am involved with biochar, I usually get a blank stare and a question: "What is biochar?" This book will answer that question...and many others.

Right up front, and in the simplest terms, biochar is charcoal produced for mixing into soil. Yes, charcoal—the carbon-rich material made from heating wood or other plant material in an oxygen-deprived atmosphere. As a soil additive, biochar offers numerous potential benefits. Those benefits are detailed in this book but simply summarized, biochar increases the capacity for soil to hold nutrients, enhances crop yields, and captures and stores carbon for the long term.

This introduction will outline the promise biochar holds for rescuing our compromised planet, leaving the detailed exploration to the chapters ahead.

## PAST IS PROLOGUE

As a teenager growing up in Australia in the early 1960s, I often thought of the folly and injustice of wastefully burning up our fossil carbon without a passing thought about the needs of future generations—and when other alternatives were apparent. One of my concerns, emerging from my formal training in physics, was that we would inevitably heat the planet in our rush to inefficiently and mindlessly consume energy, while in the process taking the planet's stored fossil carbon out of the ground and putting it back into the atmosphere.

Since that time, in the fifty years from 1960 to 2010, humans have consumed 280 billion tons of fossil fuel, and converted it to about 1 trillion tons of carbon dioxide ($CO_2$). Over 40% of that $CO_2$ has stayed in the atmosphere and about half of the balance has been absorbed into the oceans.[1] Excess $CO_2$ is a problem: in the atmosphere it acts as a **greenhouse gas**, trapping infrared radiation, inhibiting the earth from shedding solar heat, and therefore causing the planet to warm.[2] Excess $CO_2$ in the oceans changes their chemistry, making them more acidic, and threatening their living web.[3]

The ultimate outcome of this human-created condition will be determined by the interactions of numerous interconnecting feedbacks. However, accumulating understanding in science and planetary history indicate that most of those feedbacks are unfavorable, and will amplify the ominous repercussions.

## INTERTWINING PROBLEMS

As serious as they are, climate change and ocean acidification are not the only problems generated by the human footprint on the planet. In 2002, World Bank economist Jean-François Rischard identified 20 global issues that, if not addressed and on the way to resolution by 2020 will have drastic negative effects on the fate of our planet and civilization well into the future.[4] Rischard divided those issues into environmental (such as climate change, soil degradation and loss, and deforestation), social (such as poverty and over population), and regulatory (such as taxation, international labor, and migration).

These problems are laden with unfortunate consequences—and worse yet, they intertwine and reverberate:

- Deforestation, by decreasing the uptake of carbon dioxide and increasing its release into the atmosphere, accelerates global warming. Global warming stresses forests, changes their relationship with destructive pests, and increases the incidence and extent of fires. This feeds back and further amplifies global warming in a vicious cycle.

- Organized efforts to deal with social issues (such as poverty) are undermined by food and water shortages, disasters and dislocations. Yet if people cannot meet basic subsistence needs, they will have little ability or incentive to participate in solving worldwide population and environmental problems.

- Sustainability issues cannot be resolved without a consensus among nations to reinvent their tax schemes to internalize the costs of, and thus transform, unsustainable practices. However, prospects for global regulatory agreements recede as worsening physical and fiscal environments impel political expedience —and obstruct long-term political vision.

Attempts at solutions also intertwine and undermine our attempts to extricate ourselves.

- Solving climate change and peak oil (declining production with increasing demand), requires us to rapidly install vast new infrastructures for energy supply, housing, transport, and food production and delivery that use less fossil fuel and cause fewer emissions. But building these new infrastructures requires massive quantities of fossil energy and capital—and the climate and financial impacts will soon be unaffordable.

- Wealthy nations resist agreements to mitigate past and future greenhouse gas emissions, which cause damaging climate change, unless developing and undeveloped nations sign on. Yet understandably, those nations want their own chance to develop and expect wealthy nations to take fair responsibility for their past emissions—which, after all, are the prime cause of the current pressures.

- Chapter 17 of this book, "The Greener Revolution," describes the impending crisis in agriculture and the environment. That crisis, set in motion by past unsustainable practices and spiraling populations, is now magnified by a rush to biofuels (corn-based ethanol and palm oil), spawned by increased political awareness about global warming and limited petroleum. We use fossil fuel to grow our food, and now there is a headlong push to use food to make our fuel. This shortsighted "solution" is already having negative consequences on food prices and availability, as well as on the environment and species diversity.

These problems—of our own making—are complex, proliferating, and alarming. But a surprisingly simple potential solution to a broad range of problems, a solution built on ancient knowledge, is well within reach. More specifically, biochar represents a rare technological intervention into nature that, if done carefully, could have beneficial feedbacks rather than vicious ones. In order to look forward to that solution, we must first look back to its origins.

## HISTORICAL CONTEXT: ANCIENT ROOTS, BENEFICIAL TECHNOLOGY

I first became aware of biochar from the 2002 BBC documentary "The Secret of El Dorado." In 1542 the scribe of Francisco de Orellana, drifting with him down a tributary of the Amazon wrote: "...there could be seen very large cities that glistened in white...many roads that entered into the interior...and besides this, the land is as fertile...as our Spain." When the Spaniards returned 50 years later, they found only a few scattered settlements (the aboriginal people having been decimated by diseases the Spaniards introduced)—and Orellana's report was relegated to myth.

Conventional wisdom held that the typically infertile Amazon soil could never have supported large populations, and therefore these "cities" could not have existed. Betty J. Meggers, the Smithsonian archaeologist, said, "The apparent lushness of the rainforest is a sham. The soils are poor and can't hold nutrients—the jungle flora exists only because it snatches up everything worthwhile before it leaches away in the rain. Agriculture, which depends on extracting the wealth of the soil, therefore faces inherent ecological limitations in the wet desert of Amazonia."[5]

Conventional wisdom has shifted. It has become increasingly clear that the ancient peoples of the Amazon compensated for nature's limitations, leaving an enduring legacy of rich soils, known as *terra preta de Indio* (Indian black earth). In fact, their agriculture methods were *adding* wealth to the soil, not "extracting" it. This phenomenon may have profound impact for the future of agriculture (a concept further developed in Chapter 17). Modern awareness and understanding of *terra preta* and its remarkable traits have evolved only gradually, over centuries, but with dramatic acceleration this decade, as outlined in "A Biochar Timeline" following this chapter.

*Terra preta* is found in or near those sites where the Amazon Indians had established long-term villages. As such, it is a midden soil: its link to prehistoric settlement is evidenced by a liberal sprinkling of artifacts, including ceramic shards and animal bones. A less rich, brown earth, called *terra mulata*, is much more extensive; it generally surrounds the village sites where the *terra preta* is found, and contains few or no artifacts. Although the precise origins of *terra mulata* are unclear, evidence suggests that it may have resulted from relatively intensive, purposeful cultivation over extended time periods.

Both of these Amazonian dark earths, up to 2 meters deep, are darker and more fertile than the surrounding soil, which is—as Betty Meggers declared—highly weathered and poor (see Figure 1.1, left and middle photos).

*Terra preta* soils have generally retained their fertility to the present day, and the rich soil is even excavated and sold as potting soil (Figure 1.1, right photo). Their durable fertility is attributed to their high black carbon (biochar) content, which has been scientifically dated as far back as 450 to 8,000 B.C. (Chapter 7 details how biochar helps soil.)

Fig. 1 Carbon-rich *Terra preta* **Soil** (middle) and Neighboring Soil (left).

Photos: Dr. Bruno Glaser (with permission). Photo, right: Christoph Steiner

Where does the highly durable and beneficial carbon in these soils come from? From managed fires related to routine village activities such as cooking, firing of clay pots, disposing of refuse, sanitation, field burning prior to planting, and burning crop waste and forest debris. *Terra mulata* soils, in particular, appear to be the result of deliberate soil improvements. The ancient Amazonians evidently learned that somehow, their routine activities were linked to improved soil. Armed with that knowledge, they likely applied it intentionally to improve the soil—in other words, they developed a *technology*.

In present day Amazon villages, routine activities do not involve creating more *terra preta*, suggesting that past soil amendment practices were intentional, but the tradition has been lost. Low-intensity or "cool" burning, resulting in incomplete combustion, produces char that can persist in soil for thousands of years. This has been called "slash and char," as opposed to "slash and burn" fires, which are often used in the tropics as part of shifting cultivation[1] and tend to be "hot" fires set at the end of the dry season. These "hot" fires leave mostly ash, which fertilizes the soil for a season or two, but is quickly leached away by rains.

In Africa, India, and elsewhere, some native peoples still use fire management practices that purposely **carbonize** plant and animal waste to make biochar for amending the soil (see Chapters 16 and 17 for more details).

---

[1] An agricultural system in which people move from one spot to another as soil fertility declines.

## OTHER HISTORIC SOILS AND USE OF CHARCOAL*
*Christoph Steiner, PhD*

### SHARED TRAITS
Even though the *terra preta* phenomenon may attract the most popular attention, similarly fertile soils exist.

In many places and circumstances, humans have found ways to overcome environmental limitations. In northwest Cameroon, another tropical environment, grasses are intentionally carbonized for agricultural uses. In this simple in-field technique, dried grasses are covered with a layer of soil before burning. This reduces the oxygen availability and increases char formation relative to ash.

**Plaggen** were created in the Middle Ages in northern Europe by spreading cattle bedding made from peat, along with manure, to agricultural soils. Over time, plaggen soils have accumulated to over 1 meter (m) in depth.

**Chernozem** (in Ukrainian, "black soil") soils are not man-made, but are among the most productive. They are found in the grass steppes of Romania, Russia, and the Ukraine, in the prairies of North America (Mollisols), and in the pampas of Argentina. In all of these places, grassland fires have contributed a high content of durable carbon to the soil.

### HISTORIC USE OF AGRICULTURAL CHARCOAL (BIOCHAR)
There are early descriptions of agricultural charcoal use (biochar) outside the tropics. R.L. Allen's 1846 book, *Brief Compend of American Agriculture*, mentions multiple uses of charcoal mainly for conserving nutrients. Allen also observed that the pronounced benefits of top-dressing with charcoal led to extensive use of the practice in France. Most of charcoal-related benefits described by Allen have been corroborated by recent scientific studies.

There are even older descriptions of charcoal use in non-tropical agriculture. In 1697, Yasusada Miyazaki of Japan called charcoal "fire manure;" he described roasting organic wastes and mixing them with nutrient-rich manures.

Throughout Asia rice husk biochar has been mixed with nutrient-rich materials to enhance fertilization. Crops were also fertilized with a mixture of human waste and charcoal powder called "haigoe."

---

*For citations and a wider perspective on what can be learned and adapted from historical soils to bring about dramatic, sustainable global benefits, see Chapter 17.

Dutch soil scientist Wim Sombroek recognized that the fertile Amazonian soils might have been created by humans because of their similarity to the rich, black, human-created Plaggen soils of his homeland (see the text box labeled "Other Historic Soils and Use of Charcoal"). That recognition triggered Sombroek's 40-year fascination with Amazonian soils. Sombroek, and other soil scientists analyzing the *terra preta* were astonished at its ability to maintain nutrient levels over hundreds of years. Research has shown that even chemical fertilizers cannot maintain crop yields into a third consecutive growing season in cleared rainforest soils, yet *terra preta* remains fertile year after year.

In 1992, Sombroek drew attention to the potential of *terra preta* as a tool for carbon sequestration (a concept discussed below). Before his death in 2003, he rounded up like-minded colleagues into the *Terra preta Nova* group, to reinvent the ancient *terra preta* as a strategy for large-scale farming and as a carbon sink to recapture excess carbon dioxide from the atmosphere.

In 2004, New Zealand climate scientist Peter Read suggested the term "bio-char" to describe charcoal made from **biomass** and intended for use in agriculture, although another term, agrichar, was already in use. The First International Agrichar Conference was held in 2007 in New South Wales, Australia, and attracted 107 participants from 13 countries. At that conference, the name of the association was changed to The International Biochar Initiative (IBI).

In 2008, the second international conference was held in Newcastle Upon Tyne, United Kingdom, right across from the university physics department where I had once worked. This time there were 225 attendees from 31 different countries.

### THE ENVIRONMENTAL CONNECTION IS MADE

About the time of these conferences, my own long-term concern about emissions-induced climate change convinced me that in addition to mitigating emissions, the land's ability to absorb and store carbon *must* be maintained and improved. The marine and terrestrial **ecosystems** take up around three billion tons of the eight billion tons of carbon we emit each year globally (as carbon dioxide). But as the forests become stressed by warming and succumb to pests and forest fires, as deserts expand and more carbon is lost from the soil, and as the oceans warm and acidify (among many unfortunate feedbacks), the ability of the land and oceans to capture and hold carbon will continue to deteriorate.

I was struck by the idea that biochar could be used to improve the land's carbon uptake capability (see Figure 1.2). Here is the reasoning behind the potential:

*   Planet Earth is bathed in sunshine, which delivers to its surface 10,000 times more energy than humans consume globally each year.

*    Photosynthesis in living plants uses this solar energy to extract carbon dioxide from the atmosphere and synthesize it into carbon-based compounds that make up biomass. The amount of energy trapped by photosynthesis is immense— annually, about 5 times total human energy consumption. In all, photosynthetic

organisms convert around 100 billion tons of carbon into biomass each year. Humans use an alarming 30% of this biomass productivity as crops, forest products and fuel, but whether consumed as food, burned, or left to rot, virtually all biomass is broken down again so that nearly all of its carbon ends back in the atmosphere as $CO_2$.

- When waste biomass is thermally decomposed (a process called **pyrolysis**), it breaks down into gases and residual charcoal. In a modern biochar system, the gases produced by **pyrolysis** are collected and cleanly combusted, which not only provides heat to sustain the pyrolysis but also provides energy for external use—renewable energy! The gases can also be condensed into liquid fuels and other valuable products. When intended as a soil additive, the residual charcoal is called biochar.

- The carbon remaining in biochar resists decomposition in the soil for centuries to millennia, effectively locking it out of the atmosphere. At the same time, the fertility of the soil is increased—thus enhancing food yield and augmenting biomass supply for making even more biochar, energy, and sequestered carbon.

A beneficial feedback at last! Just when we need one!

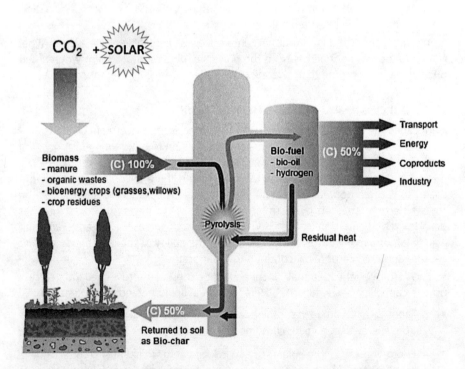

Fig. 1.2 Modern Biochar System

Source: Adapted from J. Lehmann *Frontiers in Ecology and the Environment.* 2007: 7: 381-387.

As illustrated in Figure 1.2, solar energy enables plants to synthesize carbon dioxide into biomass, which is transformed by a pyrolysis system into biochar, while producing energy and other co-products. Approximately fifty percent of the carbon in the biomass is retained in the biochar, which is stored in the soil, contributing to enhanced plant growth. As already mentioned, most of the carbon in biochar is resistant to breakdown, and will be kept out of the atmosphere for hundreds or thousands of years. Without the biochar system, nearly all of the carbon would cycle back to the atmosphere in just years, as fallen plant material decomposes. Thus, biochar accelerates the part of the carbon cycle that takes up carbon dioxide from the atmosphere (photosynthesis) and slows—by a large factor—the part that returns it to the atmosphere (decomposition). Thought of in another way, the biochar system is a solar-driven carbon pump, which rather than requiring energy to run, throws off valuable, renewable energy.

Here we have a carbon-capture technology, which appears to have the potential to play a major role in restoring our soils and our climate, while providing renewable energy and avoiding use of fossil fuels. In addition to the environmental benefits, the economic opportunity related to the scale of the coming changes is worth contemplating: sustaining civilization in the face of environmental imperative will require replacing most of the present fossil fuel industry and most of current fossil fuel-driven, unsustainable agriculture. The interlinking benefits of biochar systems are depicted in Figure 1.3.

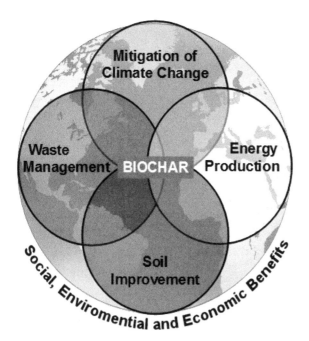

Fig. 1.3 Interlinking Benefits of Biochar

Modern biochar systems can transform waste into valuable soil improvement, which sequesters carbon and mitigates climate change, while at the same time producing renewable energy. Social, environmental and economic benefits flow from optimum implementation of the system.

Source: Adapted and modified from J. Lehmann, Biochar for Environmental Management: Science and Technology, 5

Biochar is not the only carbon-capture technology that will be part of the mix in the coming greener revolution[2], but pyrolysis technologies seem destined to pay a substantial role, and biochar's array of potential environmental, economic, and social benefits stand apart.

## BIOCHAR AND POLICY

Policy around energy security and climate mitigation will play a vital role in promoting the development of biochar systems. However, given that biochar is but one arrow in a quiver of required solutions, the sweet spot in the above diagram for making biochar most sustainable and beneficial, and to influence if not drive policy, is to first focus on how it can improve soil and food production. The remainder of this book does just that—but first, a little more about how biochar might fit into the big picture.

## CARBON CAPTURE AND ETHICAL CARBON POLICY

In a world dependent on fossil energy, it is easy to be seduced into considering the carbon capture benefits of biochar as offsets against current and future fossil fuel emissions. However, biochar is a better—and more ethical—match to recapture the *past* accumulated carbon dioxide emissions that are causing *present* climate change. In fact, many scientists now believe there is already an unsafe excess of carbon dioxide in the atmosphere; arguably, this obligates the nations that caused the excess to abate it. Only a carbon capture technology, such as biochar, can draw down this excess and repay the debt.

It is notable that from 1850 to 2000, 34% of carbon dioxide emissions have been attributed to land clearing.[6] Therefore, in a sense, the first goal of biochar is to restore the carbon lost from the soil due to the past 150 years of agricultural practice. After that, the particular durability of biochar will enable the build-up of more carbon in soils, with further fertility benefits (as the *terra preta* example has shown us). This will recapture some of the released fossil carbon back into the ground.

---

[2] Other carbon capture methods range from reforestation, no-till agriculture, pasture management, prairie regeneration, and use of biomass for long-term building products, on through "green" cement production, to new biological processes. Carbon capture technologies must be complemented by emissions reduction from efficient use of renewable energy.

## ALLOCATING RESPONSIBILITY, PROMOTING DEVELOPMENT

How should the responsibility for dealing with these past emissions be apportioned? Of those trillion tons of carbon dioxide emitted since I worried about it in 1960, over 25% are associated with the U.S. (which has 5% of the global population), and another 20% with the European Union (7% of population), and about 1.3% with Australia (0.3% of population). China has 19% of the world's population but, even as a leading developing country, has so far contributed only about 10% to the accumulated emissions, and therefore to current climate change. (Climate change actually lags decades behind the emissions due to inertia in the geo-climatic system—tables have been published that account for this.[7])

In fact, only a small number of countries have released far more carbon dioxide into the atmosphere than their per capita sustainable share. If only those countries would agree to use biochar and other carbon capture methods to withdraw those emissions, it would take pressure off the futile attempt to enroll 192 divergent nations into a carbon emissions reduction scheme as a solution to a problem caused predominantly by affluent, developed nations—a problem that now requires not just reducing emissions, but also withdrawing carbon from the atmosphere.

A carbon recapture agreement among the major responsible nations could include a trading scheme for carbon capture credits. Other nations that wanted to enter the trade could join in the agreement. Affluent nations could reduce the expense of meeting their obligations by transferring technology and funding to allow and employ poorer nations, often located in the tropics with poorer soils, to concurrently sequester carbon and remediate their soils. This would help give poorer nations their fair chance to develop, and help their people satisfy subsistence needs, thereby applying direct salve to those pressing issues.

Ultimately, a carbon emissions agreement would require all nations that exceed their sustainable per capita share of current emissions to reduce them over time to that sustainability benchmark, and allow all nations to converge on a common sustainable target (contraction and convergence). However, a carbon recapture agreement does not need to wait on this. The more rapidly the responsible nations recapture their excess emissions, the more time will be available for nations to contract and converge within the physical constraints imposed by nature.

Best of all, this kind of agreement is not as much an economic burden as a viable pathway to a solid, sustainable, and socially just future. For example, Australia's national accumulated carbon debt comes out at about 3 billion tons of carbon, which, distributed over Australia's 445 million hectares[8] of agricultural land, amounts to 6.7 tons/hectare. While numerous other agro-forestry practices could and should also contribute to carbon restoration, this scenario is actually a good match for biochar. It corresponds with a manageable rate of biochar application spread out over say 30–40 years, and also corresponds with application rates that produce soil improvement benefits (see, for example, Chapter 14).

If responsible affluent countries followed this path (either in their own land or by financially supporting the activity elsewhere), they would improve the soil's productivity, and its resilience against climate change impacts, while radically improving their ethical standing at the negotiating table for emissions reductions.

## THE GROWTH OF A MOVEMENT

Researchers around the globe are now scrambling to verify and understand all of these potential benefits of biochar, so that modern biochar systems can be applied effectively and sustainably. The original *terra preta* sites are being studied, and soils with similar traits are being sought, and found. Field studies are under way on every continent, with particular enthusiasm in Brazil, Asia and Australia. In the United States, Cornell University is conducting biochar research, led by Dr. Johannes Lehmann, who co-founded the IBI. Several other U.S. universities have strong programs, with even more work occurring in Australia and Europe. Much of that work to date on the scientific, social and economic aspects of biochar is reported in what I call the Biochar Bible: *Biochar for Environmental Management: Science and Technology* (Earthscan, 2009), edited by Dr. Lehmann and another founder of IBI, Stephen Joseph (University of New South Wales). Other review articles are listed among the references at the end of this chapter.[9]

All over the world, research labs and new corporations are working to develop modern, clean, and efficient pyrolysis processes. Japan, where biochar has been used for centuries, is a leader in commercializing biochar, developing varied biochar-related production kilns, products, and applications. The mission of the IBI is to promote the development of biochar systems that follow "Cradle-to-Cradle" sustainability guidelines.

The ease of electronic communication has pushed the biochar cause beyond the ivory towers, infusing both knowledge and momentum. Home gardeners, farmers, activists, and entrepreneurs have found a community of interest and are sharing ideas, designs, and results online. The IBI keeps the biochar community updated through its website and international conferences it organizes, and as well there are regional biochar organizations around the world, and numerous individuals championing the cause online.

In May 2009, I attended The Asia Pacific Biochar Conference, in my local area of Gold Coast, NSW, Australia. The conference brought home to me the diversity in the biochar community. There was no shortage of strictly scientific presentations, yet I found myself sitting next to and chatting with farmers, waste management consultants, economists, entrepreneurs, and even a building demolisher, all keen to see what biochar could do for them. This community concept is reprised throughout the following chapters.

That diversity is significant, and so is the opportunity for individual contribution. There are many qualities of biochar, and they depend on the type of biomass, process, and conditions used to create it.

There are yet more combinations of soils, crops, and climate zones. All of these variables and combinations need to be tested to promote rapid learning and effective application. Thus, "backyard" research can be as useful and important as formal institutional study. The following chapters provide some inspiring examples, and Chapter 14 is a guide to testing and applying biochar in your own garden or farm, with suggestions on how to gather and share data on your results.

## LOCAL DEPLOYMENT, COLLECTIVE GLOBAL IMPACT

One of the encouraging aspects of biochar is that it can be applied widely, yet *needs* to be localized. There are economic and environmental costs to transporting the bulky biomass material used to make biochar (the **feedstock**) over any considerable distance from its origin. The feedstock is best processed locally and the biochar incorporated into local soils, utilizing particularized local knowledge about conditions relating to climate, soil, crops, and species diversity.

Abundant feedstock biomass is widely available—without deforesting, and without competing with food. At present, vast amounts of biomass are left to rot or burned in field and forest, and even in landfills, or are used inefficiently in primitive and polluting stoves. (For a discussion about mitigating climate change by using "thinly distributed" feedstock and low-tech biochar devices, see Chapter 18.) Furthermore, biomass can be cultivated by **coppicing** (a woodlands management practice recalled from the early charcoal industry—see Chapter 4), or as a strategy to restore marginal lands (Chapters 19 and 20).

Granted, it does require care to gather and use this biomass harvest sustainably, and there are competing needs for it. However, biochar does not have to compete with compost, because biochar can still carry the nutrients in the biomass to the soil, and works best in *combination* with compost (see Chapter 15). Furthermore, biochar does not compete with food; rather, biochar shows great promise for enhancing food production and reducing fossil fertilizer use. Biochar also has the promise of increasing the supply of biomass over time, as soils improve and productivity increases.

Marginal and degraded soils exist in countless locales throughout the world, and must be improved as soon as possible in order to restore soils, increase food production to feed expanding populations—and recapture our historic emissions. This vital topic is expanded in Chapter 17, "The Greener Revolution," and also in the other chapters in Part V, "Changing the World."

## THE PIECES FIT TOGETHER

My own exposure to small-scale biochar came via a project to develop low-emission, low-cost biochar kilns for small farms and villages.[10] Project 540's focus is to prove that emissions from small biochar kilns can be controlled to best-practice standards, while still using simple designs, accessible materials, simple cues for checking emissions, and basic or no instrumentation. This, in fact, is a work in progress for many authors of this book, and numerous others reporting online.

Invited to present at an environment day in my local community, I was prepared to carefully explain the science on climate change in order to position and justify biochar, and then demonstrate a small low-tech, backyard biochar kiln (see Chapter 9). Everybody clamored to see only the demonstration, so they could go home and try it!

That real-world, grass-roots experience, coupled with the troubling global context, inspired this book. It aims to support gardeners, enthusiasts, small property owners, farmers, communities, and municipalities who wish to explore making biochar and using biochar to do so via techniques that are safe, low-emitting, resource-efficient, and effective for their local soil and crop. That way, we will do the most good and the least harm as we learn to achieve the local and global outcomes we sorely need.

In doing so, we revive legacies left to us by the ancient Amazonians and others, while being informed by modern science—and reaping the benefits of our own modern ingenuity.

## REFERENCES

1. Caldeira, K., and M.E. Wickett. "Anthropogenic Carbon and Ocean Ph." *Nature*, 2003: 425, 365

2. Committee on Environment and Natural Resources, National Science and Technology Council. "Scientific Assessment of the Effects of Global Change on the United States." Government Report, May 2008. http://www.climatescience.gov/Library/scientific-assessment/(accessed August 16, 2010).

3. *Scientific American*. "How Acidification Threatens Oceans from the Inside Out." August 2010.

4. Rischard, J.P. *High Noon 20 Global Problems, 20 Years to Solve Them*. New York: Basic Books, 2002.

5. Meggers, Betty J. *Amazonia: Man and Culture in Counterfeit Paradise*. Washington DC: Smithsonian Institution Scholarly Press, 1971.

6. U.S. Department of Energy (DOE). "Frequently Asked Questions." Carbon Dioxide Information Analysis Center. n.d. http://cdiac.ornl.gov/pns/faq.html (accessed August 16, 2010).

7. Climate Analysis Indicators Tool (CAIT) Version 7.0. Washington, DC: World Resources Institute, 2010.

8. *Demographia*. "Agricultural Land: Australia: 1981-2005." http://www.demographia.com/db-aus-ag.htm (accessed August 16, 2010).

9. Sohi, S., *et al.* "Biochar, Climate Change and Soil: A Review to Guide Future Research. Australian Commonwealth Scientific and Industrial Research Organization (CSIRO). Land and Water Science Report 05/09, February 2009. Woolf, D. "Biochar as a Soil Amendment: A Review of the Environmental Implications." February 2008 (unpublished). http://orgprints.org/13268/ (accessed August 16, 2010).

   F. Verheijen, *et al.* "Biochar Application to Soils: A Critical Scientific Review of Effects on Soil Properties, Processes and Functions." European Commission, Joint Research Centre Institute for Environment and Sustainability. Scientific and Technical Report. Luxembourg: Office for Official Publications of the European Communities, 2010.

10. Moxham G., P. Taylor, P. Gibson, and J. Seed. "Project 540: Low-emission, Low Cost Biochar Kilns for Small Farms and Villages." Asia Pacific Biochar Conference, 2009.

## A BIOCHAR TIMELINE - Albert Bates

8000 BP  Earliest radiocarbon dates for Amazonian Dark Earths

1542  Francisco de Orellana descends the Amazon River. His scribe, Gaspar de Carvajal, writes, "Inland from the river at a distance of 2 leagues [6 miles] more or less, there could be seen some very large cities that glistened in white. This, the land, is as good, as fertile, and as normal in appearance as our Spain."

1670  German Jesuit missionary John Phillip Bettendorff provides the earliest known use of the term *"terra preta."*

1866  After surveys by Landsford Hastings, "Confederado" settlements established on *terra preta* sites in the lower Amazon, relocating Southern plantation culture to Brazil following the American Civil War.

1867  Ex-Confederate Admiral John Randolph Tucker charts the Amazon River for the government of Peru. In Brazil: Home for Southerners, Ballard S. Dunn writes "... for about twenty miles ... are lands of the best quality, producing every description of crops ... in the greatest perfection and abundance."

1868  Geologist and explorer James Orton writes of the Confederado settlements that "the soil is very black and fertile. It beats South Carolina, yielding without culture thirty bushels of rice per acre."

1874  Charles Frederick Hartt, first Dean of Geology at Cornell University, conducts a geological survey of Brazil, collecting 500,000 samples.

1876  British geologists C. Barrington Brown and William Lidstone observe deep black soils mixed with broken pottery in Guyana and later in the lower Amazon, concluding soils were "undoubtedly of artificial origin."

1879  Hartt's assistant, Herbert H. Smith, describes for Scribners Magazine "the rich *terra preta*, 'black land,' the best on the Amazons. It is a fine, dark loam, a foot, and often two feet thick."

1895  Friederick Katzer studies the "Schwarze Erde" [black earth] and concludes that the lower Amazon region's "more distinguished wealth lies in its soil."

1903  In Sarajevo, Katzer subjects his *terra preta* samples to loss-on-ignition, chemical leaching, and other tests and concludes that these soils were not formed by nature, but were cultivated in ancient times when Brazil was more densely populated.

1921-  Hypotheses of origins of dark earths by U.S. anthropologist William Farabee
1974   (1921), Brazilian agronomist Felisberto Camargo (1941), French geographer Pierre Gourou (1949), and Brazilian pedologist Italo Falesi (1967).

1925  Percy Harrison Fawcett vanishes looking for the fabled "City Z."

1923-    Brazilian anthropologist Curt Nimuendajú systematically maps and
1945     samples the *terra preta* sites in the lower Tapajós region.

1927     Henry Ford establishes his large rubber-growing community,
         Fordlândia, along the Tapajós River.

1934     Fordlândia is moved upstream to the much more fertile setting at
         Belterra, a former Confederado *terra preta* site.

1960     Brazilian-American geographer Hilgard Sternberg carbon-dates
         ceramic fragments in *terra preta* soils to 100 BP.

1966     Dutch soil scientist Wim Sombroek performs laboratory analysis of
         Belterra samples and distinguishes *terra preta* from *terra mulata*.

1970     Katzer's tests are repeated by Wim Sombroek.

1979     Bayreuth University in Germany launches research on black carbon,
         organic matter stability, micromorphology, chemical and mineralogical
         analysis, and microbiology, beginning with Wolfgang Zech and
         continuing with Bruno Glaser, Johannes Lehmann, Christoph Steiner,
         and others.

1980s    Interdisciplinary programs are begun at institutions in Brazil, Colombia,
         the United States, Japan, Australia, and elsewhere to study soil carbon
         processes and *terra preta* formation.

1980     U.S. geographer Nigel Smith publishes "Anthrosols and Human
         Carrying Capacity in Amazonia," compiling dark earth research to
         date.

1987     Thousand-year-old dark earth sites located in Africa by Brooks and
         Smith.

1990s    Archaeologists Michael Heckenberger, James Petersen, and Eduardo
         Neves excavate large, long-term villages on dark earths in the Upper
         Xingu and along the lower Rio Negro, including likely site of "City Z."

1992     Charcoal carbon sequestration proposed by German energy researcher
         Walter Seifritz as sink for anthropogenic carbon dioxide in the
         atmosphere.

1997     Japanese researchers Ogawa, Okimori and Takahashi propose carbon
         sequestration and forest conservation under U.N. Clean Development
         Mechanism, using pyrolyzed biomass residue and forestry waste.

2001     A *Terra preta* Symposium at the Conference of the Latin American
         Geographers in Benicassim, Spain brings together Geographers,
         archaeologists, and soil scientists from Europe and Latin America.

2001     U.S. Department of Energy report by Spath, *et al.*, shows that pyrolytic
         conversion of biomass provides best path for hydrogen production
         because of co-products.

|  |  |
|---|---|
| 2001 | British Museum opens display, "The Unknown Amazon." |
| 2002 | First International Conference on Anthropogenic *Terra preta* Soils in Manaus, Brazil. Sombroek and others propose *"Terra preta* Nova" as a global carbon sink initiative. |
| 2002 | "The Secret of El Dorado," a BBC Horizon television documentary, furthers global awareness of *terra preta* soils. |
| 2003 | Lehmann, Kern, Glaser and Woods publish Amazonian Dark Earths: Origin, Properties, Management, the first comprehensive anthology of *terra preta* soils. |
| 2003 | Findings by Heckenberger, Erickson and others show that the prehistoric civilization of the Amazon was more populous and complex than previously assumed, attributable to soil management. |
| 2004 | Small-scale pyrolytic kilns such as the Adam-Retort® are produced in India and Africa. Many backyard stove experiments are begun. |
| 2004 | New Zealand climate scientist Peter Read coins the term "bio-char" to describe biomass-derived charred carbon used in agriculture. |
| 2004 | At Conference on Energy and Carbon Utilization at University of Georgia, Danny Day introduces plan for integrated energy, forestry, and agricultural carbon cycle to combat climate change. |
| 2006 | The International Agrichar Initiative is formed at a side meeting of the World Soil Science Congress in Philadelphia. |
| 2007 | Tom Miles launches *terra preta* list and website in support of the Agrichar Initiative. |
| 2007 | First International Agrichar Conference is held in New South Wales, with 107 attendees from 13 countries, and the International Biochar Initiative (IBI) is established. "Agrichar" is trademarked by an Australian company. |
| 2008 | Second IBI conference held in Newcastle, United Kingdom with over 225 attendees from 31 different countries. |
| 2009 | Lehmann and Joseph publish *Biochar for Environmental Management*. |
| 2009 | Woods, Texeira, Lehmann, Steiner, WinklerPrins and Rebellato publish *Amazonian Dark Earths: Wim Sombroek's Vision*. |
| 2009 | Biochar is proposed as a climate mitigation strategy at the United Nations Conference of Parties to the Framework Convention on Climate Change in Copenhagen. |
| 2009 | "Cool Vegetable" campaign to market biochar-grown produce is launched by Japanese grocery store chain. |
| 2010 | Third IBI conference is held in Rio de Janeiro, Brazil. |

Chapter 2

# Making a Difference with Biochar: From the Ground Up

Karen Siepen
Owner, Renewable Carbon Resources Australia (RCRA)

**IN THIS CHAPTER YOU WILL LEARN:**

- How one entrepreneur was introduced to biochar and its commercial production.

- How biomass, charcoal, and biochar are related.

- How biochar can replenish depleted soil and help resolve the current global food crisis.

- The financial benefits of biochar.

- Traditional ways to make biochar and how one method has been adapted for modern commercial production.


"Biochar is biomass charred for application to soils, and biomass is *everywhere*."

# MY INTRODUCTION TO BIOCHAR

I was introduced to biochar by serendipity. A couple of years into the charcoal business, I noticed that the grass and trees around my charcoal production site were growing faster than anywhere else on the property. After extensive research and telephone calls to scientists, I discovered the word "biochar."

My research also revealed the growing global interest—rather, *excitement*—surrounding the idea that a charcoal product could turn infertile soil into productive farmland. The boundless societal and economic potential for food production became clear to me, and I wanted to learn more.

In May 2009, I attended the Asia Pacific Biochar Conference. I was struggling with the jargon and science-speak that followed every question put to the speakers, and I was not alone. Finally, one attendee pleaded with a speaker to describe biochar in one line. The speaker paused, squirmed, and said, "It's just not that simple." I left the conference looking for a simple touchstone I could understand, work with, and explain to others.

Shortly thereafter, another colleague came to the rescue with the following simple insight: "Biochar is biomass charred for application to soils." And what's biomass? "If it rots and it smells, it's probably biomass."

Then biomass is *everywhere*. Biomass is grass clippings and dead trees. It's manure, crop waste, and vegetable scraps. It's cardboard, paper, wood shavings, or even dead animals. I have since learned that because biochar can be made from biomass, biomass is as good as gold.

## THE GARDEN OF AWARENESS

That simple insight about biomass took me back to my youth, when I watched veggie gardeners in my area turn their garden beds with a variety of natural materials. They would work in manure, straw, grass clippings, vegetable scraps, ash, and charcoal.

Yes, charcoal. Gardeners would gather charcoal and ash from the wood stove or fireplace and spread it over the garden patch, turning the soil to work it in.

They did it to help the tired soil recover. The previous crop had sucked the nutrients out, and putting these natural materials back in the soil provided abundant nutrients for a new crop.

Depletion of soil is natural. Like an expectant mother passing nutrients from her body to help her baby develop, the development of healthy plants depends on sufficient nutrients from the soil. While women generally have breaks to recover between pregnancies, the soil may not. To produce food, crops are often grown season after season in the same soil, without respite, and this can be achieved only by using a brew of fertilizers every year.

As a child, I would squeeze the rich brown, moist soil between my fingers. It smelled earthy but somehow clean. It produced food that was rich with flavor and "good for me." I now know this was made possible by the gardeners, who had restored the soil with ample carbon-based nutrients that fed the plants throughout their growth cycle, from seed to mature, food-laden plants.

Whether those gardeners understood the underlying science of soil and plants, or merely mimicked their parents or grandparents, the results were the same. The produce of my youth was better than what we can typically buy in shops today. Simply put, no one using chemicals and genetically altered plants can mass-produce food that compares to those old gardens in taste or nutrients.

These hints from the past show how biochar can help resolve both the growing global food crisis and the escalating soil crisis. Along with the increasing need for food, there is a desperate need to replenish the soil, spent from delivering crops year after year, and return it to health.

Because biomass is everywhere, the solution is staring us in the face. Every time vegetables are thrown into the trash, every time the grass is cut or the hedges are trimmed, biomass is created. Biomass can be turned into biochar, and biochar can durably remediate our depleted soil. But instead of using this valuable, renewable resource, we are throwing it away at an ever-increasing rate. We thoughtlessly—or ignorantly—toss it in a heap or bury it in bulk, in landfills, so it is simply wasted.

Some believe it's too late for complete recovery of the planet's soils. But I've seen what biochar can do. If we used it properly, plants would thrive automatically and sustainably. They would be abundant, healthier and cheaper to produce.

We can turn our refuse into gold.

Fig. 2.1 A handful of biochar

## CHARCOAL VERSUS BIOCHAR

Biochar and charcoal may be identical in many respects, but the telling difference is in how they are used. Charcoal is used as a fuel. Crushed charcoal used in the soil is biochar, a valuable soil amendment.

This simple description may not be scientifically precise, but this is what I've seen with my own eyes. Biomass, in the form of crushed charcoal, kept the verdant vegetable garden of my youth healthy and productive, year after year. Now I see the same beneficial effect where we make charcoal—our little green oasis in an otherwise brown landscape.

## HOW BIOCHAR IS MADE FROM BIOMASS

Here is how it works. Biomass is heated to a sufficient temperature so it can cook thoroughly, just like baking a cake. While it's cooking, the sap and moisture are driven out and dried up so that what's left is biochar—a black and very light, shrunken version of what you started with. Under a microscope the material looks like a honeycomb.

Quite literally, a dead plant has been transformed by heat into a new substance that can draw in water and hold it like a sponge. This structure of biochar provides excellent tunnels and caverns for microbes to live in—and plants need microbes in the soil to help nourish them. Good quality biochar retains nutrients from when the biomass plant was alive and plants can draw on those nutrients (carried to them via the microbes) and water when they need to.

## THE COMPONENTS OF BIOCHAR

Generally, dry biomass contains, by weight, approximately 50 percent carbon, 5 or 6 percent hydrogen, and about 40 percent oxygen. Biomass also typically contains smaller amounts of other components of living matter, such as minerals (ash), nitrogen, sulfur, phosphorus, and calcium.

When biomass rots, the carbon and hydrogen are released into the atmosphere as carbon dioxide ($CO_2$), methane, and other gases, including rotten-smelling hydrogen sulfide. A similar result is obtained when the biomass is burned to ash. The proliferation of these gases in the atmosphere—another serious problem we're facing—exacerbate the **greenhouse effect**. As a **greenhouse gas**, the methane released has a **global warming** potential up to 70 times worse than $CO_2$.

On the other hand, when biomass is cooked to make charcoal, up to 40 percent of the carbon remains in the charcoal, along with the minerals and most of the plant nutrients.

## YOUR ROLE...AND MINE

All of us are responsible for, and are affected by, the contamination of our air by carbon dioxide and methane and the uninformed mismanagement of valuable biomass. We can, however, start setting things right. We can participate in—and help build—the global movement to convert biomass into biochar.

We can all play a role, in numerous ways and on many levels:

- When you purchase biochar you enable more biochar to be manufactured, taking more harmful gases out of the atmosphere and reducing waste on the planet.

- If you leave the biochar in the bag and don't ever use it, you have still assisted in converting biomass to a stable form, which is itself a productive activity.

- If you use the biochar to improve the soil at your home, workplace, or farm you create a further benefit: healthier soils that require less water and fertilizer to produce food.

## SHOW ME THE MONEY: THE FINANCIAL BENEFITS OF BIOCHAR

There is another, very exciting prospect about biochar and the biomass it comes from. Converting biomass to biochar opens a new spectrum of business opportunities; doing *good* aligns with doing *well*.

These new businesses will:

- Manufacture and sell a significantly superior natural soil health product.

- Help prevent carbon dioxide and methane (among other polluting gases) from entering the air—and simultaneously reduce landfill requirements.

The demand will develop and accelerate. Gardeners everywhere will use biochar. Councils will vote to buy or manufacture biochar for their counties, because it will concurrently deliver long-term soil improvements for public green areas and lower expenses for biomass waste management. In short, everyone will benefit in some way because the manufacture of biochar has air, water, and food benefits for all.

Next, we will examine the financial benefits of biochar.

### RESIDENTIAL

If you use a 10 kg bag of biochar in your home garden, you can save up to 30 percent of the water you now use to keep your garden alive. (See the text box labeled "@Home Biochar: Saving Water, Clearing the Air.")

---

**@HOME BIOCHAR: SAVING WATER, CLEARING THE AIR**

Here are compelling calculations based on a biochar containing 60 percent stable carbon. (For a discussion of biochar's carbon component, which remains stable in the soil for generations, see the chapter of this book titled "What *Is* Biochar?")

- If every house in Brisbane, Australia used biochar in their gardens at the rate of 10 kg per 2 square meters, **Brisbane water usage could be reduced by 14 million liters per week.**

- Just as important, if the 450,000 households in Brisbane used just one 10 kg bag of biochar in their garden, then **Brisbane will prevent 2.5 million kilograms of carbon from entering the atmosphere.**

Because biochar lasts for generations, it's cost effective.

---

Home gardening with biochar would also save money on fertilizers, because a garden requires much less fertilizer when biochar is used. (Notably, biochar coupled with fertilizer performs better than fertilizer or biochar alone.)

Finally, biochar lasts for generations, making it extremely cost-effective.

### CROP FARMING

While many of the at-home benefits just described also apply to crop farming, the circumstances and scale change—and so do the stakes—due to the sheer volume and food quality of produce being grown.

As previously mentioned, farmers have long been forced to push out crops season after season to make a profit, or at least a living. The worldwide demand for food is increasing but the soil is tired, losing its ability to grow and develop produce at the rate required. The future looks bleak unless something is done—and done quickly.

Granted, many farmers already use crop waste to "feed" their soil. But in many cases, crop waste offers little benefit to soil, or it breaks down too slowly to help the farmer much.

The crop farmer can instead turn waste from his previous crop into biochar. By transforming the waste on his own property, he can improve crops faster with more volume of produce while increasing the long-term fertility of the soil.

This is fine in theory, but this is not backyard gardening. As a practical matter, adding appropriate biochar levels to large fields can be daunting and expensive. However, seasonal applications will build up the soil over time, translating into better yields, and less fertilizer applied, with each crop.

Fig. 2.2  Biochar in seed-raising mix

## TARGETED BIOCHAR APPLICATIONS
More targeted methods of working with biochar are available.

Farmers can drill biochar into the planting lines only. Targeted drilling of biochar is cheaper than "broadcasting," enabling the farmer to more efficiently manage his limited resources. After all, farming is a business. This method will deliver a good result for the plants while improving the soil over several seasons.

Some farmers use biochar in the seed-raising mix as a cost effective way to get stronger, healthier seedlings. This method also leads to a steady build-up of biochar in the soil.

The amounts of biochar necessary per site/paddock will vary with each type of soil and crop planted. For example, sandy or granite-based soils prosper with a heavier dose of biochar. Renewable Carbon Resources Australia (RCRA) has trialed sand and biochar in a 50/50 ratio (a ratio not viable for a commercial farmer) and grown better chives than any we have ever seen in the market. In other trials using modest amounts of biochar—as little as ¼ cup per plant—tomatoes, corn, broccoli, cabbage, and peas all surpassed expectations in development and yield. (Note: "Cup" is used as the unit of measure because biochar made from **greenwaste** will weigh less than biochar made from hardwood timber; therefore a kilogram of hardwood biochar has less volume than a kilogram of greenwaste biochar. So far, results have shown that less hardwood char is required to get a desirable result than chars made from lighter density waste. Moreover, hardwood biochar is more resistant to displacement by wind and water than soft biomass biochars like greenwaste.)

- *Tomatoes:* Plants grew significantly faster with deeper color in the foliage, and bore more fruit. In fact, more than double the per-plant yield of plants without biochar-treated soil.

- *Corn:* Produced a minimum of two additional cobs per plant; the cobs were also larger and deeper in color, flavor, and texture.

- *Broccoli:* A dazzler, with heads 30 percent larger and with deeper color and flavor.

- *Cabbage:* Increased head size by over 100 percent, without affecting the usual fridge shelf life (one month). Even the outer leaves were green and healthy.

These results show how amending soils with biochar benefits crops.

## GRAZING

As mentioned at the outset of this chapter, at the RCRA production facility, the grass and trees growing around the facility—and as far out as 3 km—are greener and more prolific than outside that radius. The 3-km radius is noteworthy because that's how far the wind carries char dust from RCRA's charcoal grading operations. Wind-borne biochar particles are not necessarily common; this occurs at RCRA because of our grading process, which creates dust while sorting the charcoal into size and quality classifications.

We lease the RCRA property from a grazier. He is thrilled to have his soil carbon levels increased year after year as the biochar dust works its way into the soil with wind and rain. His cattle spend a lot of time in the biochar-treated area because the grass is sweeter with fleshier stems and leaves.

Graziers face a significant problem when considering biochar for their properties because grazing properties are large in area and their produce—meat—is not harvested as often as many plant crops. Nevertheless, graziers could make biochar from downed timber.

Many graziers burn downed timber in their paddocks or leave it to rot. Burning the timber to ash releases nearly all of its carbon (say 98%) into the atmosphere as greenhouse carbon dioxide ($CO_2$). Leaving the timber to rot and be colonized by termites is even worse, because rotting and termites both release methane, a greenhouse gas 70 times more potent than $CO_2$. A controlled burning of the timber until it transforms into charcoal, and extinguishing the fire before ash forms, will save a much larger portion of the carbon contained in the waste timber, in the form of long-lasting, stable charcoal. By spreading this charcoal in the soil as biochar, much of the carbon in the biomass can be kept out of the atmosphere while at the same time building up the soil long-term.

A grazier desiring to make biochar in a controlled open burn should handle the fire responsibly, and proceed as follows:

- Make sure sufficient water and a transfer pump is on hand to quench the fire. For each one cubic meter of the fire, 1,000 liters of water should be available.

- Pile or push up the downed timber on clear ground to prevent the fire from spreading.

- Light the pile, keep it contained, and spray with water any areas that start developing white ash.

- When the timber pile is predominantly glowing red, extinguish the fire by spraying the water out over the hot coals. (Caution: The ash may contain hot coals for some time so make sure they are fully cooled and extinguished.)

- When the char has completely cooled (after several days), it can be transported across the paddock using a drag frame made of concrete reinforcing mesh behind a tractor.

This primitive yet effective style of open-fire charring is currently used in the bamboo forests of Japan. This char-making process is further described in the chapter titled "From Blacksmith to Biochar: The Essence of Community," along with more efficient and clean methods that should be adopted as they become available.

Some graziers believe that simply burning their paddocks to clear fallen timber produces the same result as creating biochar and spreading it. However, uncontrolled burning largely creates ash with only around 2% of the original biomass carbon kept intact as char. This highlights the difference between traditional "slash-and-burn" agriculture, which can fertilize soil with ash for a small number of years, and "slash-and-char" as practiced by the Amazon Indians to make *terra preta* (the black earth of the Amazon), which created enduring fertility for hundreds of years.

Graziers who are not able to make biochar themselves, or are not interested in doing so, can buy bulk biochar and spread it in a single small paddock that can then be used for weaning calves or finishing the cattle prior to sale. As we observed at RCRA, both informally and via field trials, cattle will gravitate towards the "carbon grass;" they instinctively know to eat it. The biochar-treated paddock will retain more nutrients and hold moisture better in dry times than the remaining property—just like our little oasis around the production facility. Healthier, fatter cattle with glossy coats invite higher prices and more profit.

## INDUSTRY

Many commercial and industrial sites have gardens that could benefit from biochar, and also have an abundance of biomass to use or offer others.

For example, sawmills and timber-associated manufacturers are currently under pressure to remove their biomass waste products. For these businesses, the cost of having the sawdust and timber off-cuts removed is eroding their profits and increasing the volume of landfills.

The same can be said for tree trimmers and landscape gardeners. Clearing land for larger-scale developments, electricity and gas lines, and mine sites creates biomass. Stables, piggeries, and feedlots generate considerable manure and bedding, which can be used to produce nutrient-rich biochar rather than the gaseous cocktail this biomass now creates.

As illustrated by these examples, many industries have a potential biochar feedstock that is currently considered a problem rather than an asset. Fee-for-service mobile biochar units could convert this industrial biomass into biochar for resale—or can reduce expenses for biomass removal. In either case, profits are increased.

## WHERE TO FROM HERE?

As the above discussion demonstrates, everyone from a city resident to a major corporation can actively use biochar for the benefit of all. This factor alone has interested parties circling the industry looking for a way in.

Australia exemplifies the overall business potential of biochar. With so much area to cover, Australian retailers and distributors have the chance to introduce to the marketplace, and popularize, a little-known natural, environmentally positive product.

Profit is there to be shared and enjoyed—and it is clean, green profit.

## MAKING BIOCHAR – THE OLD FASHIONED WAY

People have been making charcoal (and therefore biochar) for centuries. The *terra preta* phenomenon in the Amazon basin began with ancient methods of making char and adding it to the soil.

## TRADITIONAL METHODS

One of the oldest methods for making char originated at the hearth. Wood was burned for cooking and when the food was cooked, the fire was quenched before the wood turned to ash. Since char is significantly lighter than wood, this was also a good way to carry long-burning and less smoky fuel when travelling.

Next is the earth oven method, where a pit was dug and timber placed inside. The timber was set on fire and allowed to burn to a certain level before soil was heaped on top of it. Some oxygen would still enter the pit so the wood smoldered, releasing thick smoke. When the smoke stopped and the contents cooled, the pit was excavated and the char was removed.

After that people started to get creative and built mud igloos resembling a beehive pottery kiln. The wood was loaded into the igloo, which was all but sealed so only a small amount of oxygen could enter to keep the smoldering alive. When the smoke went blue or stopped, the igloo was completely sealed with mud and dirt and allowed to cool. The batches were relatively small but sufficient to service the needs of villages in rural communities. This batch-style manufacturing is still used in many countries.

## ADAPTING TRADITIONAL METHODS TODAY

These days—at least in Australia—commercial char is produced on a large scale for restaurant use. One Australian favorite, Charcoal Chicken, is cooked with char made in huge pits with corrugated iron roofs. Many popular ethnic restaurants use char made the same way.

This large-scale method requires skillful management by a **collier** (char maker). High-quality combustible charcoal must have specific burning characteristics, and commercial pit-style production involves substantial quantities of timber and extreme heat—some pits contain 20 tons of charcoal. There are no dials to tweak for making adjustments, so the collier must be able to interpret the activity inside the pit. A skilled collier can actually maneuver the main body of heat inside a pit to ensure all timber is properly heated, and can "cook" a pit in all weather conditions. In the past, this process has been extremely labor-intensive, but processing developments and heavy machinery have made it easier.

This kind of hands-on char making is more than a curiosity. Recycling timber into char or charcoal has helped many farmers survive long droughts; char producers pay royalties to use their timber as feedstock and to run production on their land. This partnering has also allowed sufficient char production and supply to carry on popular ethnic styles of cooking.

Provided the collier cooks the char properly, the traditional pit method makes good quality biochar. The biochar component of the charcoal is typically called screenings, because the smaller particles are screened out leaving the larger barbecue-size charcoal.

Current interest in biochar is spurring development of more advanced techniques and devices for making char—including do-it-yourself methods—that continue to evolve. Those devices and techniques, which are more efficient and have lower emissions, are described in greater detail elsewhere in this book. As they become economically viable, they will be adopted by RCRA.

Next, we offer a more detailed description of how the traditional pit method is used in Australia today for commercial charcoal and biochar production.

## PIT PRODUCTION OF COMMERCIAL CHARCOAL

### The Timber Used

Making commercial charcoal or biochar begins with selecting and collecting timber. RCRA uses gidgee timber due to its extremely high density. Gidgee[3] grows in dense black soil in a band starting in northern Queensland and extending southwest to New South Wales. Gidgee timber charcoal is preferred for cooking, heating and by blacksmiths because it burns longer and hotter, making it more cost-effective for commercial use. For feedstock, RCRA uses already-downed timber, which would otherwise be field-burned or left to rot. RCRA does not deforest.

## The Pits

RCRA makes charcoal generally following the earth oven or pit method. RCRA's charcoal pits are dug in very specific soil types to retain the integrity of the walls. The pits vary in size, but most often they are rectangular and as deep as four meters. Because each pit has a slightly different shape, it will cook slightly differently. The collier must therefore be aware of the characteristics of each pit.

## The Process

Timber is cut, loaded, and waiting near the pit. The collier first ignites a covering of wood at the bottom of the pit to create a bed of hot coals. When the hot bed is ready, the timber is tipped into the pit and a center support pipe is placed along the pit's midline. A corrugated iron roof is laid over the pipe, leaving air gaps on each end. The air gaps allow the collier to regulate the oxygen entering the pit so that the timber will smolder rather than flame. Flame, which occurs with excess oxygen, would convert the timber to ash instead of charcoal. On the other hand, an insufficient burn will result in incomplete conversion of the wood, leaving volatile material in the charcoal that will make it smoky for cooking, and a less desirable biochar.

The oxygen is drawn into the pit through an air gap, down the end wall to the level of smoldering coals, across that level of the pit, and then expelled through the other gap at the far end of the pit. As the timber chars, and the main body of heat moves up towards the roof, the oxygen flow must be reduced to compensate.

Fig. 2.3 Loading timber into biochar pit for second burn

Controlling oxygen flow is the key to making quality charcoal. Wind, air temperature, and weather can all dramatically influence the process. For example, the pit can become fan-forced with wind or affected by the moisture in the air from rain; charcoal pits cook better in winter than they do in summer.

The collier must therefore keep the pit smoldering as the char starts to form, and make fine and timely adjustments to regulate the flow of oxygen. This requires careful monitoring throughout the days and into the evenings. Inattention will not only affect product quality; a fire can erupt in the pit, which if unchecked will rage out of control and within minutes the immense heat will buckle the roof (letting in more oxygen), then collapse the roof—and destroy the pit.

After 24–48 hours, the "first burn" is cooked. The collier closes the oxygen gaps at either end of the pit and sands up the joins to make sure no oxygen can enter, which stops the smoldering reaction and preserves the charcoal.

---

[3] Gidgee is a gaseous tree that forecasts the rain; when rain is imminent, gidgee releases gas that smells like rotten eggs.

When the pit has cooled to a manageable level, it is loaded with more timber, since the first batch has shrunk in volume as the heat has driven off its moisture. The roof is replaced, and the cooking continued. This process, which maximizes the efficiency of charcoal and biochar production, is repeated until the pit is full of charcoal.

## CONCLUSION

Whether you choose to become a user of biochar or try your hand at making it, the paramount point is this: everyone can be involved in this movement at some level, and that involvement will make a difference.

In this cause, no one is powerless. Everything we need to assist in healing the planet is within our grasp, in our own homes, yards, and fields, awaiting only the resolve to turn biomass into gold.

## KEY POINTS FROM THIS CHAPTER

- Global interest is growing around the idea that a charcoal product —biochar—could turn infertile soil into productive farmland.

- Biochar is biomass charred for application to soil. Biomass includes grass clippings, dead trees, manure, crop waste, and vegetable scraps.

- Biochar made from biomass can help durably nourish the soil, making crops abundant, healthy, and cheaper to produce.

- Biochar and charcoal are similar, but their uses are different. Charcoal is used as a fuel. Biochar is crushed charcoal developed for use in the soil.

- To make biochar, biomass is cooked without, or with limited, oxygen. The cooking reduces and transforms the biomass into a black, light new substance—biochar.

- Biochar can draw in water and hold it like a sponge. This structure of biochar provides an excellent habitat for plant-nourishing soil microbes.

- When biomass decomposes or is burned it contributes to the greenhouse gases in the atmosphere. By converting biomass to make biochar and putting it in the soil, greenhouse gases are kept out of the atmosphere.

- Converting biomass to biochar opens a new spectrum of business opportunities and financial benefits at every level: residential, crop farming, grazing, and industry.

- People have been making charcoal and therefore biochar for centuries. Traditional methods are being adapted and further developed for modern use.

- Everyone can be involved in the global movement to convert biomass to biochar, and that involvement will make a difference.

# Chapter 3

# On the Farm: A Biochar Biography

Bob Wells

**IN THIS CHAPTER YOU WILL LEARN:**

- How a former boat salesman turned an overgrown, infertile piece of land into an organic farm.
- How biochar was pivotal to his success.
- The hope biochar offers to future generations.

"A nagging thought kept haunting my subconscious that this biochar stuff was just too good to be true. But I kept getting great results wherever and however I applied it."

# INTRODUCTION

In 2005, my wife and I found ourselves in the happy position of owning a small overgrown and undevelopable piece of land next to our house on Cape Cod, Massachusetts. I wanted to set up a small organic market-farm and adopt a simpler, healthier lifestyle. So with naïve fervor I quit my 9 to 5 job in the marine industry and threw myself into clearing away the trees and vines.

Soon, however, my noble thoughts about organic farming and "managing my woodlot" collided with harsh reality. The soil had been abused and grazed to death before it was abandoned seventy-five years ago, to be taken over by every nasty invasive plant in the neighborhood.

## CLEARING THE LAND—AND MY HEAD

When my wife and I purchased our "farmland," it was so thickly overgrown that it was impassable. If I wanted to farm this land, I would have to clear it first. Clearing this land felt like trying to tame a stray cat the size of a Buick. Every day, I would come home sore, bruised, and bleeding.

Multiflora rose, brought in generations before to make hedgerows, had grown up and over many desirable trees (like white cedar), smothering them in the process. Doing battle with these spiked barriers meant donating a pint of blood to the cause—daily. Their thorns aren't just sharp: they're evilly angled so that any effort to extricate yourself from them sinks the points in deeper. My wife, a history buff, enjoyed the oft-repeated joke that I was going off to fight "the War of the Roses."

The multiflora had many other partners in crime. Black locust also has thorns on its young shoots but they're long, thin, and straight so that once they get into you they break off and leave behind a stinger under your skin. The other problem with a locust tree is that it grows tall and thin with a very shallow root system. Cape Cod—an exposed, sickle-shaped peninsula that hangs out into the Atlantic Ocean from the mainland—has some of the strongest winds in the country. That combination means lots of broken or toppled locusts everywhere. And even when I came across a nice oak or cedar, it usually had a broken or uprooted locust sprawled across it in just such a way as to destroy any potential for the native species to grow straight and healthy.

Bull briar must have been the inspiration for barbed wire. Its vines are so strong that they have stalled the hydraulics on my tractor. They love to hide just above the ground, where they will catch your foot and trip you—especially if you happen to be carrying a running chain saw.

The soil was apparently fertile enough for something: I didn't know that poison ivy could grow so big—and high. Stumps nine inches across supported poisonous canopies thirty feet in the air where they too smothered more desirable plants. Run through one of those vines with a chain saw and you'd spray yourself with a nasty skin irritant. I spent many nights in itchy torment, caused by poison ivy sawdust getting inside my gloves, under my belt, or into my shoes.

To top it all off, we are infested with wood ticks that can leave a scar from a single bite. Even more dreaded are the deer ticks; they're the size of a poppy seed and carry Lyme disease, which has disabled many people in our area and taken the lives of two men I knew.

After months and months of fighting this battle daily my resolve was being tested. Scratched up, bruised, itchy, and tired, at times I wondered: What was I *thinking*?

However, doubt was always driven away by the vision that brought me here— that someday I would have a lovely little farm where I could serve my community by growing healthy, fresh, local fruits and vegetables. And besides, I had told my friends and family that I was going to farm, so there was no going back to selling boats now.

## FIRST PLANTING

I eventually cleared enough space for high bush blueberries—my first plantings. I reasoned that blueberries already grew in the wild here on the Cape and therefore would probably survive even with my inexpert help. I also knew that they would grow in the acid soil on my plot—and I had seen organic blueberries selling for over $20 per pound.

The downside was that it would take a few years for these new, little bushes to produce any significant return. So I started seeking out other specialty crops that might give me a chance of seeing some more immediate cash flow. I spent many intense hours reading and searching websites of agricultural schools trying to glean as much knowledge as I could about everything that I was trying to grow. As I crammed, the hints from my wife about getting a "real job" were becoming more frequent.

But I was determined to make this farm work for us. After all, I did have *some* farming experience.

## FORMATIVE FARMING, BIG AND SMALL

### BIG FARMING IN WESTERN NEW YORK

My mother grew up on a farm in western New York State. During my high school years I spent my summers there.

By that time, the farm had expanded from the original 300 acres my grandfather bought when my mom was just a youngster. It had become an agribusiness conglomerate, managed by two of my uncles and containing thousands of acres of various crops.

When school got out for the summer, I would rent a room from my dear Aunt Rindy and spend long days in the scorching sun picking stones out of fields. I worked alongside huge, muscular, migrant workers who only tolerated the stumbling little white boy because they knew that he was the "boss man's nephew."

I learned many life lessons in their rough shadows during the day—and each night from dinner-table political lectures from my Uncle Bob. I was young and naïve. (Now I'm older and naïve.)

Above all, those summers gave me a perspective on what it takes to farm on a large scale. My uncles' farm had hundreds of acres of spinach, thousands of acres of green beans, tractors that would plow 100 acres a day, six giant pea combines that would run around the clock when the peas were ready to pick, huge truckloads of chemical fertilizers and pesticides (some of which were applied by helicopter), storage barns that could pass as football stadiums—and I saw them all as normal parts of farming. It was generally understood that any poor farmer in that area with less than 500 acres would just struggle along and when he could no longer turn enough profit, he'd get devoured by one of the bigger farms.

## SMALL FARMING IN WEST VIRGINIA

My youthful summers on the farm in New York ended after high school. But a few months later, I had the chance to gain another valuable perspective.

When I graduated, my parents were very upset with me. I'd announced that I didn't know what I wanted to do with my life and therefore couldn't possibly go to college—that would just be a huge waste of time and money. So I decided to travel about and see the world with the hope that something would pique my interest and give me more focus.

After a few months of going here and there and trying various dead-end jobs, my brother's wife suggested that I visit her sister Natalie in West Virginia. Natalie's husband Bob had left behind a successful chiropractic practice in New Jersey to start a family in the clean, natural environment of a backwoods homestead nestled in a hollow beside a creek. With a small bag of belongings and a bus ticket, I was off to West Virginia thinking that I would see some countryside and get to know some relatives.

I'll never forget the evening I arrived. My brother's wife's sister's husband Bob (I'm not sure what that makes him to me) picked me up at the closest bus stop, which was about 25 miles from their home (a 45-minute ride on rough, switchback roads and single-lane bridges) and drove me down to the creek-side homestead.

I had assumed that I would stay for the weekend—or maybe a few days. But other arrangements had been made: when we entered the farmhouse, Bob told me that by the end of the summer I would know my way around their 40 acres pretty well.

The culture shock I experienced in West Virginia was tempered by family connections similar to what I had experienced in western New York. In both cases I enjoyed safe, loving, supportive farm-family households. Both places were full of kids, animals, family activities, work, community connections, and a generally heartwarming, country-style environment. But aside from that, the two farms could not have been more different.

**A TALE OF TWO FARMS: WESTERN NEW YORK VERSUS WEST VIRGINIA**

In New York, my uncles would fly their own airplane between the plots of land they owned in different counties to check on crops or deliver equipment parts. In West Virginia, I could have delivered a message across the farm with a fold-up paper airplane.

In New York, my daily chores included things like loading tons of seed and fertilizer for the planting crews and filling the fuel on the huge diesel tractors. In West Virginia, I got up at 5:00 a.m. to hand-milk the single Jersey-Guernsey cross cow before breakfast.

The New York farm stretched for miles so flat that the biggest hills were the nearby overpasses for the New York Thruway. In West Virginia, the only flat spot on the farm was down next to the creek—where we would only grow hay because of the regular floods.

In New York, irrigation was handled by miles of heavy metal pipe and huge V8 diesel-powered pumps running full blast. In West Virginia, it was handled by yours truly and a heavy metal bucket.

In New York, every planting was accompanied by chemical fertilizers and pesticides. In West Virginia, the standard amendments were compost and manure.

I could go on, but by now you get the picture. Going to West Virginia was like going back 150 years in a time machine. The reason for sharing all this is not to pretend that because of my experience with both extremes, I know what works best. I just want to let you know that I *have* seen both sides of farming. It seems obvious to me now that both styles have strengths and weaknesses. I don't like to judge anyone's methods too harshly—mostly because I strongly believe that we all, large and small, can do a lot better.

**...BACK TO MY LITTLE CAPE COD FARM**

**SANDY SOIL, NEED HELP**

By the time I tunneled into the tangled woods with my trusty chain saw, and chewed up enough vines and cut down enough trees and dug out and pulled enough stumps to actually plant something, I was faced with another harsh, unfertile reality. What little topsoil I had, I unfortunately dispersed in the act of pulling stumps and roots. What was left looked like it would make a nice, large sandbox for the preschool down the road.

This soil condition was common for Cape Cod. The Cape was formed by the northern glaciers of the ice ages scraping their way down the east coast of the United States. When they retreated they left behind big piles of pebbles and sand with the odd boulder mixed in and an occasional clay bank where the melt waters went through. Sometimes I feel like all of my soil came out of a huge street sweeper, emptied out after cleaning roads that were sanded all winter. Sand and pebbles made up 99 percent of what I started with—the soil resembled beach sand, extremely acidic, and had very little organic matter.

Putting in my first blueberries, I dug large holes and mixed in what I hoped would be good amendments for long-term fertility, since I intended these plants to outlive me. But when I had cleared enough room to start growing vegetables—which, by the way, took about three years—I had to figure out how to build good soil.

### ENTER *TERRA PRETA*

> I picked up and began to read the book *1491* by Charles C. Mann, which contained a few pages about *terra preta de indio.*
> Little did I know that this book would start me on a path that would change my life.

When faced with difficult problems, I start reading. I buy or borrow books, and spend hours online, looking for coaching that will help me over my next hurdle. I tend toward how-to books aimed at the specific things I need to learn. So it was very unusual (I must have been bored) when I picked up and began to read a book that my wife, the history buff, had brought home from the library. The book was *1491* by Charles C. Mann. Little did I know that this book would start me on a path that would change my life.

This book revealed the story of *terra preta de Indio* to me. "Aha!" I thought. If ancient people with simple technology could turn washed-out sandy soils into the most fertile, sustainable soils on the planet, then just think what I could do here with modern methods and understanding. The book was very much a godsend to me. I had all the ingredients at hand: poor soil that needed major help, huge piles of cleared **biomass** to get rid of—and some experience in making charcoal.

### *TERRA PRETA* IS ROCKET SCIENCE

My experience with making charcoal stemmed from my boyhood hobby of model rocketry. Never satisfied with putting together someone else's designs or living within the adult world's rules, I learned how to make my own rockets and solid fuel rocket engines. (Don't tell my mom.) Without going into details that I would not even teach my own kids, let me just say that very fine, willow wood charcoal was one of the key ingredients in a good rocket engine.

So off I went to build a **retort** and see what charcoal might do to propel my vegetables. And by the way, for elitists who look down their noses at us dumb farmers, this experience conclusively proves that farming really *is* rocket science.

## MY FIRST BATCHES OF CHAR

Here's how I made my first batches of good, clean char on the farm:

- I would fill an 18-gallon steel drum with black locust limbs and secure the top, leaving only a single, ¾ inch hole in the top for a vent.

- I would then roll the drum into a small brush fire and let it cook on its side while I continued to gather up more sticks, limbs, and cordwood. Soon, an impressive jet of gas (yes, like a rocket) would be blasting out of the vent as the wood gases escaped. If I aimed the hole into the wind and downward toward the hot coals these gases would ignite and flare back over the can accelerating the whole process with some vigor.

- When the vapors stopped escaping, I would simply roll the can back out of the fire, stand it on end with the hole now flush against the ground, so that no air could enter, and leave it to cool down while I put out the brush fire and saved what charcoal I could from that.

By the next morning I could empty the cooled drum which, based on what I'd learned from my research, felt like mining gold. It was very exciting to pop off the lid and dump out the beautiful, black char that yesterday had been a pile of useless sticks. Turning junk into useful charcoal! Alchemy!

I know what you are probably thinking: yes, I like to play with fire. I have even earned the nickname "Arson Wells" but I can honestly say that I have never burned anything down that I didn't mean to, nor have I ever hurt anyone while indulging my pyromaniacal tendencies.

Since the 18-gallon drums were so much fun, I graduated up to 55-gallon drums with a resulting increase in the volume of charcoal I could produce in a day. Soon, I had collected a nice pile of beautiful charcoal and was ready to begin some crude field trials.

## TRYING MY BIOCHAR IN THE FIELD

In my second year in the vegetable business, a friend gave me some seeds for a local species of turnip called the "Eastham Turnip." She said, "You live in Eastham. You *have* to grow Eastham Turnips." This encounter turned out to be another godsend.

There is a long and legendary history behind the Eastham turnip. It's so important to the town culture that there is even an annual turnip festival. I can't remember ever eating a turnip before I started to grow them but I love them now. Mostly, that is because they provide me with a niche market that is hard to beat. They sell for more than $3 per pound at the farmers market, and I have actually sold a single turnip for $24. It was an 8-pounder, and I grew it using biochar.

After my friend gave me the seeds, I decided to try out the *terra preta* idea on my turnip crop. First I spread out all the compost that I made over the winter. Then I devoted my entire biochar supply to turning enough earth black for two 100-foot rows.

I ground up the charcoal small enough that it would pass through a ¼-inch screen. I then covered my rows an inch deep with it and tilled it in. Next, I planted the whole field and laid out my drip irrigation that I feed from a dedicated well with a solar powered pump.

I was not at all expecting the results that I got. I knew I was amending really poor sandy soil, but I am not exaggerating when I say that the turnips in those two dark-earth rows were twice as big as the turnips in the rest of the field. After only 30 days of growth they were so much bigger and greener that they looked like a different species than the rest of the field. I was amazed. I thought I might really be on to something here.

The turnips in the two rows tilled in with biochar were twice as big as in the rest of the field. After only 30 days of growth they were so much bigger and greener that they looked like a different species.

I have actually sold a single turnip for $24, an 8-pounder grown using biochar.

Fig. 3.1 Turnips in field dressed with biochar (Photo: Doug Clayton)

It was at this point that I decided to go online and see if anyone else had been farming with biochar. Sure enough, I found a whole international community trying to learn the ins and outs of this stuff.

I then threw myself into reading anything I could find on the subject. At the time, there wasn't very much. Dr. Lehmann's book[4] had not come out yet so mostly I followed online links to as many papers and articles as I could find.

Simultaneously, I tried to make as much char as I could and threw it on every plant in sight to see what would happen.

During that period I started top-dressing raw char onto my blueberry bushes. Then I read an article that said that char can be used as a liming agent to bring up the pH of acidic soil. In horror I realized that I had just spread a liming agent on my young blueberries—which require strongly acidic soils. In fact, when I planted them I had used sulfur to make the soil even more acidic than it already was. Until now the plants had been doing very well but I was terribly afraid that I might have damaged the ones given biochar. Fortunately, I had not gotten very far but I knew that I had put it on around 100 bushes.

---

[4] Johannes Lehmann and Stephen Joseph, eds. *Biochar for Environmental Management: Science and Technology* (London, UK and Sterling, VA [USA]: Earthscan, 2009).

It wasn't until about half a year later that I noticed something strange. I was walking past the blueberries on my way to the vegetable field when I suddenly noticed that the plants were much smaller in the last third of each row. (By then, I'd forgotten that I'd spread charcoal on some of them.)

My first thought was that there must be some kind of blockage in the irrigation system. Blueberries don't have root hairs like other plants and given our sandy soil, irrigation is essential to keeping them alive, let alone making them productive. When I planted this field, I put in drip irrigation feeding a ring of ¼-inch soaker hose around each plant. This was all fed by my solar-powered pump.

But on further examination, I could see that the irrigation system was working fine. The drippers were working the same on the big plants as well as the stunted ones.

Next I thought that the bushes were of different varieties. I had planted seven different varieties over two years' time, but once again that was not the answer. All the plants in those rows were the Jersey variety. So, why would two-thirds of those rows be three feet tall and one-third be two feet tall? I had been meticulously treating every plant with equal care since I had put them in.

Then it dawned on me. I knelt down and started pulling away the pine needle mulch around the base of each plant and sure enough, chunks of charcoal could be clearly seen around the bigger plants. I had been afraid that I had poisoned them when I had applied that biochar. But in fact here was clear evidence that it was helping them. Once again I was stunned by my good fortune even though I can't explain the mechanism involved in making this happen and had feared exactly the opposite result.

I started thinking that biochar was some kind of magical substance that helped all plants grow and couldn't hurt anything. As I continued to study all the literature I could find related to making and applying biochar, I decided to get more scientific in my approach. I did my best to keep notes on what I was doing and began testing it on a number of other crops.

## THE RESULTS
I kept looking hard for the downside of biochar. A nagging thought kept haunting my subconscious that this biochar stuff was just too good to be true.

But I kept getting great results wherever and however I applied it. I tried it on eight varieties of peas with very good results. I planted green beans by digging a six-inch ditch, filling it half way up with 50:50 biochar and compost mix, wetting the mix, then putting in the seeds and covering them with soil. I have honestly never seen faster growing, more productive, or better tasting green beans anywhere on any farm.

My beets love the biochar; my carrots love the biochar, my potatoes like the biochar. My corn loves the biochar, my lawn loves the biochar. I have grown Swiss chard, arugula, lettuces, and squash all with great results after adding biochar, either tilled in before planting or as a top dressing after the plants have been established.

My tomatoes seem to be the only holdouts. They have shown little response, and my wife says that the biochar-amended potting soil I mixed for her had very poor results for her tomato starts.

Having looked hard, I have noted one potentially detrimental effect. Biochar-fed plants may mature much faster than normal. In most cases this would be a great advantage, but with crops like lettuce and spinach, rapid maturity could cause them to bolt before you are ready to harvest.

Whenever I give or sell someone a biochar sample, I encourage them to experiment on a small scale first so that no one is betting the farm—perhaps literally—on the hope that applying biochar to their whole crop will yield enormous increases.

There are also ways of pushing it too far. The only time that I can say that I did any real damage was when I used fresh, un-aged, un-inoculated, unfortified biochar when planting peas. My understanding of this phenomenon is that fresh biochar can actually compete with the plants as it adsorbs its initial load of nutrients before it settles into its role of acting like a coral reef in the soil. But the following year that same piece of ground did very well with other crops. Since then I have been careful to warn anyone using biochar for the first time to make sure that they mix it first with compost or compost tea. It also helps to age it. Unlike compost, spreading the char in the fall for it to be tilled in the spring is an advantage.

## RICH SOIL OR POOR SOIL, BIOCHAR MAKES SENSE

If you are fortunate enough to be farming soil that is rich and balanced, then the advantage of biochar for you is that it will help you keep it that way without using as much fertilizer. You probably won't see the dramatic results that I have. But that doesn't mean you won't see some strong, long-term advantages.

The economic advantages of biochar are very hard to define because we are so used to thinking in terms of how much fertilizer I need to buy *this year*. Imagine for a moment that I offered to sell you a wonderful new source of nitrogen that would make your crops grow better than before. Now suppose I claimed that the application you're putting on this year will work even better for next year's crop without adding any more. Either you would figure I was selling snake oil, or you would want some of my magic fertilizer because you could save on next year's fertilizer expenses.

Yet biochar in the soil is something like that. Unlike fertilizer, whether man-made, chemical, or natural, biochar has an extremely long life in the soil. Biochar also attracts microbes and beneficial fungi, holds on to the nutrients that are put into the soil, and increases the **cation exchange capacity** of soil more and more over time. In truth, biochar works better the second and third year than it does the first.

Another important advantage of biochar in soil is its ability to hold moisture. As water issues become more important in the world, we need to be aware that we can save on irrigation through the use of biochar. Saving on irrigation means saving on both water and energy.

I was suspicious that soil darkened with biochar would heat up more in the sun, speeding evaporation. My sandy soil dries out very quickly as it is. Once again I was surprised when my experiments showed that biochar helps the soil stay moist even in full sunlight.

Biochar is not itself a fertilizer, although some might argue that point since a certain fraction of biochar will be minerals that may in fact act as nutrients.

## THE LEGACY

One of the things that really enthuses me about biochar is the legacy it will leave. By using it, I can make my soil better over the long-term. Biochar will still be benefiting the soil long after I become compost and my grandchildren are farming.

Along with the extended list of practical benefits of biochar, I have discovered something else, something very meaningful: biochar also can nurture hope.

This is what I mean. As I learned more about biochar and went about telling everyone I knew about this great, simultaneously new and ancient technology, I started receiving invitations to come and speak to people about it. Garden clubs and organic farmers were the first to be interested. Then, to my surprise, my 17 year-old daughter Marina asked me if I would come to her school and explain biochar to her Green Club.

I was surprised because she had heard me tell so many people about biochar that I figured that she was sick of hearing it. Nonetheless, I was flattered that she asked so I took her up on the offer. I was nervous because I knew that teenagers can be a tough audience. If they were not fascinated, I would put them right to sleep. I asked myself if I was crazy to go and talk to a group of teens about my dirt.

Like any parent, I have often worried about my kids and all the things that they have to face in their future. Sure, when I was little we lived with the ever-present threat that someone would press the wrong button and all of humanity would vanish in a bright flash of atomic explosions. We even had duck-and-cover drills at school, which really hammered that worry into our little minds. Even in first grade, I wondered how a sheet metal school desk was going to save me from an atom bomb.

But my kids can talk intelligently about asteroids that will wipe us out or super-bug diseases that we have created through the overuse of antibiotics. Rampant STDs, drug use, alien abduction, animal extinctions, super volcanoes, giant tsunamis, ozone depletion, massive pollution, rampant consumerism, terrorist threats, overpopulation, energy shortages, human trafficking, war … the list goes on, thanks to our sensationalist media. And now on top of all of these concerns our young people have the mother of all worries, global climate change!

But the most amazing thing happened in that classroom. I told the dozen or so Green Club kids that right in my back yard I had a simple device that can effectively mine carbon out of the sky, put it in the ground, make the soil better for growing food, and offset the use of fossil fuels at the same time. They didn't fall asleep—they understood. They got excited by the idea. One girl insisted that I needed to tell the principal of the school right away so that an assembly could be arranged for me to tell the whole school about this. Mind you, this is a school of around 1,000 students. That was the point at which I saw how much these children needed *hope*. Their questions were not what I expected. They asked: "How can we get started doing this right now?" and "How can we help spread the word about this to others?"

Since that day this little Green Club of teenage students has done much more than hope—they have taken action. They have arranged field trips, helped make biochar on my farm, promoted field trials, set up tables at community gatherings to explain about biochar, and even won a competition with their video explaining biochar. Independent and classroom studies have been set up in their school in order to learn more about the uses of biochar. And all of this is happening because the kids are making it happen, not because some adult is pressing an agenda on them.

## NEXT STEPS, MORE PROOF

Since my classroom epiphany, I have pressed on as well. I joined forces with a business partner in order to create better systems for producing biochar faster, more efficiently and—most importantly to me—without making smoke. (That subject will be covered in another chapter.)

I have continued my farm experiments. The most accurate trial that I have done to date is again with my Eastham turnips. With soil amended for a couple of years with compost, minerals, and manures, we planted eight rows of turnips and tried to control all the variables so that everything would be even and consistent across the plot. After the plants were established, we top-dressed four of the eight rows with biochar, using a light application of around eight ounces (one cup) to the square foot.

After around 30 more days of growth, a puzzling thing happened, which I have also observed in other trials by other people. The plants *without* the biochar looked much more lush and healthy. The greens were darker and larger. I was afraid that I was going to have to eat an awful lot of my words about the miracle of biochar.

Another 60 days passed and it was time to harvest. We harvested our trial plots and weighed each and every turnip. Once again biochar surprised me. Across the board, the non-biochar rows looked big and healthy—but the actual yields showed 20 percent less turnips. The weight of the greens was very even in both cases. Looking at the roots as we pulled the plants, one could see that biochar has a lot of influence *underground* where you can't see what is going on, stimulating the growth of bigger root systems that yield bigger turnips.

> Biochar was working *underground*. The root systems were bigger and so were the turnips. I could expect to realize an additional $6,400 per acre by applying biochar.

Extrapolating conservatively, I figured I could realize an additional $6,400 per acre by applying biochar this way on this particular crop. Plus, it will still be there next year to help whatever I plant.

I thank God that there are people out there who have the power, influence, and conscience to try to make good things happen on a national or global scale. But honestly, I suffer from the MEGO affect (My Eyes Glaze Over) when the subject turns to "Cap and Trade," "carbon credits," or other political solutions. If farmers on any scale begin to see the financial benefits of using biochar, we will have no need to sell them on the idea that it is good for the environment. Just explain how it will help make them money and stand back and watch them make it happen.

## WHAT'S STANDING IN THE WAY?

The technology to make biochar is not at all difficult by today's standards. What is difficult is to get us all out of our mental ruts to look at things in new ways. For example, when I see a pile of dead branches by the side of the road, I don't see a pile of waste. I see an opportunity to sequester carbon, offset fossil fuel use, make my farm more productive, and feed my family better—all at once.

When I'm out teaching groups about biochar and its use I am often asked "If this is all so great, why isn't everybody doing it?" That question elicits two responses in me. First, it makes me think that as a society we have developed a pervasive arrogance that makes us believe that we already know the best way to do things. Second, I think that biochar is actually something that doesn't fit the "bigger is better" mentality, and therefore is of no interest to big corporations that live on economies of scale. If you imagine a big company considering a factory to produce biochar out of wheat straw for farmers, how could they ever justify the expense of energy and infrastructure to move so many raw materials—with very little density—to the factory to be processed and then moved back to the farms for application?

Maybe smaller is better in this case. If the farmer who grew the wheat had a device like mine that would heat his home, barn, and greenhouse while making biochar for use right there on his farm, it would make excellent economic sense for him. Small- and medium-scale production of biochar right on the farm, or maybe community-wide, seems an ideal—and realistic—arrangement for sustainable economic and environmental efficiency.

## CONCLUSION

One day I was explaining to my oldest brother Jim how inadequate I felt as a teacher on the subject of biochar. Various groups invite me to share my experiences with them, but I tend to think that it's because not many others know much about biochar, so those who do are in demand.

Jim's heartening response was, "In the land of the blind, the one-eyed man is king." I submit this chapter with the hope that the vision of this one-eyed man will inspire much more experimentation, study, and perhaps even a little hope for the future.

## KEY POINTS FROM THIS CHAPTER

- Biochar traces back to an ancient, simple technology that turned infertile, sandy soils into fertile, sustainable soils.

- Biochar can be made from sticks, fallen tree limbs, and cordwood using basic equipment.

- Biochar makes a big difference in crop yields.

- Biochar can be tilled into the soil before planting or applied as a top dressing after plants have been established.

- People who want to try biochar should experiment on a small scale first.

- Fresh biochar can compete with plants for nutrients. Before first-time use in the soil, biochar should be mixed with compost or compost tea, and aged.

- Using biochar has long-term advantages. Biochar stays with the soil for years, attracts microbes and beneficial fungi, and holds on to soil nutrients. Biochar works better the second and third year than it does the first. Biochar also holds moisture. For these reasons, biochar saves money on fertilizer and on irrigation.

- For those worried about global warming, biochar offers long-term hope. It can make the soil better for growing food, and offset the use of fossil fuels at the same time.

- Farmers on any scale can discover the financial benefits of using biochar and will be motivated to use it. The environmental benefits will naturally follow.

- Small- and medium-scale production of biochar on the farm, or community-wide, seems an ideal—and realistic—arrangement for sustainable economic and environmental efficiency.

Chapter 4

# From Blacksmith to Biochar: The Essence of Community

Peter Hirst
New England Biochar

**IN THIS CHAPTER YOU WILL LEARN:**

- One man's special journey from the corporate world to village blacksmith to biochar producer, entrepreneur, and advocate.

- The transforming power of contained and controlled fire—an ancient technology and community focal point—and how that same power is embodied in a low-tech modern "retort," turning biomass into biochar and inspiring new perspectives on the meaning of "scale" and "community".

- The potential of low-tech, high-ingenuity methods, combined with strong community, to reclaim infertile land and establish a sustainable, environmentally balanced biochar system.

*[This chapter offers the author's personal story and perspectives about biochar and the meaning of community, and provides a backdrop for his chapter on basic biochar production, "Biochar Production Basics: From Colliers to Retorts," which appears later in this book.]*

"Finally, it all clicked: the extraordinary turnips; the small, local scale of the technology; the potential to restore the original rich, black earth of Cape Cod; and the potential for carbon-negative energy...It all pointed to biochar! I'd come to a fork in the road, and following the wisdom of Yogi Berra, I took it."

## INTRODUCTION: THE POWER OF FIRE

Fire fascinates us. It is embedded in our lore, our mythology, and our culture. As applied technology, perhaps the oldest known, fire is vital, practical, transformational.

Fire is also at the heart of biochar technology. Fire transforms **biomass** into char.

Wherever we make char now, we see the firing of the **retort** taking on the role of the ancient cooking fire: not only a device for meeting the community's practical needs, but a place and occasion for celebrating community itself.

My journey from blacksmith to biochar producer and advocate has taught me a great deal about community and appropriate scale.

### MEDITATIONS OF AN ASPIRING BLACKSMITH

#### ABOUT COMMUNITY

Before I became a char maker, I was a blacksmith. After a career in the energy industry, I sought a simpler life: a life of meaning, human scale, and local community. I aspired to become "The Village Blacksmith" in Longfellow's poem. Longfellow's blacksmith pursues a valued, ancient craft; through his "honest sweat" and his relationship with his community—family, neighbors, church, village—he achieves a revered grace and enlightenment. His mere example serves as "the lesson" to his community about the "flaming forge of life."

In Longfellow's poem, that community was a small town in eastern Massachusetts and following my romantic muse, I went looking for my community there, on Cape Cod.

I would soon realize that my vision of community did not match contemporary reality. While developing my blacksmith business plan, I worked part time in a local store. During most of the 1900s—until the 1980s—this store had been the authentic incarnation of that other community center of Longfellow's time, the general store. In this one place, you could get cast iron cookware, clam rakes and shrimp net crimps, kitchen matches that you really could "strike anywhere," and a fresh cup of coffee. You could sit around the hot coal stove in the morning with the village sages and solve the world's problems, before the workday started.

No more. Cast iron from Pennsylvania had been supplanted by imported Teflon. The merchandise was intended for day-trippers from "over the bridge"—who wouldn't know a shrimp net from a shrimp cocktail. Almost everything in the store, including the computer-carved cod—the esteemed Massachusetts state symbol, the "Cod" in Cape Cod—was made on the other side of the world.

The local residents had lost the special community aura of the once-beloved store. They'd say: "You work at The Store? I never go there. I live here."

Something had gone wrong; the meaning of "community" had changed since Longfellow's day. Back then, the geographic proximity of small groups of people made for a commonality of interest, perhaps as basic as subsistence. To my disappointment, this seemed forever lost.

I longed for something on a local scale, made locally for the locals—some *authenticity.* "The Store" now lacked it. I resolved that my blacksmith shop, and my life, would not.

## ABOUT COAL

Of all the pathways to *authenticity* in my new life as a blacksmith, finding the source for forge fuel would prove the richest. Although this search almost ended the whole endeavor, it ultimately led me to biochar.

For over 150 years, the traditional blacksmith's forge fuel has been a bituminous coal called "blacksmith's coal." I found an affordable source nearby. But I also found out, according to the dealer, that "it makes the thickest, blackest smoke you ever saw." My nineteenth-century muse had taken another blow, this time colliding with my twenty-first century, clean-energy conscience. I bought enough coal to get started, but knew that long-term I'd need cleaner fuel—and went to the library.

Fossil coal appeared during the Industrial Revolution. Before then, blacksmiths had to be using something else. Again, I found insight in Longfellow's poem:

> And children coming home from school
> Look in at the open door;
> They love to see the flaming forge,
> And hear the bellows roar,
> And catch the burning sparks that fly
> Like chaff from a threshing-floor.

There it was. Bituminous coal doesn't make "sparks that fly like chaff." Only one fuel makes sparks without smoke: charcoal.

I decided to make charcoal.

## MAKING CHARCOAL, PRESERVING FORESTS

I did know a little about making charcoal. At one time, I was a serious student of Eric Sloane, the American chronicler of early American rural crafts, tools and industries, including the craft of the **collier**—making coal from wood. We call it charcoal now, but back when it was the fuel of the early industrial age, the word "coal" meant the black fuel made from wood.

The fact that charcoal is a biofuel bolstered my decision to make it. As a biofuel, charcoal is a renewable resource. Even though, over the last five centuries, human activity has left the woodlands of Cape Cod sparse and of poor quality (see textbox), they still have abundant slash and standing deadwood. If left alone, all of this material decays, returning its carbon to the atmosphere as carbon dioxide ($CO_2$) and in some cases methane, a greenhouse gas much more potent than $CO_2$.

If I could use this renewable biomass as fuel, I could capture its energy while releasing no more, and possibly less, greenhouse gas to the atmosphere. In other words, I could establish a sustainable, carbon-neutral fuel system.

---

**THE CAPE WOODLANDS AND SOIL: POOR, BUT NOT ALWAYS**

They found it [Cape Cod] to be a small neck of land; on this side where we lay is the bay, and the further side the sea; the ground or earth, sand hills, much like the downs in Holland, but much better; the crust of the earth a spit's depth excellent black earth; all wooded with oaks, pines, sassafras, juniper, birch, holly, vines, some ash, walnut; the wood for the most part open and without underwood, fit either to go or ride in.

—William Bradford, *Mourt's Relation,* 1622

---

Furthermore, a conscientious woodlot management program could actually improve the health of the woods and increase its total biomass beyond its current neglected state, thereby drawing net carbon from the atmosphere and sequestering it in that biomass. I could actually aim for a carbon *negative* fuel.

In Europe, woodlots had been conserved for centuries through **coppicing**, providing a sustainable fuel source for the charcoal needed to heat the smithy's forge. Coppicing is the practice of harvesting mature trees without removing the stumps, which are left to sprout new shoots. With an established root system, these juveniles grow fast, and continue to build the overall biomass of the woodlot, both by adding wood above ground and building more massive root structures below. Each harvest leaves intact the mature root structure, which is capable of supporting ever more woody material above.

This ancient practice was virtually absent on this continent. Why bother? When the Europeans first settled here, the woodlands of New England appeared limitless. Today, we know they are not; the Cape Cod woodlands have been deforested, overtaken by invasive vines and scrub, and left infertile and unproductive. (See also Bob Wells' chapter, "On the Farm: A Biochar Biography.")

I would do my part to remedy that. I'd find a woodlot to manage that would provide sufficient fuel to make charcoal for my little forge, and perhaps a surplus of charcoal I could sell to other smiths nearby, who were already expressing interest. I developed a passion for the idea that one of the industries mainly responsible for deforesting the Cape—**ironmongering**—could contribute to its recovery.

## TRADITIONAL CHARCOAL MAKING: AUTHENTIC, BUT OBSOLETE

As I looked for a woodlot to manage, I was also looking for a way to produce charcoal. I reviewed the ancient methods that supported the early industrial revolution. They offered valuable instruction on the rudiments of low-tech charcoal production. (For more on these rudiments, see my later chapter on basic biochar production, "Biochar Production Basics: From Colliers to Retorts.")

However, authentic as the traditional methods might be, they were dirty, dangerous, and environmentally suspect. Here was another reality check for my romantic notions; I'd have to find a way to modernize. Online, I found diagrams of a modern "retort"—essentially, an oven within an oven. The outer oven was a burn chamber; it would heat wood in the inner oven, baking the wood until it charred. The wood gases, given off as smoke in traditional methods, would be recycled into the outer burn chamber to sustain the bake. I decided to build one from readily available materials: a fuel oil tank, a standard 55-gallon (200 liter) drum, and standard plumbing fixtures.

## QUESTIONS OF SCALE

Of course, for my ideas about restoring land and selling surplus charcoal to work I would have to produce more char than I needed for smithing. This introduced issues of scale, involving not only the size of the local market and the size of the production unit, but the scale of effort needed to obtain feedstock. In securing access to management of a suitable hardwood lot, I'd have to convince the owner that I'd make a real difference on the land. I'd have to move a lot of slash and deadwood off an acre of land to show any progress in contributing to its health. Coppicing a single stem could provide over a cord of wood. If I did this right, I would produce a lot of charcoal.

I realized balancing feedstock, production technology, and charcoal demand would be a dynamic process, requiring continuous adjustment—like, in fact, most things in nature. After all, the producer of biochar, like the ancient collier, is a participant in natural processes, not a dominating force. This balancing of resources and needs is—as much as production technology—at the core of biochar systems. Modern agronomic colliery will be a craft encompassing many skills.

## A TURN IN THE ROAD – FROM CHARCOAL TOWARD BIOCHAR

### ENTER BOB WELLS

While I continued to develop my retort design, I explored the market potential for my surplus.

I visited the local farmers market and pitched the idea to sell my locally grown agricultural product—my charcoal. Gretchen, the manager, didn't exactly jump at it. "Charcoal?" she said. "I'm not sure that would qualify as 'locally grown'...But I know someone who makes charcoal—that guy over there across the way."

"Over there across the way" was Bob Wells, complete with straw hat, suspenders, and a stand full of fine looking produce, especially butternut squash. Wait a minute. Butternut squash? In August? The only stand in the market with winter squash.

Bob was friendly and approachable. I told him I intended to make charcoal—a lot of charcoal.

Bob perked up; I'd struck a chord. "Charcoal?" he asked. "Yeah, I make charcoal. Lots of it. I'm putting it in my soil, as biochar."

That was the first time I had ever heard the word "biochar." "You're doing *what* with it?" I asked. And I wish I had a dollar for every time I've heard that question since.

It wasn't long before I learned the fundamentals of biochar, including its soil qualities, carbon-capture and energy potential. And the retort design I was working out on paper? Bob already had the exact device—fuel oil tank, 55-gallon drum, and plumbing fittings—half-assembled and sitting outside his workshop. We agreed to get together at Bob's farm to try a few experiments and produce a little char. I had found a partner in the crime of colliery. (Bob Wells' own introduction to biochar is described in his chapter "On the Farm: A Biochar Biography.")

When I showed up at Bob's Redberry Farm, the first thing he showed me was his turnips. The Eastham turnip was a local legend, ripening around Thanksgiving and favored for retaining a rich sweetness despite its large size, typically a couple of pounds each.

Bob's turnips were in neat rows, showing large growths of greens still over a month after harvesting. Two rows showed marked differences from the others. The plants were more massive—about twice as big as the others, and a much darker green color. I saw immediately why he was so enthusiastic about biochar, for these beauties were the ones he had treated with the stuff.

### BREAKTHROUGH: THE CLOSED RETORT

We got around to making char. Bob had experimented with closed retorts; his yard boasted a motley collection of drums and barrels, pipes, nipples, elbows, and other plumbing artifacts. Most of it came from the Eastham dump, which would become our favorite supply depot.

Despite all the hardware and experimenting, most of Bob's actual production had been from controlled open burns, a traditional method of making char—educational, but not a long-term production solution. Bob and I started working on a retort.

Our first experiments were crude, yet effective. We built a controlled open fire, and placed enclosed cans or barrels of wood on a grate, on or near the open flame. After a few weeks, we were cooking full 55-gallon drums of wood. Then we attached a two-inch pipe to the standard fitting on the drum to redirect the **pyrolysis** gases—the flammable gases given off when heating wood at high temperature—back under the drum sitting horizontally on a grate. After an hour or two, this crude retort produced impressive quantities of pyrolysis gas, in a feathery gas flame so hot that it began to melt the grate.

We stared at this hot, gassy flame with the old fascination, impressed by the huge, clean energy output from this primitive rig. We knew if we enclosed it properly to contain the heat we could achieve one of my original design goals: self-sustaining and efficient char production.

I remarked to Bob, "A lot of blacksmiths are going to want this."

Bob replied, "You can have the blacksmiths. There are a lot more farmers and a lot more soil out there than blacksmiths with coal forges."

Finally, it all clicked: the extraordinary turnips; the small, local scale of the technology; the potential to restore the original rich, black earth of Cape Cod; and the potential for carbon-negative energy...It all pointed to biochar! I'd come to a fork in the road, and following the wisdom of Yogi Berra, I took it.

## THE TIN MAN – THE FIRST COMMUNITY-SCALE UNIT

Bob and I researched, designed, and built a "55/30," a 55-gallon outer drum containing a 30-gallon inner drum. The 55 would contain the main heat source, and the inner 30 would be the enclosed retort.

This 55/30, which we now call the Tin Man, proved our breakthrough—our first practical community-scale unit. The 55/30 can cleanly and reliably produce batches of about 20 pounds (10 kg) of biochar at a time, suitable for a single household with a few hundred square feet of plantings. It is built simply from readily available materials. It is reasonably durable and light. One person can manage the whole operation, from gathering feedstock to production to in-soil application.

## LESSONS FROM THE TIN MAN

Making and using the Tin Man taught us many valuable lessons.

### BIOCHAR FIRST

Of all the benefits of biochar, the top three are soil, soil and soil. Our priority is to make the best biochar for the soil that we can. If we do that, all the rest will follow.

We acknowledge the excitement around the prospect of capturing the waste heat from small biochar systems to generate renewable power and avoid the use of fossil fuels. These are, in fact, core principles for producing and using biochar ethically because they aim to maximize the use of valuable feedstock and maximize carbon capture. The prospect of harnessing renewable power from biochar is tantalizing; we persistently work toward it and encourage others to do so.

However, in real-world practice, this potential is elusive in low-tech retort biochar production. As it turns out, tapping waste heat energy impedes the thermal performance on which good char production depends. Diverting even a modest amount of producer gas from the gas burn around the retort lowers the heat input to the retort below the level required to achieve complete pyrolysis. Similarly, any substantial obstruction of the exhaust stream, or removal of heat from it, reduces the chimney draft that pulls in the air needed for complete, clean combustion of the starter fuel and the producer gas.

Simply put, producing quality biochar with energy capture requires substantially more technology and cost than we have found feasible at the Tin Man scale. That's why we consciously follow this tenet: biochar for soil first.

### KEEP IT CLEAN

One consideration that we do put on an even level with biochar quality is clean production. We tinkered with the airflows, feedstock preparation, and energy conservation (insulation), and did not consider the Tin Man "finished" until we achieved consistent, repeatable burns that produced a lot of char with little or no smoke.

### ECONOMIC FEASIBILITY – LOW TECHNOLOGY, HIGH INGENUITY

As we began to envision moving past the Tin Man and pursuing New England Biochar as a commercial enterprise, we learned about ongoing efforts to develop large-scale, automated biochar production systems. However, for many reasons we maintained our consciously low-tech approach.

First, we were in no position to compete with these large-scale efforts. Second, we wanted to match our scale of production to our identified markets. We had discovered the most intense enthusiasm for the biochar movement among Bob's peers in the agriculture business—small farmers with local markets and a devotion to sustainable, low-tech methods. Third, we realized that charcoal had been produced for thousands of years with virtually no technology, and during the last hundred years using more advanced technologies that had been thoroughly tested and proved. We concluded that everything we hoped to accomplish could be put together mostly from junkyard or off-the-shelf components. In alignment with the community values I'd been seeking in my Village Blacksmith scenario, low technology, high ingenuity methods remain the bedrock of everything we've done.

## COMMUNITY RE-FOCUSED

With all this, we continued to learn about the communities we hoped to serve and the scale of production needed to serve them. My "biochar community" was not necessarily identical to the idealized "Village Blacksmith" community.

In starting the blacksmith shop, my community ideal had been based on a unifying interdependence intertwining the myriad interests and needs of people living in proximity. As we learned more about the interdependence of needs and resources that a biochar operation brings together, a different sense of the community to be served emerged.

Now I realized the biochar community is not interdependent for a broad, generalized collection of social benefits, but rather shares a *community of interests* in the specific needs and resources that biochar engages: soil and its products, compost, wood feedstocks, retort technology, materials recycling, and renewable energy capture and use. Each of these categories involves numerous variations. Go to any biochar demonstration or presentation, and you will find an impressive variety of interests represented.

On the other hand, this more diverse, dispersed community aligned with my blacksmith ideal in one crucial respect: our endeavor was evolving naturally and organically from the bottom up, not from the top down.

This group dynamic—identifying or forming the community to operate and be served by biochar production—is and will continue to be an important part of making the biochar movement work. It is one of the keys to identifying the appropriate scale of biochar technology and production for each locale.

## BEYOND THE TIN MAN: SCALING UP

The Tin Man was a great start, a good unit for the single household with some time to dedicate to building top quality soil in a good-sized garden plot. For more serious operations—market gardeners and small farmers—we would have to scale up.

We designed and built another low-tech retort device we called the Shotgun. The outside chamber was made from two pieces of standard fuel tanks welded together, and accommodates two side-by-side 55-gallon drums as closed retorts. The Shotgun nearly quadrupled the Tin Man's capacity, without adding technical or operational complications.

The simply designed Tin Man and Shotgun confirmed that we were on the right track. Along the way, the market for our biochar expanded yet further. To serve that market, we needed another step up in scale—we needed a new technology.

Our ideals encountered more turbulence. Scaling up our use of technology conflicted with the priority of building whatever we needed by using or modifying readily available, common components. We scoured the biochar websites, but didn't find actual, working technologies in the scale we were seeking to achieve. We had to look elsewhere.

Eventually, we found the right technology for us in the Adam-Retort[5], a masonry unit neither designed nor advertised to produce biochar. However, the Adam-Retort epitomized our low tech/high ingenuity approach: it had few moving parts, was easy to build, and could be adapted to make biochar. It also burned clean; in Auroville, India, the Adam-Retort made production of village-scale charcoal fuel 75 percent cleaner.

Incorporating the Adam technology, we built a transportable steel unit. Everything we had learned and proved with the Tin Man and the Shotgun also proved applicable to the Adam-Retort.

Just as with our smaller units, our transportable Adam-Retort allows us to travel far and wide to do contract work for property owners, and to provide training and education in biochar benefits and production throughout our region. As a result, our community of interest—our biochar community—has expanded even further, and larger-scale biochar production has been introduced to other locales.

In fact, our extended community has come to resonate with my original ideal. It is every bit as real and vibrant, and our Flow Farm experience would prove it.

## FLOW FARM: AN INSTANT COMMUNITY PHENOMENON

Fig. 4.1 Masonry Adam-Retort at Flow Farm

*Water vapor is emitted from the first phase chimney*

In March 2010, we traveled to Flow Farm in North Carolina to build the first original masonry Adam-Retort in North America. Flow Farm is the brainchild of Mark Epstein, who relocated from Chicago to create a small, high-quality farm and learning center. Mark's vision—executed under Baj Kourkian, his farm manager— is to establish and sustain the highest achievable organic and vegan principles.

Mark and Baj had decided that biochar would integrally promote those principles, and that their biochar program would be based on the Adam-Retort. We carefully worked out the construction, training, and production details.

---

[5] "Adam-Retort®" is a registered trademark owned by Christoph Adam, the inventor.

During this planning phase, the project drew outside interest that would transform it. Dr. Deborah Hanmer, a plant pathologist at the University of North Carolina at Pembroke, contacted me to ask how she might learn about biochar through the project. She was invited to attend a burn and bring along a few interested students to assist.

Dr. Hanmer in turn introduced me to Dr. Richard Parret, executive Director of the NC Farm Center, a 6,500-acre facility near Fayetteville, North Carolina. Dr. Parret directs an important, well-funded biochar trial and production project.

By the time I arrived at Flow Farm in March, my work week had been extended to include a burn of the Adam to be attended by Dr. Hanmer and her students, Dr. Parret, and a number of other biochar enthusiasts. It had developed into quite a gathering.

We began by loading and starting up the new Adam-Retort, assisted by the UNC students. While the main unit was warming up, we demonstrated a tiny gasifier and retort, a small open burn, a TLUD, and the Tin Man, all of which Baj and I had constructed as part of the training for the Flow Farm crew.

By the time we sat down to a beautiful vegan lunch under the tall longleaf pines, it was clear that something special was happening. People who had for the most part never met were meeting over biochar and over the retort, and sharing their enthusiasm.

After lunch Mark, Baj, Deborah, and Richard took a walk in the woods. When they returned an hour later, a new cooperative program had been formed. This group of strangers—in the space of one day—had met, discovered a community of interest, and forged an agreement to start a cooperative biochar production and application program around the new Adam-Retort.

I had come full circle. I had witnessed, and was a part of, an *authentic* community—the cooperative kind I'd sought all along. The controlled fire of the Adam-Retort, like the stove in the general store, had created a place to gather and commune. It thus became the quintessential community biochar unit—literally, with its first fire.

Chapter 5

# The Accidental Scientist: Lessons in Farming, Biochar and Collaboration

Robert Quirk

**IN THIS CHAPTER YOU WILL LEARN:**

- How a sugar cane farmer in Australia, struggling with acid soil, collaborated with landholders, researchers, and local government to create an innovative solution.

- How that collaboration addressed the problem of greenhouse gas emissions from soil treated with nitrogen fertilizer.

- The potential of biochar to reduce greenhouse gases.

*[This chapter offers the author's personal story about how he was introduced to biochar and became both a pioneer and respected authority in the field. His story frames his chapter "Producing Biochar on Sugarcane Farms: Industry Benefits, Local and Global Implications," which appears later in this book.]*

"A journey that began over a cup of tea has taken me a long way down an instructive, and ultimately higher, road."

## THE FISH KILL OF 1987

For 35 years, I had been farming sugar cane in the coastal flood plain adjacent to the Tweed River, in northern New South Wales (NSW), Australia—and doing so quite successfully—or so I thought—right up until the catastrophic fish kill of 1987. Heavy rains that year, following a prolonged dry period, strongly acidified the entire Tweed River estuary. At one point, the pH in the estuary measured as low as 3.5. The water of the estuary was completely clarified. All gilled organisms in it were killed.

The community, area fishermen, and local council all pointed an accusing finger at sugar cane farmers, arguing that runoff from our pesticides had poisoned the water and killed the fish. Livelihoods were in danger and tempers ran high. Both farmers and fishermen received death threats.

At the time, the canegrowers believed such fish kills happened naturally. In fact, history bore this out. The first recorded fish kill followed the flood of 1893, and back then there were few if any drainage channels on the flood plain. By the 1940s, settlers on the flood plain had discovered that their cattle would not fatten in the paddocks if their only water was pumped from the ground. This, it was later learned, was because of the aluminum and iron content of the water.

### 1990: THE MOMENT OF ENLIGHTENMENT

Canegrowers knew what the settlers knew, and therefore rejected the notion that we were to blame for the fish kill. Our conviction was so strong that we also rejected any idea that scientists could prove anything to the contrary, and for months fought against allowing them to poke around our farms to do needless research.

That all changed in one afternoon.

Sitting under a tree over a cup of tea, Associate Professor Mike Melville from the University of New South Wales visited with me and Robert Hawken (another concerned canegrower). Mike confirmed our long-held belief—yes, the fish kill was a natural phenomenon. The sulfur that had come from the ocean during the last sea level rise was now making its way back to the ocean, and killing all the fish on its way.

Mike also explained that the fact we were right made no difference. It was simply no longer acceptable for this to happen. More than 85% of the 38,000 hectares of sugar plantations on the NSW river floodplains are underlain by acid sulfate soils. The problem was bigger than the canegrowers; it affected everyone in the coastal floodplain. It was *immense*.

Mike's comments changed my life. He became a great friend, and my new life as scientist began. From then on, being right was no longer important—we wanted to fix our acid sulfate soils.

During the next ten years, I formed working relationships with two other men who also became my friends, Professor Ian White and Dr. Ben Macdonald, both with the Australian National University. Many others joined our collaboration, eventually forming a team generating research papers that have been peer reviewed both nationally and internationally. The practices we have developed are recognized worldwide as best practices for growing sugar cane in these landscapes.

## 1992: THE WORK BEGINS, A PARTNERSHIP IS BORN

Having awakened to the wide implications of this natural soil condition, we began to discuss how we could go about fixing it. We recognized early on that first and foremost, a collaborative partnership was needed among landholders, researchers, and local government. Second, extensive research would be necessary.

But even with these fundamentals in place, as canegrowers, we had to make sure that the research was tethered to the real world. We made it clear that any proposed solution had to satisfy two criteria: First, we landholders would have to believe it would work before we would try it. Second, it would have to be affordable. If the work didn't meet both these criteria, then it would not be considered.

An agreement was reached, and the research began. Rarely has such a successful collaboration occurred between the ivory towers of science and the farmer.

## 1992 – 1997: THE RESEARCH RESULTS

Fig. 5.1 B Double Tanker

The research, ambitious and broad in its scope, was conducted by university students and resulted in nine PhDs. After a few years, we established that the water moved only vertically through the old root zones. These soils were impervious as concrete in terms of lateral movement of water within the soil. We also established that the soil contained *50 tons* of sulfuric acid per hectare, the equivalent of a B-Double tanker. (A hectare (ha) is a unit of surface area equal to 10,000 square meters. One hectare equals 2.471 acres.)

This problem actually originated before Europeans settled in Australia. Sulfur deposited by a previous sea level rise had oxidized in droughts, creating the existing sulfuric acidity. Now, during inundations, this acidity was leaching aluminum and iron from the soil and flooding them into the field drainage ditches. In effect, runoff from the acid soil was spiking the river and estuary with sulfuric acid and heavy metals, toxic to plants and fish.

It was impossible to neutralize that amount of acid. Instead, we decided to design a system that would accept and contain the acid in the landscape and farm on top of it.

## THE INNOVATIVE APPROACH

An innovative approach was needed. Here's what we did:

- We laser-leveled the fields to sheet off the water before it had a chance to move through the soil profile using the old root zone, and bring the acid to the surface.

- Because we had discovered that the main body of acid was coming from the banks of the drains on the property, we filled in 6 km of the property's 16 km of drains.

- We installed automatic, electric pumps to keep the water levels in the drains low so that during rain events, the drain would have extra capacity to handle runoff.

- We started green cane harvesting. This meant that the iron and aluminum in the soil would be trapped by organic matter and no longer discharged into the waterways to kill the fish.

- We installed an extensive monitoring system to track pH, salinity, temperature, and dissolved oxygen.

Through this approach, we have recorded continuous improvement in the pH of the discharge water, increasing from 2.6 in the start-up phase to 5.6–7.0 now. This was a good start.

These collaborative efforts have resulted in an 80% decrease in acidic discharge from acid sulfate soils in the lower Tweed River, while generating an increase in cane yield. There were no losers. In fact, audits of compliance with the agricultural and soil management practices we collaboratively developed show an astounding 100% compliance.

## THE WETLAND

Although we had reduced the amount of acidity leaving the property by 80%, we thought we might be able to do more. We constructed a wetland of 2 ha on slightly sloping ground, consisting of 6 leveled bays with a reduction of 100 mm between each bay. The bays were bermed so that each would hold back 200 mm of water. The retention of water in the bays allowed organic matter in the wetlands to remove the toxic elements.

The result amazed even the most optimistic of us. We were able to raise the pH from 3.7 to 7.0, reduce iron levels by 90% and aluminum levels 50%. Dissolved oxygen was also increased, from almost zero to saturation. We became confident that all was going well and that we'd overcome the problems of farming in these high acidic (low pH) soils. But the nitrous oxide ($N_2O$) problem still loomed.

## THE NITROGEN BOMBSHELL

### THE MURWILLUMBAH SOIL TRIAL

In 2005, a more extensive acid soils trial was set up near Murwillumbah, with some of the most advanced monitoring equipment available. Fields using numerous nitrogen treatments were studied over a one year period. In 2006, the bombshell hit.

The Murwillumbah research found that our acid sulfate soils discharged ten times more nitrous oxide ($N_2O$) than the Mackay sugar cane soils in Queensland did. The extrapolated, explosive implications of that trial: *30% of all the $N_2O$ in Australia might be coming from NSW sugar cane fields.*

This was a shocking setback, especially because five years earlier we'd already researched the Tweed soils to determine the discharge of **greenhouse gases** (GHGs) from sugar cane fields following the application of nitrogen fertilizer. After a month of extensive monitoring the results were inconclusive, showing little to no fluxes of GHGs.

In hindsight, this was a false reading. Other research had shown that either a rainfall event or a low barometric pressure event was needed to trigger release of GHGs, but neither had occurred during the monitoring period. For the next several years we farmed on very happily, thinking there was no problem and if there was, it was very small.

But once again the ball was in our court to show that either the figures or the extrapolations on the Murwillumbah trial were wrong. We knew we needed further trials now to show how we might reduce these GHG figures to at least the background levels of sugar-producing areas outside of the Tweed. Our previous research had shown that the Mackay district sugar cane fields had much lower discharges of GHGs than the Tweed.

With warning bells going off, it was time to get proactive and, instead of complaining, work on a solution—as we had done with the acid soil issue. I spoke to the researchers at Industry and Investment NSW, and what followed was an agreement to set up the first biochar trial in the Australian sugar cane industry.

### THE BIOCHAR TRIAL: SMALL AGRONOMY BENEFIT, HUGE GHG IMPROVEMENT

To investigate the $N_2O$ problem, a 15-plot, fully replicated, three-year trial was set up in a paddock of plant cane with the aim to test if we could reduce the $N_2O$ levels leaving the field. Each trial plot consisted of three rows, with biochar, amendment, or other variable applied to the soil in all three rows but only the middle row to be weighed and recorded (to avoid contamination by edge effects).

The trial is continuing. To date, the trial has shown minimal agronomic benefits associated with applying the char. On the other hand, lab tests have shown that *after application of biochar, $N_2O$ levels declined by as much as 70% or more.*

## CONCLUSION

A journey that began over a cup of tea has taken me a long way down an instructive, and ultimately higher, road.

I first learned how a collaborative effort among stakeholders could resolve a common problem with our local acidic soils. Together, we recognized that our $N_2O$ emissions had to be reduced; if not, we'd be out of business. We learned that biochar, while not yet a proven agronomic boost for us cane farmers, may offer a sustainable solution to GHGs—and that our cane farms are almost ideal for producing biochar. (See the chapter of this book titled "Producing Biochar on Sugar Cane Farms: Industry Benefits, Local and Global Implications.")

Overall, we have learned that our local solutions hold global promise as well. Our work is continuing.

The team working on the trial presented early results at the Gold Coast Asian Pacific Biochar conference in 2009 and to the International Society of Sugar Cane Technologist triennials meeting in Veracruz, Mexico in 2010. Papers have also been submitted to the International Biochar conference to be held in Rio, Brazil in September 2010.

**KEY POINTS FROM THIS CHAPTER**

- In 1987, a catastrophic fish kill occurred in the Tweed River sugar cane farming region. The fish kill was a natural phenomenon, caused by sulfur that had infiltrated ground water from acid soils.

- This condition, although natural, had adverse implications for the entire region. Something had to be done; the very soil itself needed fixing.

- A landmark, collaborative, partnership of landholders, researchers, and local government came together, intensively researching and creating an innovative approach that successfully addressed the acid soil problem.

- However, the research for this initiative revealed the soils in the NSW cane farms, treated with nitrogen fertilizer, discharged an excessive amount of nitrous oxide —a harmful greenhouse gas—into the atmosphere.

- The same collaborative approach was used on this problem, resulting in an agreement to set up the first biochar trial in the Australian sugar cane industry. It was discovered that cane farms are ideal for producing biochar.

- Lab tests have shown that after application of biochar, $N_2O$ levels decline by as much as 70% or more.

- Local collaboration led to local solutions with global repercussions: biochar could be a sustainable way to mitigate greenhouse gas emissions.

# Part II
## Understanding Biochar

"It has been found that, with some soils and crops, productivity can be increased eight-fold. For the atmosphere that's a treble whammy — fossil fuel left in the ground, stable biochar carbon in the soil, plus increased labile carbon bound up in the life-cycle of the greater weight of crops and their in-soil roots. Devoted researchers are working...to realize these benefits..., passing the treble whammy on to farmers on the ground..."

—*Dr. Peter Read, Massey University*

Chapter 6

# What *Is* Biochar?

Hugh McLauglin, PhD PE
Director of Biocarbon Research, Alterna Biocarbon Inc.

**IN THIS CHAPTER YOU WILL LEARN:**

- What biochar is…and what it is not.
- How biochar is produced through carbonization and pyrolysis.
- Biochar's unique structure, chemical composition, and long-term durability.
- Factors that determine the properties of biochar, and their relevance for application to soil.

"Thermal modification, which converts biomass into charcoal, renders carbon virtually impervious to biological degradation and thus, stable and persistent in the soil."

# INTRODUCTION

Biochar is "thermally-modified biomass" that is destined for addition to soils. Biochar can be made from many raw materials (called biomass feedstocks), the same way as charcoal. However, unlike charcoal—which has been used primarily as a fuel for cooking—the properties of biochar are optimized to enhance agricultural performance.

Potential biochar sources include conventional lump charcoal, residual char from open biomass burning (including forest fires), char residuals from gasifying stoves and furnaces, by-products or co-products of **fast pyrolysis** and **slow pyrolysis** technologies, and carbonized biomass manufactured in processes dedicated for specific **feedstocks,** including chicken litter and other bio-solids.

Biochar is both a class of materials capable of sequestering carbon in soils and the centerpiece of an ambitious program to improve long-term soil productivity. Soil improvements attributed to the addition of biochar include increased moisture retention, improved air permeability, elevated **cation exchange capacity,** increased buffering of soluble organic carbon, and synergistic interactions with soil microbe populations.

Much of the current enthusiasm for the properties of biochar is inspired by studies of a centuries-old phenomenon in the Amazon rainforests known as **"terra preta"** ("black earth" in Portuguese). In the Amazon, aboriginal tribes developed a method for achieving enduring soil productivity, which modern biochar application seeks to replicate—and possibly improve. Unfortunately, precise understanding of ancient **anthropogenic** (man-made) influences on the *terra preta* sites is elusive.

Biochar therefore remains something of an enigma. Although biochar's positive attributes have generally been recognized and acknowledged, extensive debate and research continues about its *specific* principles, properties, and benefits—and how best to utilize them. Nevertheless, some insights can be gleaned from the known properties of carbon-rich substances and their observed effect in soils.

## DEFINING BIOCHAR

### WHAT BIOCHAR IS NOT

Biochar is carbon-rich, containing significant fractions of amorphous **graphitic** domains (that is, "tiny pockets" of carbon in its form as graphite). The graphitic domains in biochar, including samples isolated from historical *terra preta* sites, have been documented to be stable in the soil for millennia.

Although one might propose that the presence of graphitic carbon atoms gives biochar its unique soil-improving properties, the answer is "likely not." If the mere presence of graphitic carbon atoms improved soils, then "carbon black" or "tire black" materials—and coal dust spilled over the ages—would perform like biochar. Such benefits are rarely, if ever, observed.

Biochar also has properties and molecular structures that resemble activated carbon, a common industrial material that has unique properties for adsorbing vapor and liquid phase organic molecules. As will be discussed, **adsorption** properties are believed to play a significant role in biochar phenomena, but adsorption effects alone do not account for the composite of observed biochar attributes. If adsorption alone were the dominant phenomenon, then powdered activated carbon, with its maximal surface area, would be the ultimate soil amendment—which also has not been observed. Similar logic can be applied to many common carbon-rich substances, such as shredded tires and pulverized plastics, none of which exhibit any properties even vaguely similar to those of biochar. To the contrary, detrimental impacts on plants and soils are often observed. Thus, other natural and synthetic carbon-rich materials demonstrate scant similarity to the desirable properties of biochar.

### WHAT BIOCHAR IS

Biochar can be broadly characterized as "thermally modified biomass." This "definition" is more a description of how the vast majority of existing biochar found in soils was formed than an actual requirement to qualify a material as biochar.

The thermal modification of biomass is significant because it results in a pivotal property of biochar—the ability to persist in the soil indefinitely by not being susceptible to biological decay. This persistence essentially makes biochar a soil "catalyst": biochar facilitates reactions beneficial to soil dynamics without being consumed in the process. In contrast, common soil additives—substances like fertilizers and other amendments—are either assimilated by living systems (plants, soil microbes) or gradually transformed, as is the case with the breakdown of peat moss, compost, or manure in soils.

In the absence of thermal modification, essentially all forms of biomass (plants, animals and microbes alike) are 100% biodegradable. This concept is illustrated in Figure 6.1. As the figure shows, un-charred organic matter rapidly decomposes due to the actions of soil microbes, which return the vast majority of the carbon back to the atmosphere within the first few years. In contrast, while conversion of biomass to biochar by pyrolysis releases roughly half of the carbon atoms immediately, it renders the remaining half dramatically more resistant to decay by microbial activity.

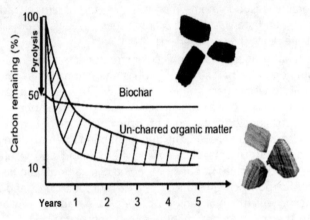

Fig. 6.1 The Essential Stability of Biochar

Source: Lehmann et al., 2006, Migration and Adaptation Strategies for Global Change 11, 403-427

The specific thermal modification that converts biomass into biochar can be viewed from two closely related perspectives—**pyrolysis** and **carbonization**:

- The pyrolysis perspective focuses on the chemical breakdowns that result in the liberation of pyrolytic gases.

- The carbonization perspective focuses on the chemical build-ups of the carbon atoms into solid structures, as other smaller volatile components are formed and released as vapors.

The bulk of pyrolysis and carbonization reactions occur in the temperature range from about 200°C to 500°C. One can think of pyrolysis and carbonization as simultaneous physical-chemical processes, changing the biomass into pyrolytic gases and char.

At sufficient temperatures, generally above 300°C, carbonization modifies the chemical bonds within the remaining solid such that it is less likely to be consumed as food by living systems. The chemical bond modifications consist of dehydration, conversion of less stable **aliphatic** (single or linear chain) bonds into more stable **aromatic** (stackable) bonds, and the consolidation of those aromatic bonds into local **graphene** complexes (which can be visualized as a complex of layers, with each layer resembling chicken wire and made of carbon atoms and their bonds).

## DEFINITIONS FOR NON-SCIENTISTS

*Carbonization*
The chemical build-up of carbon atoms into solid structures.

*Aliphatic/Aromatic*
Carbon-composed compounds are divided into two classes:

- Aliphatic compounds, made up of linear chains of molecules

- Aromatic compounds, made up of more stable molecular rings

*Graphene*
Graphite's major structural element, graphene is an isolated sheet of joined, hexagonal, carbon rings.

This chemical transformation is what gives biochar its long-term, essential stability. Chemically, here is why: in living systems, enzymes facilitate individual chemical reactions, and enzymes are very specific to the unique chemical bonds they transform. When carbonization occurs, the chemical bonds between the carbon atoms become randomized, creating locally varying molecular structures—and a much larger percentage of stable graphene chemical bonds. Due to this diversity of chemical structures and overall greater bond stability, living systems did not evolve enzymes to transform carbonized bond structures. In simple terms, biochar has long-term durability because it is too difficult for living organisms to consume.

The long-term stability of biochar raises an interesting question. If a portion of carbonized biomass is immune to biological decay and if natural forest fires continually generate additional carbonized biomass, then why isn't the soil replete with accumulated, persistent biochar? The basic reason is that there are very slow, non-biological, ambient temperature reactions between carbonized biomass and atmospheric oxygen, which slowly degrade exposed graphene bonds over the course of thousands to millions of years. That is why reservoirs of oil and coal—fossil carbon that remains stable long-term—are only found deep in the earth, far from gaseous oxygen. Even at ambient temperatures, atmospheric oxygen will react with—and degrade—carbon-carbon and carbon-hydrogen bonds, given enough time.

This is why thermal modification, as in the conversion of biomass into charcoal, is so critical. This process renders carbon virtually impervious to biological degradation and thus, stable and persistent in the soil.

## CARBONIZATION AND PYROLYSIS

### INTRODUCTION

In light of the above analysis, it is tempting to conclude—and many do—that biochar is made simply by pyrolysis of biomass, or some variation of this concept. While it is true that creating biochar from biomass involves pyrolysis, as in heating biomass under controlled conditions, pyrolysis is hardly the entire story. This section of the chapter will dissect the conditions that lead to the formation of biochar. Doing so will lay the foundation for correlating trends in processing conditions with observed biochar properties.

As previously mentioned, carbonization is the conversion of a substance into a more carbon-rich form. This is what happens to the residual solid biomass during pyrolysis. Therefore, examining carbonization as it relates to the creation of biochar focuses on the remaining solid phase and measuring or predicting its properties.

Biomass consists principally of organic compounds—**hemicellulose, cellulose,** and **lignin**—in addition to a suite of inorganic ash constituents. Pyrolysis transforms the organic portions of the biomass: it fractionates the organic compounds into volatiles and reorganizes the remaining carbon atoms into biochar. The non-organic portions are also altered, but in ways that are outside the scope of this article. The following analysis will thus focus on the organic portion, also referred to as the "**ligno-cellulosic**" fraction, of the biomass.

### THERMAL TRANSFORMATIONS OF BIOMASS DURING PYROLYSIS

Figure 6.2 shows the sequence of thermal transformations that the principal constituents of ligno-cellulose in biomass undergo during pyrolysis. The temperatures are referred to as the "**heat treatment temperature**" or **HTT**, the highest temperature the biomass experiences as it is being modified by heat. HTT is important because HTT is the main determinant of a char's properties. Above 325°C, the residual char continues to consolidate and incremental volatiles are emitted, as will be discussed later.

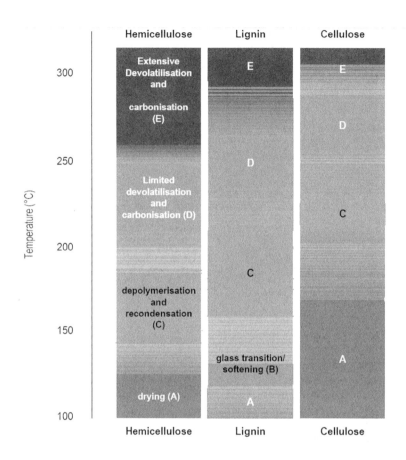

Fig. 6.2 Thermal Transformation of Ligno-Cellulosic Constituents during Pyrolysis

Figure 6.3 and Figure 6.4, respectively, depict the complexity of the physical and microscopic structures of wood, with the latter showing individual organic polymers interwoven at nearly the atomic level. Figure 6.4 also provides insight into the complexity of the molecular relationships as the hemicellulose, cellulose, and lignin compounds undergo thermal transformation. Thus, as individual polymers lose volatiles and carbonize to yield residual char, there is a melding of individual constituents, and many new carbon-carbon bonds are created within the char.

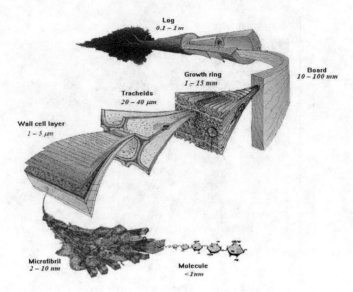

Fig. 6.3   Wood Physical Structure*

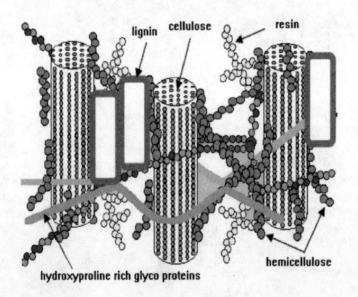

Fig. 6.4   Wood Microscopic Structure*

*Source: Jianghong Peng, *"A Study of Torrefaction for the Production of High Quality Wood Pellets"* (August 23, 2007), page 7.   http://www.techtp.com/orrefaction for High Quality Wood Pellets.pdf

During pyrolysis and the concurrent carbonization, water vapor, carbon dioxide, and smaller volatile organic compounds are formed within the biomass and immediately evaporate, exiting as vapors. The remaining solid phase forms new chemical bonds, collapsing into a more carbon-rich structure that continues to react, especially if the temperature continues to increase. Above 300°C, the material turns black in color and is generally referred to as "char." Biomass that has not exceeded 300°C may still exhibit levels of tan to brown coloration and is characterized as "torrefied" (derived from an obsolete term meaning "dried" or "roasted").

Figure 6.5 depicts the graphene domains that are formed as a result of the consolidation of carbon atoms, principally from the cellulose and lignin constituents of the biomass. These graphene domains, at a molecular level, have been characterized as "potato chips" or "corn flakes." As additional consolidation of the char occurs at increasingly higher temperatures, a complex, porous, 3-dimensional structure develops, as depicted in Figure 6.6.

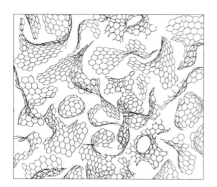

Fig. 6.5 Development of Local Graphene Domains during Carbonization.

Source: *Philosophical Magazine* 84, no. 29 (11 Oct 2004): 3165

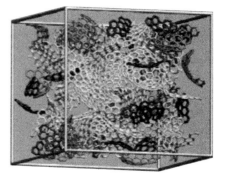

Fig. 6.6 Development of Porous 3-Dimension Structure during Carbonization.

Source: "Condensed Matter," *Journal of Physics* 19 (2007): 3.

## SLOW PYROLYSIS CONDITIONS AND CARBONIZATION CONSEQUENCES

The sequence of chemical transformations described above is associated with a set of char-forming conditions referred to as "**slow pyrolysis**." This helps distinguish the likely properties of a slow pyrolysis char from other chars generated under "**fast pyrolysis**" and "**gasification**" conditions. The most commonly used char-making methods accessible to individuals are slow pyrolysis techniques and the following discussion is limited to those chars.

As previously suggested, based on Figure 6.2, one might be tempted to conclude that the highest temperature (the HTT) that a biomass experiences during thermal modification is the sole determinant of the properties of a particular char. Such a conclusion would be probably the best single assumption when predicting char properties, but would likely overlook the important role of several other influences on the char. Research shows that important roles are also played by the rate of heating, the rate of escape of volatiles, and the magnitude of temperature gradients in the transforming material.

Figure 6.7 below reflects how two important conditions (discussed below) of biochar change with HTT. Time and temperature are crucial interacting factors. Among local regions, temperature differences of just a few degrees would create a variety of chars with different properties depending on the HTT reached in that region, and whether enough time was spent at that temperature to reach equilibrium. The particular properties of a char resulting from temperature non-uniformities will depend on the speed of heating and the chunk size of the biomass, with longer times and slower heating required to ensure larger chunks reach a uniform HTT for sufficient time.

The unifying ideal for all slow pyrolysis chars is that the temperature gradients are gradual enough that to go any slower would not make a significant difference in the conditions within the biomass. Then the local char properties are determined by the biomass as it rearranges and breaks down into a thermally modified char and exiting vapors. As the temperature rises, the char is further consolidated, as more and different volatiles evaporate and leave the transforming char behind.

Under the circumstances just described, the char properties are most strongly dictated by HTT—which, again, is the highest temperature the biomass experiences for a long enough period for the biomass molecules to rearrange and the volatiles to form and leave the char mass as vapors.

Char properties can be markedly affected by how fast the volatiles are liberated during the pyrolysis process. Although the volatiles are formed within the biomass during its conversion to char, many factors can influence the subsequent vaporization of the volatiles. This second step is important, because it differentiates the properties of slow pyrolysis chars that are produced at a given temperature. This differentiation is attributed to an independent char-creating (and modifying) process called "secondary char formation."[6]

---

[6] Antal and Gronli summarized the complexity of the interactions in their 2003 review titled "The Art, Science, and Technology of Charcoal Production," Ind. Eng. Chem. Res. 42: 1619-1640. They wrote:

Klason established the key role of secondary (vapour-phase) pyrolytic reactions in the formation of charcoal 88 years ago; [however,] today, many researchers still assume that charcoal is solely a product of primary (solid-phase) pyrolytic reactions. In reality, charcoal contains both "primary" charcoal and "secondary" charcoal that is a coke derived from the decomposition of the organic vapours ("tars") onto the solid carbonaceous solid (1627-28).

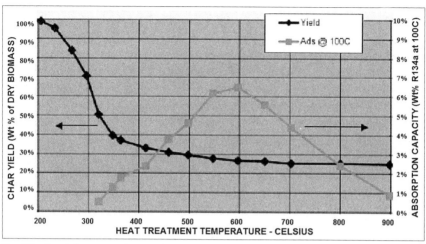

Fig. 6.7    Trends in HTT on Char Yield and Adsorption Capacity

Thus:

• Primary char is char formed directly from the solid-phase biomass carbon atoms.

• Secondary char is formed from volatiles that redeposit within the structures of the initial primary char.

Many factors influence the formation of secondary char, including the size of a particular biomass particle, the pressure of the pyrolysis reactor, and the relative composition of the vapors within the reactor. In larger particles, the exiting vapors have greater distances to migrate, but elevated pressures and inert gases also influence the relative partition between volatiles adsorbed within char and evaporated into vapor. Consequently, within any group of chars produced at exactly the same pyrolysis temperature, the extent to which secondary char is formed will determine the range of resulting char yields and biochar properties.

In addition to dictating yield and char properties such as fixed carbon content, and as previously noted, HTT strongly impacts a desirable biochar property known as **adsorption capacity**, which is related to the internal surface area of the char. As shown in Figure 6.7, chars exhibit an increasing surface area with HTT up to a fairly high temperature (generally between 500°C and 700°C), after which the surface area "collapses" (attributed to the consolidation of single layer graphene domains into more consolidated graphitic plates). Thus, it is possible to overheat a char and destroy desirable adsorption properties.

The adsorption capacity of char also has real-world economic impact (see text box titled "The Real-World Value of Adsorption Capacity").

**THE REAL-WORLD VALUE OF ADSORPTION CAPACITY**

Figure 6.7 shows two trends that provide an important consideration for producing and marketing biochar.

Consider the case of starting with a fixed amount of biomass, say 100 units of dry weight, and converting it to either a 350°C biochar or a 600°C biochar.

The 350°C char will yield about 40 units of char and have an adsorption capacity of about 1.25%. The 600°C char will yield about 27 units of char with an adsorption capacity of 6.50%.

If the biochar is sold without giving any consideration to adsorption capacity, then the 350°C char is the more profitable product (assuming near-equivalence in raw material and production costs) since the yield is 40 units instead of 27 units (50% more saleable product).

In contrast, if biochar is valued on the basis of adsorption capacity per unit weight, the 600°C char could command over five times the price of the 350°C char per unit of char weight.

When the yield is multiplied by the adsorption capacity—which represents the adsorption capacity created per 100 units of raw material biomass—the 600°C char is 3.5 times the value of the 350°C char for equivalent initial biomass weights.

In summary, when chars are formed under slow pyrolysis conditions, the highest treatment temperature is the strongest influence on the resulting char properties. The HTT has to be high enough to form the primary char from the biomass, and even higher to promote the development of adsorption capacity in the primary char. However, vapor phase effects may create secondary char, which generally increases net char yield, but reduces its available adsorption capacity; this is because secondary char occupies the adsorption sites formed within the primary char.

Given all of the interacting phenomena described in this chapter, one can appreciate the need to test the char once it is made and before it is put in the soil. The following chapter of this book addresses this topic in detail.

## CONCLUSION

High-quality biochar is not automatically created when a biomass undergoes pyrolysis. Biochar, like good wine, requires a carefully controlled production process—the best biochars are formed under a relatively narrow set of conditions.

The most favorable conditions for creating beneficial biochar properties are those that allow the original biomass to consolidate into graphene domains under slow pyrolysis at temperatures that maximize development of surface area and adsorption capacity. Once a quality biochar is formed, subsequent conditions must avoid depositing excess secondary char, removing primary char carbon atoms, or subjecting the residual char to excessive temperatures, all of which lead to deterioration of valuable biochar properties.

Any secondary char deposition will improve the mass yield of a biochar, but can simultaneously result in the loss of adsorption capacity. This is a classic case of "more is not always better," since the value of the greater mass of char is generally diminished by the loss of adsorption capacity to an extent that manifests lower overall biochar efficacy in the soil.

## KEY POINTS FROM THIS CHAPTER

- Biochar, made by heating biomass, is intended for addition to soils to enhance agricultural performance.

- Many raw materials (biomass feedstocks) and processes are available for producing biochar.

- When biomass is heated to above 300°C, the material turns black and is referred to as "char."

- The "thermal modification" involves two transforming—and concurrent—reactions: pyrolysis and carbonization. In pyrolysis, gases are liberated. In carbonization, carbon atoms are changed into the solid graphite structures that give biochar its long-term durability.

- Biochar is a carbon-rich material that is virtually non-biodegradable and thus stable in the soil for millennia. In contrast, common fertilizers and other soil amendments (such as peat moss, compost, or manure), and all regular biomass, break down over time.

- The primary determinant of a particular char's properties is "heat treatment temperature" (HTT), the highest temperature reached by the biomass during pyrolysis. HTT strongly impacts a desirable biochar property known as adsorption capacity.

- HTT is not the sole determinant of a char's properties. Several other factors influence a char, including the duration of heating, the temperature gradients, the rate at which volatiles are released during pyrolysis, and the type and particle size of the feedstock.

- Under some carbonization conditions, "secondary" char is formed. This will increase overall net char yield, but may reduce adsorption capacity—and the char's value to the soil.

- Biochar is capable of sequestering carbon in soils and improving long-term soil productivity. Soil improvements attributed to biochar include increased moisture retention and synergistic interactions with soil microbes.

- There is still much to learn. Biochar's specific properties are subject to debate and are being extensively researched to better understand how those properties impact plants and soils, and how biochar can be best applied.

Chapter 7

# How Biochar Helps the Soil

## Hugh McLauglin, PhD PE
Director of Biocarbon Research, Alterna Biocarbon Inc.

**IN THIS CHAPTER YOU WILL LEARN:**

- The constituents of biochar and how they act.
- How biochar mitigates physical deficiencies in the soil.
- How biochar helps the soil do more with less.
- How biochar restores the soil to its natural biological role.

"Biochar helps conserve plant nutrients by storing them within its matrix and making the nutrients available when crops need them."

# INTRODUCTION

We know that biochar can help the soil. Biochar-amended soils have had documented beneficial effects on crop yields. However, it is not fully understood *how* biochar delivers those benefits.

Better understanding of how biochar works is essential. Optimizing the use of biochar will help feed soaring populations saddled with depleted or poor soil.

Ongoing research will clarify this important, complex subject. In the meantime, this chapter attempts to offer some coherent and plausible explanations.

## BIOCHAR – A TEAM PLAYER

Biochar is a permanent soil amendment, but does not act alone. There are few direct biochar-crop interactions.

Biochar in effect acts as part of a team, working in combination with the local soil and its amendments, the individual crop or grouping of crops, and the local climate. As a soil-amending teammate, biochar improves how the soil functions as the host medium for a growing crop, even as both are subjected to the buffeting variability of growing seasons and climate.

---

**THE ONGOING DIALOGUE ON BIOCHAR**
*Additional Reading*

Those interested in exploring the breadth of the current dialogue on biochar are invited to download the following reports, all of which can be accessed and downloaded at http://biocharinfo.com:

- "Biochar Application to Soils—A Critical Scientific Review of Effects on Soil Properties, Processes and Functions." Report of the EU Joint Research Centre, Institute for Environment and Sustainability.

- "Biochar, climate change and soil: a review to guide future research." *CSIRO Land and Water Science Report*, May 2009.

- "Biochar as a soil amendment: A review of the environmental implications." Dominic Wolf (unpublished).

These reports are balanced and comprehensive, and leave the reader with an awareness of both the extent and limitations of the research to date.

Short research summaries on specific themes, as well as biochar fact sheets, white papers, technical bulletins, and practical guides, are available from the International Biochar Initiative (IBI) at:

http://www.biochar-international.org/publications/IBI.

An extensive list of scientific literature and hundreds of reports, updated monthly, can be found on the IBI website at:

http://www.biochar-international.org/biblio.

---

## THE CONSTITUENTS OF BIOCHAR

To better understand the general action of biochar in soil, it is helpful to examine biochar as a small number of constituents, each of which has predictable roles in the soil.

As shown in Figure 7.1, one useful approach is to view the biochar as being made up of two portions: the "mobile" portion that will dissolve (leach) into the soil water and the "resident" portion that will remain as a stable part of the non-leachable soil matrix.

Each portion contains both **organic** and **inorganic** fractions—and each has a different destiny. In general, the mobile portion will have its greatest impact over the first one or two growing seasons, and the resident portion will remain in the soil, with sustained impact, for a very long time (decades, centuries, even millennia).

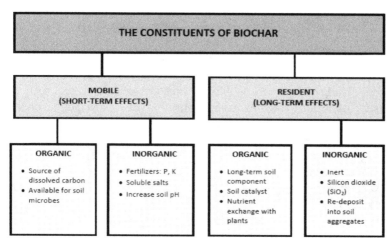

Fig. 7.1 The Constituents of Biochar

## MOBILE PORTIONS

The mobile portion of biochar—the portion that can move in water or be rapidly decomposed by microbes—contains both organic and inorganic parts.

### Mobile Organic Portion

The function of the mobile organic portion is fairly straightforward: it will be a source of dissolved organic carbon and will also be available organic matter for soil microbes (as later discussed in greater detail). In this regard, the biochar acts like many other sources of degradable soil carbon, such as compost and naturally deposited detritus. Over a short time frame, on the order of years, the leachable and biodegradable organic portions of the biochar are metabolized by the microbes in the soil, or washed away into streams or ground water.

Concerns have been raised about possible toxicity in soil due to mobile organics from biochar. Indeed, biochars can introduce toxic constituents, but almost invariably the toxic constituents were present in the original biomass before its conversion to biochar. For example, treated lumber can be the source of heavy metals that remain in the biochar. The actual process of **pyrolysis**—which converts biomass to biochar—has not been shown to generate significant quantities of toxic products such as **PAHs (polycyclic aromatic hydrocarbons)**. If fire produced significant toxic constituents from biomass, then every forest fire would leave behind a legacy of toxicity. Instead, renewed growth typically follows. Biochar is also well known to **adsorb** these toxic compounds when they are present in soil, in a sense "locking them up."

## Mobile Inorganic Portions

The inorganic portion of biochar is transformed into ash after the biochar is burned or heated at high temperature to oxidize and remove the organic portion (which includes the carbon atoms of the char). Measurements have shown that most biochar ash is soluble in water. This is to be expected, since the ash originated as dissolved minerals in the soil water, which were then transported into the growing plants that later formed the biomass from which the biochar was created.

The mobile inorganic portion of biochar may include fertilizers, such as phosphorus and potassium, and other components that have a liming effect on the soil (that is, raise its **pH**). Generally, these inorganic constituents have the potential to improve soil fertility and crop yield in places where the specific nutrients are limiting and higher pH levels in the soil are desirable. Increasing soil pH can diminish some soluble metal toxicities (such as aluminum), when such toxicities are present. On the other hand, in alkaline soils, additional liming may not help and can actually make fertility conditions worse.

The mobile inorganic portion also contains compounds that act like salt, including sodium chloride and other neutral ion pairs. These compounds may be benign or can introduce excess dissolved salts (**total dissolved solids or TDS**), resulting in saline soil conditions. Such excess dissolved salts do not help the plants and can, in fact, inhibit or prevent seed germination and healthy crop growth. In general, salts wash out of the soil with precipitation and normally do not build up to levels that cause concern. Problems result when excessive salts are added, such as by excessive irrigation with brackish water, or where the climate provides insufficient precipitation to flush away the accumulating salts. For this reason, applications of biochars that contain salts need to be coordinated with and balanced against the local irrigation practices and precipitation patterns.

## RESIDENT PORTIONS

The resident portion of biochar—the portion that stays put within the soil matrix—also contains both organic and inorganic parts.

## Resident Inorganic Portion

Some plants convert dissolved minerals into stable insoluble forms, such as silica (silicon dioxide). This non-leachable component of biochar ash is a minor constituent of the biochar, and is typically inert or slowly dissolved and re-deposited into soil aggregates over time. In some plants, carbon can be locked up in these silica structures, and they have been proposed as making a significant contribution to long-term carbon sequestration. (See "Next Generation Carbon Bio-Sequestration Solutions" at http://www.plantstone.com.au/AboutPlantstone.html.)

## Resident Organic Portion

The most fascinating and unique fraction of biochar is the organic portion that becomes a permanent soil component. This portion, which can also be described as "recalcitrant" or "resident," is insoluble (non-leachable). It is not consumed by growing plants, but appears to be degraded by both non-biological and biological processes over a very long time scale—stretching literally into millennia.

In light of this longevity, it is reasonable to label biochar as a "soil catalyst." The bulk of biochar remains substantially unchanged, yet enables improvements in the overall environment that the soil provides for the plants and microbes that live in it. This notion is key to many of the attributes of biochar discussed next.

## BIOCHAR MITIGATES SOIL'S PHYSICAL DEFICIENCIES

One of the significant and predictable impacts of biochar is on soil drainage. Some soils, typically those containing elevated portions of clays and which are poorly aggregated, are too tight and do not drain effectively. Ineffective drainage results in extended periods of inadequate soil aeration. Other soils, especially those dominated by sandy matrices, may drain too efficiently. Overly efficient drainage can shorten the benefit of periodic wetting. In both cases, the addition of biochar compensates for the native soil deficiency in the following ways:

- Clayey and poorly aggregated soils become less compacted and provide better aeration.

- Sandy soils acquire additional bulk moisture storage capacity.

In seeking to improve bulk moisture dynamics, the initial soil texture will dictate how biochar should be introduced. To improve aeration in clay soils, the biochar must be mixed throughout the root zone; plowing or tilling is likely required.

For sandy soils, biochar can also be introduced by working it into the root zone, or by top-dressing and surface incorporation. Through the latter approach, surface water will eventually transport the biochar downward, deeper into the soil matrix; however, the biochar must be protected from erosion by wind and water until it has had time to migrate deep enough.

One way to protect the biochar after incorporating it into the surface of sandy soil is to mulch on top of it, although in some cases only deeper incorporation will protect from water erosion.

Regardless of soil texture, biochar can be applied in bands in situations where turning the soil is undesirable (for example in reduced tillage or no-till agriculture), or to avoid disturbing root integrity in perennial crops.

Using biochar to correct soil drainage properties can be a one-time fix that usually requires a significant volume of biochar to achieve the desired result. Other biochar contributions to soil dynamics can be achieved through a series of smaller, incremental applications.

## BIOCHAR HELPS THE SOIL DO MORE WITH LESS

One of the major challenges in agriculture is to make the nutrients in the soil available to the plant when the plant can benefit from them. Fertilizers can often only be applied early in the growing season, before the crop canopy closes and field operations are no longer feasible. Unfortunately, between the time the fertilizer is applied and the crop takes it up, fertilizer can be leached out of the soil by excess rainfall, consumed by weeds, or metabolized by microbial activity in the soil.

Biochar helps conserve plant nutrients by storing them within its matrix and making the nutrients available when the crops need them. This happens because of a property in biochar, certain clays, and soil organic matter known as **cation exchange capacity** (CEC). CEC is a measure of a biochar's capacity to retain positive ions, such as ammonium and potassium **cations**, in an exchangeable form that is available to plants.

CEC not only helps conserve the fertilizers added to the crop during the growing season, but also improves the soil's ability to capture and retain nutrients from other sources available at other times. For example, at the end of the growing season crop residues are often left in fields to decompose. When this organic matter decomposes, biochar captures some of the nutrients released, saving those nutrients for the next growing season. Moreover, biochar's inherent capacity for storing nutrients, as measured by CEC, has been shown to actually increase as the biochar interacts with the soil matrix over long time periods.

Biochar also modifies and improves the soil's performance by retaining moisture and making it available during periods of low precipitation and hot, dry soil conditions. This is possible because many biochars have very large internal surface areas—typically over 100 square meters per gram in biochars that have good **adsorption capacity**. This internal surface area adsorbs moisture when water availability within the soil is high and releases it back into the soil when water availability is depressed.

Thus, during annual cycles when rainfall is sparse—and in drought conditions—biochar can improve retention of soil moisture. In many areas of non-irrigated agriculture, crops are planted during the rainy season, followed by a growing season that ends due to lack of moisture. In this situation, the biochar helps the soil conserve precious moisture reserves, in effect extending the growing season.

In sum, biochar helps save precious water where irrigation is used and provides critical support where it is not, improving crop performance during periods of drought.

## BIOCHAR RESTORES THE SOIL TO ITS NATURAL BIOLOGICAL ROLE

Healthy, natural soil involves more than simply metering nutrients to plants. A healthy soil-plant nutrient exchange involves a pivotal intermediary: innumerable soil microbes, which synergistically participate in cycling those nutrients. One example of this remarkable partnership is **mycorrhiza**[7] (from the Greek words for "fungus" and "root"), the symbiotic association between beneficial fungi and plant roots. A more detailed description of how it works follows in the box labeled "Amazing Mycorrrhiza."

This exchange effectively improves the plant's ability to absorb minerals, allowing nutrients such as phosphorus and zinc to be passed from the soil into the fungus, and then into the plant roots.

This soil-microbe-plant troika has developed over billions of years and is essentially a life-or-death proposition for plants. Of the 17 necessary elements for plant growth, 13 are derived from mineral matter in the soil. Only the remaining four— carbon, oxygen, hydrogen and nitrogen—are obtained from the atmosphere. And nitrogen acquisition, in the absence of commercially produced fertilizers, requires the assistance of microbes.

Since 95% of all plant families are mycorrhizal, this exchange phenomenon is the norm rather than the exception for natural plant growth. Simply put, plants make their own food (see the text box labeled "Plants Make Their Own Food")— although now we know they do it with the help of microbes.

If plants are fed nitrogen and other nutrients from synthetic fertilizers, mycorrhizal exchange is inhibited. After all, the exchange does draw energy from plants in the form of excreted sugar, which plants can use for other survival needs if alternate nutrient sources are available that do not demand investment in mycorrhizal exchange.

### HOW DOES BIOCHAR FIT IN?

Biochar makes a significant contribution to mycorrhiza by promoting soil microbe populations. Specifically, biochar:

- Detoxifies soil water by adsorbing compounds that inhibit microbe growth.

- Provides a protective habitat for microbes (see Figure 7.2).

- Improves soil moisture management, as discussed above.

---

[7] The term "myccorrhiza" refers to both this symbiotic relationship and a participating fungus. In the latter sense, the plural is "mycorrhizae."

## AMAZING MYCORRHIZA: HOW DOES THE PARTNERSHIP WORK?

Soil microbes and fungi live in intimate contact with soil particles and moisture, aided in this by their large surface area to cell volume ratio. A fungus has a large mass of filaments called mycelia (singular, mycelium), which are much smaller than plant root hairs. These filaments give the fungus extensive surface area and, with it, a high capacity for absorbing water and mineral nutrients. (Biochar has the same property.) However, for the fungus and other soil microorganisms to thrive, they need energy in the form of carbohydrates.

Plants photosynthesize sugars (such as glucose and sucrose) from carbon dioxide, water and sunlight. To carry on this activity, plants need minerals from the soil for myriad enzymatic processes and to form chlorophyll (which is similar to hemoglobin in animals except with the iron replaced by magnesium). However, while all plants can extract some minerals from the soil through their root hairs, they benefit from increased mineral nutrients that support their areal growth and fertility.

So, here's the deal: The mycorrhizae (fungi) make soil nutrients available and extend their filaments into plant roots, thereby providing nutrients for uptake by the plants. The plants in return send sugar from the leaves down to the roots where it is excreted to feed the fungi.

But the deal goes deeper: deep roots of trees and grasses bring minerals up from lower in the earth and deposit them to the topsoil in the form of leaf and other plant litter. Fungi break this dead material down into simpler components (they extend their filaments into dead material also) and extract energy from it, as well as building it into the organic structures of their bodies. When the fungi and other soil organisms die and decompose, they provide organic nutrients to the plants.

In the natural world, leaf litter, decaying animals, and plants provide a moist and aerated protective mat, resulting in a perfect environment for the soil microorganisms and fungi. In human agriculture, mulching and composting can replicate this environment to grow strong, disease resistant, and nutritious plants.

—*Paul Taylor (Ed.)*

## MORE GOOD NEWS ABOUT MICROBES

- **Phosphorus Uptake.** Plant roots on their own may be incapable of taking up demineralized phosphate ions—for example, in alkaline soils. However, the mycelia of mycorrhizal fungi provide access to this phosphorus, and transmit it to the plants they colonize.

- **Getting Nitrogen.** The Haber-Bosch process, invented in the early 1900s, paved the way for commercially produced nitrogen fertilizers. But before then, virtually all farmer-applied nitrogen fertilizers were recycled animal manures. And before there were farmers—or even animals—plants obtained their nitrogen via nitrogen fixation, by forming nodules with certain bacteria.

PLANTS MAKE THEIR OWN FOOD

As Arthur W. Galston discussed in *Life Processes in Plants* (Scientific American Library, 1994):

We have not always understood that plants synthesized their own food. The ancients believed that plants derived their food from the soil, and that the root system was a kind of diffuse mouth sucking nutrition from the earth's breast. This notion was proved wrong early in the seventeenth century, when a Dutch physician named Jan Baptista van Helmont planted a 5-lb willow sapling in a container of dried soil weighing exactly 200 lb. For five years, he added nothing to the container except rainwater. When he harvested the tree, he found its weight to be 169 lb, while the dried soil now weighed 199 lb 14 oz, a small loss he attributed to experimental error...

Van Helmont also concluded ... that plants derived no materials at all from the soil other than water. He did not appreciate that the approximately two ounces lost by the soil included mineral elements that were in fact essential to the well-being and growth of his tree [page 18]. ...

If the plant is fed any form of fixed nitrogen, especially ammonia or amino acids, both nodulation and nitrogen fixation are strongly inhibited. This makes good sense, since both processes are "expensive" from an energy point of view. Plants obviously prefer to take the easy road to obtaining their fixed nitrogen by adsorbing ready-made compounds if they are available, but they can switch to a more independent, energy-intensive mode when required [page 202].

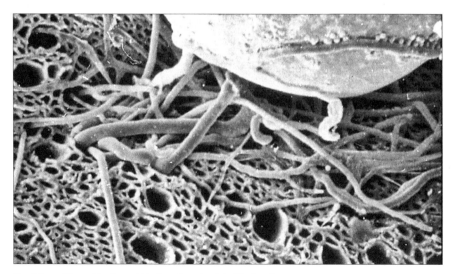

Fig. 7.2    Mycorrhiza Fungal Hyphae Growing into Biochar Pores

Source: Ogawa (1994)

## BIOCHAR WAS SOIL'S FIRST AMENDMENT

"Biochar" is merely the current name for natural or manufactured pyrolyzed biomass; nature has in fact deposited "biochar" in the soil via groundcover fires for billions of years. The soil-microbe-plant interaction has developed over time via natural selection, with the successful combinations prospering and the failures fading away.

Today, there are many ways to promote crop productivity. In modern industrial agriculture, fertilization is the dominant approach. Although such fertilization can replace depleted nutrients, it is a temporary solution and does not contribute to overall, long-term soil quality.

Biochar does. Given the significant soil benefits described in this chapter, biochar—an original soil amendment created and validated by nature—offers immeasurable potential in the modern world for helping to grow food sustainably, especially when used to address deficiencies in local agriculture.

## CONCLUSION

Using biochar will not cause plants to grow in a new way. Rather, it helps the soil provide conditions more conducive to plant growth.

## KEY POINTS FROM THIS CHAPTER

- Biochar's constituents have a predictable role in the soil that enables conclusions about the benefits of biochar in specific growing situations.

- Biochar works in combination with other soil components and soil microbes to permanently improve the overall soil dynamics and plant nutrition, which in turn improves plant growth and yield.

- Biochar is made up of two portions. One portion is mobile, and includes biodegradable and leachable constituents. The other portion is resident: it is non-leachable and decomposes extremely slowly.

- The resident organic portion of biochar has unique internal structure and properties that give biochar its compelling benefits. This portion will remain in the soil, with beneficial amending impact, for a very long time—decades, centuries, and even millennia. Although conventional fertilizers may provide short-term benefits, they do not contribute to overall, long-term soil quality.

- Biochar is a natural material that has been deposited into soil by groundcover fires for billions of years. In its modern application, however, biochar can be manufactured and applied to improve soil fertility.

- Biochar thus offers substantial potential to the modern world for growing food sustainably, especially where soils are poor.

# Chapter 8

# Characterizing Biochars: Attributes, Indicators, and At-Home Tests

## Hugh McLauglin, PhD PE
Director of Biocarbon Research, Alterna Biocarbon Inc.


**IN THIS CHAPTER YOU WILL LEARN:**

- The quality indicators and attributes of biochar.

- The four constituents that characterize biochar, and the importance of each.

- How these four constituents are measured, with useful at-home tests and consumer tips.


"Each biochar can and should be tested prior to addition to the soil."

# INTRODUCTION

"Biochar" is a somewhat ambiguous term that is applied to a broad range of charcoal end-products intended for addition to soils. Those products are generated by various raw materials and conversion processes, resulting in differing characteristics that may affect their performance in their intended application.

This chapter offers a simple scheme for characterizing specific biochars before adding them to soils. It will detail those characteristics and the logic behind them, how to test for each characteristic, and the limitations of each test.

## QUALITY INDICATORS OF BIOCHAR

Biochar quality indicators fall into three general categories: physical attributes, constituent attributes, and soil-relevant attributes (see Figure 8.1). These categories, and the quality indicators in each, are discussed in greater detail below.

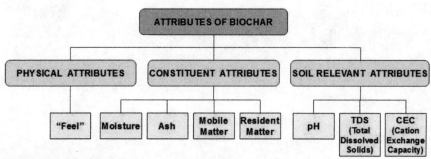

Fig. 8.1 Attributes of Char

## PHYSICAL ATTRIBUTES – THE "FEEL" OF BIOCHAR

Properly carbonized wood intended for use as biochar is very different from the cinders left behind when a campfire goes out. Open air campfires burn in an uncontrolled, non-uniform environment. As a result, the leftover material is likely to be a mixture of unconverted material (**torrified wood**), and material fully converted to ash, as well as some charcoal.

Properly carbonized wood:

• Is a surprisingly light, rigid, but friable (easily crushed) material.

• Is uniform and fine-grained without pockets of under-carbonized (unburned) material.

• Is not greasy to the touch.

• Produces abundant black powder that will wash off with plain water.

If soap is needed to remove char's black powder from the skin, the char contains substantial mobile matter. The significance of mobile matter when applying biochar to soils is discussed later.

## CHARACTERIZING CHAR: THE FOUR CONSTITUENTS

The four essential constituents that characterize biochar are moisture, ash, mobile matter, and resident matter.

**Moisture** refers to the water content of the biochar, and as measured may include some highly volatile organic compounds that evaporate along with the water.

**Ash** refers to the portion of moisture-free biochar that is not organic.

**Mobile** matter (also known as labile matter) is the organic portion of moisture-free biochar that can migrate into the soil and become a source of food for soil microbes.

**Resident matter** (also known as recalcitrant matter) is the organic portion of moisture-free biochar that is expected to remain stable in the soil for a very long time.

**CONSUMER TIP 8.1**

*Measure for Moisture and Ash*

Moisture and ash are found in every bag of biochar, yet add little value to the long-term performance of biochar in the soil. These components are fairly easy to measure, and any candidate char should be tested for both before purchase or application to soil.

Each biochar constituent can be further subdivided. First, this chapter explores the significance of each constituent, how it is measured, and what the measurement represents. The chapter then addresses other considerations related to applying biochar to soils.

Throughout the chapter, look for "@HOME BIOCHAR" text boxes containing instructions for biochar assessments you can do at home. Remember to always follow the safety precautions given, and protect yourself from the hot materials and noxious vapors that may be produced by some of the procedures.

## MOISTURE

The amount of water present in biochar can vary greatly, depending on how the biochar is produced and whether it has accumulated moisture during storage or shipping. In order to assess and compare properties of various biochars on a uniform "**dry basis**", it is necessary to determine how much of the biochar is not water.

The moisture content is measured by weighing a sample before and after drying in an oven at a specified temperature just above the boiling point of water. The "moisture" measurement may include not only water content but also other low-boiling organic solvents.

For most biochars, only water vapor is driven off when drying at low temperatures (below 105°C). However, some biochars will release lesser amounts of organic vapors, typically methanol and acetic acid. These are easy to detect by their odor: Methanol, which is an ingredient in paint and varnish removers, has a slightly alcoholic odor when pure and a repulsive, pungent odor in its crude form. Acetic acid is what gives vinegar its sour taste and pungent smell.

A convenient standard of "moisture-free biochar" can be determined by drying a sample at 105°C until a constant weight is reached (that is, no further weight is lost when drying is continued). This is typically done overnight in a drying oven with internal forced convection. (For an easy, at-home way to measure the moisture content of a biochar sample, see the text box labeled "@Home Biochar/An Easy Way to Measure Moisture.")

> **CONSUMER TIP 8.2**
>
> *Don't Buy the Water!*
> Many biochars are highly hygroscopic (or hydrophilic) and will take up significant moisture if exposed to humid air—an important property in the soil.
>
> If you're using homemade chars, no problem; the extra water won't harm the ultimate performance of the biochar.
>
> The real concern here is commercially produced chars. Generally, they have less than 5% and not more than 10% residual moisture. If higher, you've bought "char with water added"—and paid for the water!
>
> The lesson for consumers: water should not be a significant component of commercial char sold by weight or shipped a long distance.

**@HOME BIOCHAR**

**An Easy Way to Measure Moisture**

Moisture is relatively easy to measure, but requires patience—especially if you're drying wet biochar or larger quantities you plan to test later for other properties.

**What You'll Need:**

- A simple toaster oven (not a microwave oven).

- A thermocouple (or standard oven thermometer suitable for use inside the toaster oven). Don't rely on the thermostat of an inexpensive toaster oven.

- An inexpensive scale, accurate to 0.01 grams. (Scales that read to 0.01 grams up to 200 grams are available online at prices below US$20.) Alternatively, you can use a kitchen scale for a larger sample of char (which will also require a longer drying time).

- A piece of aluminum foil, perforated to let excess moisture escape and allow vapor to circulate.

**What to Do:**

1. Weigh the biochar sample.
2. Put the sample in a drying dish or in small tin can with open top and perforations in the bottom for airflow. Don't seal the vessel.
3. Place the perforated aluminum foil over the top of the biochar vessel to shield the sample from direct radiant heat of the toaster oven heating element(s).
4. Insert the thermocouple (or oven thermometer) into the center of the biochar sample to measure its internal temperature.
5. Heat the sample until its interior target temperature is reached, which is usually 100–105°C for determining moisture content.
   **NOTE:** Because of the cooling effect of evaporating moisture, make sure that the interior of the biochar itself has reached the requisite temperature and is not less than 100°C. This is especially important for larger samples.
6. Weigh the sample again.
7. Calculate the percentage difference: this is the moisture content.

It takes a bit of practice to achieve consistency and reproducibility with this technique, but after half a dozen tries, you'll be a seasoned moisture content analyst!

However, drying at 105°C removes only part of the actual moisture contained in a biochar sample. Most biochars are **hygroscopic** (also known as **hydrophilic**)—they readily attract and hold large amounts of moisture from the environment, and this moisture is released and evaporated at temperatures at or above 100°C.

Water may also be **adsorbed** to the large internal surfaces areas inherent in biochar (discussed below), or held in more tightly bound forms as water of hydration within the ash present in the biochar or as water molecules associated with the organic portions of the biochar.

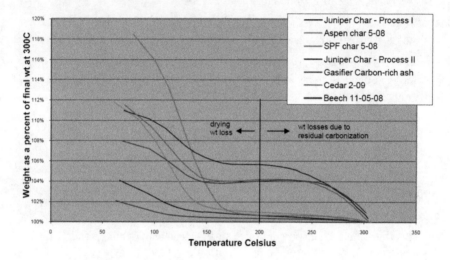

Fig. 8.2    Weight Loss Curves for Seven Chars

Source: "All Biochars are Not Created Equal, and How to Tell Them Apart." Hugh McLaughlin, PhD, PE, Paul S. Anderson, PhD, Frank E. Shields and Thomas B. Reed, PhD. Version 2 (October 2009), superseding the original version issued at the North American Biochar Conference, Boulder, CO (August 2009).

Figure 8.2 shows the weight losses as measured for seven biochars when heated from below 100°C to 300°C. A temperature of 200°C falls on a stable weight plateau, where most of the water and other volatiles have been removed but before the char begins to lose mass due to further carbonization at higher temperatures. Thus, drying at a temperature of 200°C conditions the biochar by **desorbing** volatile substances, including water vapor, which have been adsorbed in the pores of the biochar. If these volatiles are not desorbed, they would interfere with the subsequent measurement of adsorption capacity (discussed later). The biochar, as conditioned, is technically "desorbed," but is usually referred to as "oven dry" biochar in order to distinguish it from "moisture-free" biochar.

An at-home process for getting biochar "oven dry" is provided in the textbox labeled "@Home Biochar/Drying Process for 'Oven Dry' Biochar."

**@HOME BIOCHAR**

### Drying Process for "Oven Dry" Biochar

Here is the recommended process for drying biochars to remove additional moisture and to subsequently measure adsorption capacity:

### What You'll Need:

The same equipment used for "An Easy Way to Measure Moisture."

### What to Do:

1. Set the oven for the target drying temperature plus 25°C. (This is the maximum internal temperature referred to below.)

2. Turn the oven off when the biochar's internal temperature reaches the target temperature.

3. Keep the biochar in the drying oven until the maximum internal temperature is measured and noted.
   **Important note:** If the biochar's internal temperature exceeds the oven temperature, the biochar has begun oxidizing, which will lead to invalid results; the drying study should be repeated at a lower oven temperature.

4. Cool the biochar in the drying oven or a sealed container to inhibit adsorption of moisture from the surrounding air.

### Safety Tip: Ventilation!

Because some biochars, when heated to internal temperatures above 150°C, may emit significant volatiles, and even generate smoke, drying should be done either under a laboratory hood or in a well-ventilated area, such as an open garage or outdoors.

When heated to above 150°C, some biochars may exhibit incremental carbonization, emit significant volatiles (flammable gases), and even generate smoke. These are indicators that the biochar is not fully carbonized or that it contains torrefied wood. Biochars containing significant portions of torrefied wood are likely to behave differently and possibly less beneficially in soil than fully carbonized biochars. Soil and plant scientists are researching this subject further.

## ASH

Once a biochar sample is moisture-free or oven-dry, the next category of interest is ash: that is, the fraction of the moisture-free biochar that is not organic. Depending on its nature and amount, the ash portion of any biochar may be considered a beneficial component or a detriment. In any event, low ash numbers are desirable in a biochar—and therefore it is in the interest of the char producer or purchaser to measure it correctly.

### Measuring Ash

Ash content is measured by grinding a dry biochar sample (either moisture-free or oven-dry) to a coarse powder and placing it into an open-top ashing crucible. Next, the sample is heated in a muffle furnace, open to air, at a temperature of 500–550°C, for at least 30 minutes. (Depending on the sample, ashing—even for finely powdered samples—can take much longer.) Heating continues until the sample becomes a pale gray to white powder with *no* black particles. The ratio of the ash weight to the original dry sample weight provides the ash fraction on a dry basis (either moisture-free or oven-dry, depending on the sample's starting point).

A completed ashing process will burn off all organic material, leaving behind inorganic ash. Black powder in an ashed sample indicates residual carbon—and the presence of uncombusted organic material. If this is observed, the samples should be stirred and re-ashed. Because ashing yields a very stable material, erring on the side of extra time at furnace temperature, under controlled temperature limits, will have no detrimental effect on the ash content of the biochar sample.

### Ash Levels and Implications

Most chars made from clean wood yield less than 5% ash by weight, while agricultural residues, such as corn stover, may yield significantly higher levels. If the original **feedstock** material (that is, the original living or formerly living material [**biomass**] to be made into char) is new, clean wood or agricultural residues, there is generally little worry about ash level or composition. However, whenever the origin of the biomass is unknown, or the ash levels are significantly higher than 10% by weight, it may be worth testing the ash for soil pH impact and the presence of metals. The pH, which will indicate how much the ash will act like lime in the soil, can be easily measured by using pH test paper. For acidic soils, additional alkalinity is welcome, but for high pH soils, additional liming may lead to poor crop performance.

Testing for metals should be conducted by a qualified laboratory, which can also help interpret the analytical results. Not all metals in the ash are bad, but all metals in the ash need to be understood as to their fate and role in the soil.

**@HOME BIOCHAR**

## Measuring Ash
Like moisture, ash is fairly easy to measure at home.

### What You'll Need:
- The same scale you used to measure moisture, with accuracy to 0.01 grams.
- A propane-fueled camping stove.
- A clean, dry, open-top tuna fish or cat food tin can (not aluminum).
- A sample of finely crushed or powdered, dried biochar.

### What to Do:
1. Heat the empty can to burn off any coatings from the manufacturing process.
2. Weigh the container after it cools, and record.
3. Spread a ½-centimeter (or ¼-inch) layer of dried char over the bottom of the can and note the container's new weight.
4. Record the difference; this is the weight of the dry biochar.
5. Heat the open tin can on the camping stove over an open flame that uniformly heats the entire bottom of the container.
6. Stir the contents periodically and uniformly to facilitate ashing, but take care not to knock or blow away any of the ash.
   **Important note:** Don't let the contents of the tin can catch fire and burn with an open flame. That will carry ash away as particulates in smoke emissions.
7. Continue this process until the tin can contains only gray to white ash residue.
8. Weigh the cooled can including the ash therein.
9. Remove all ash and weigh the empty can.
10. Record the difference; this is the weight of the ash.
11. Record the ratio of ash to dry biochar weights, using the values recorded in Steps 4 and 10.

*Voila!* You've calculated the percent of ash on a dry char basis.

## MOBILE MATTER

Moisture-free biochars still contain organic matter that will not remain permanently as beneficial carbon agents in the soil. This material is "mobile" (sometimes also referred as **"labile"**) because it can leave the biochar by leaching into the soil or being ingested by soil microbes, yet its carbon is not likely to be released as a gas component. The term "mobile matter" is the analogue of "volatile matter," a term derived from **proximate analysis** (a standard test used in coal science), and which refers to matter that becomes gaseous when heated to 950°C. Proximate analysis has been adapted to analyzing biochars. However, for biochar, the term "mobile matter" is more descriptive, and thus more suitable. (For more discussion of modifying proximate analysis to make it more suitable for characterizing biochars, see: "All Biochars are Not Created Equal," available online at http://www.biochar-international.org/node/1029.)

### Measuring Mobile Matter

In order to more accurately partition the organic portion of a particular biochar into mobile matter and soil-stable resident matter—and recognizing that biochar is a soil amendment rather than fuel—the proximate analysis temperature is lowered from 950°C (the temperature for testing coal) to 450°C.

A bone-dry biochar sample is placed into a proximate analysis crucible (that is, a self-sealing ceramic crucible). **This test must exclude air in order to avoid oxidizing the remaining resident matter.** Next, the biochar is heated in an oven at 450°C for 30 minutes. This process will drive off mobile matter in the biochar, leaving behind the ash and resident matter constituents.

## RESIDENT MATTER

Resident matter is the portion of organic matter in biochar that is expected to remain stable in the soil for a very long time. It is the portion of moisture-free biochar that is neither mobile matter nor ash.

Conceptually, resident matter (or recalcitrant matter) is analogous to "fixed matter," another term used in coal science (proximate analysis).

### Analytical Sequence for Determining Resident Matter

Determining resident matter is an analytical sequence, building on the processes already described.

1. Dry a biochar sample to 175°C to 200°C, creating at least 25 grams of moisture-free biochar, and divide it into two smaller weighed parts.

2. Ash one part at 500–550°C in air (see "Measuring Ash" above).

3. Heat the other part, air-free, to 450°C, which will remove the mobile matter; the residue can be saved to measure resident carbon, as described below.

4. Calculate the resident matter portion by subtracting the ash and mobile matter fractions from the moisture-free biochar fraction.

This analytical sequence parallels the **ASTM** D-1762 procedure for **Chemical Analysis of Wood Charcoal** (an industry-accepted standard test), except that the temperature ranges have been modified. Because biochar is destined for soil and not for use as a fuel, the drying temperature has been raised to 175°C to 200°C, and the ashing and mobile-volatile matter temperatures have been lowered. As biochar science evolves over time, the relative merits of these modified analytical procedures will be established, and appropriate adjustments will be made.

### Measuring Resident Carbon

Not all the material in the resident matter is carbon. As well as ash (which is measured and subtracted), various amounts of other elements will remain in the sample, such as nitrogen, hydrogen, oxygen, phosphorus, and sulfur. For typical biochars created from clean wood and grass biomass by **slow pyrolysis**, the carbon fraction is typically in the 60–90% range.

---

**CARBON DIOXIDE IS NEARLY FOUR TIMES HEAVIER THAN CARBON**

Carbon dioxide is 3.67 times heavier than atomic carbon:

Atomic weight of C = 12
Atomic weight of O = 16
Molecular weight of $CO_2$ = 44
$$(= 12 + 16 + 16)$$

The average annual emission per person in Australia and the United States from burning fossil fuel is over 5 tons of C, which translate into 19 tons of $CO_2$.

---

Resident carbon can be measured by performing a chemical analysis on a portion of the residue left from the mobile matter analysis. This gives a basis for estimating the carbon- or carbon dioxide-sequestering potential of that biochar in the soil: each weight unit of pure carbon is equivalent to 3.67 times that same weight unit of carbon dioxide that could be kept out of the atmosphere and safely and stably sequestered in the char.

### Mobile Matter vs. Resident Matter

As mentioned above, one potential impact of mobile matter, when leached from biochar, is its interaction with soil microbes. Depending on the soil and crops, additional soluble soil carbon may be good (by promoting microbial activity in the soil) or may have drawbacks (such as stimulating microbial competition for available soil nitrogen). In addition, mobile matter is not stable and will likely not be present as a beneficial carbon agent in the soil after one—or perhaps a few—growing seasons. For these reasons, mobile matter is likely of lower value in a biochar than an equivalent weight of resident matter.

**CONSUMER TIP 8.3**

Because mobile matter can leave a biochar after one or two growing seasons, resident matter is likely the more important biochar component to consider when purchasing biochar.

## SOIL-RELEVANT ATTRIBUTES

The above tests break a biochar into its constituents and provide insight into its make-up. But this does not end the story. Other specific biochar properties are believed pivotal for assessing how a particular biochar will impact the soil—specifically, levels of **pH** and **total dissolved solids** (TDS), and **cation exchange capacity** (CEC) and adsorption capacity.

These important properties will now be discussed in greater detail.

## BIOCHAR TDS AND PH

Two tests—for total dissolved solids (TDS) and for pH—can predict the short-term impact of adding a particular biochar to a particular soil. TDS and pH gauge two different properties. TDS measures the total dissolved salt content in water, including fertilizers and neutral salts that are in solution. TDS in soil is not necessarily a bad thing, but too much salt (excessive TDS) has an adverse effect on most plants. This is a significant concern with biochars made from materials containing manure, such as chicken litter.

Excessive TDS is also a concern for biochars with significant ash content. Dissolvable soil salts migrate into the soil water, and in the biochar are measured as ash. Since these salts can leach into the biochar-amended soil, high-ash biochars have a much greater likelihood of elevating TDS in the soil. (See text box labeled "Technical Aside/Total Dissolved Solids (TDS).")

---

**TECHNICAL ASIDE**
**Total Dissolved Solids (TDS)**

Total Dissolved Solids (TDS), the most common indicator of water quality, is a measure of the combined content of all substances dissolved in water that remain after the water is evaporated. TDS is proportional to electrical conductivity of water.

The lower the TDS/conductivity level, the purer the water.

Handheld TDS meters can test for TDS easily and inexpensively. However, TDS meters are actually conductivity meters and detect only mobile charged ions. Therefore, the term "total dissolved solids" is somewhat misleading when applied to these meters: "total charged ions" more accurately describes what's being measured.

Ultimately, the lower the total charged ions, the purer—the more de-ionized—the water.

Sources: Randy Holmes-Farley, "What is TDS?" *Reefkeeping*. http://reefkeeping.com/issues/2004-04/rhf/feature/index.php. "Water Quality 101," *Water Quality Products* 13, no. 1 (January 2008) http://www.wqpmag.com/Water-Testing-101-TDS-article8837.

---

Soil pH is much more critical, especially if the added biochar pushes the pH in an unfavorable direction, either too high or too low. Many biochars have a significant "liming" effect and can elevate soil pH. For many soils this is a good thing, but alkaline soils may not tolerate additional lime loading.

### Testing Biochar for pH and TDS

Levels of pH and TDS can be measured using inexpensive handheld meters on a sample created by mixing a portion of pure biochar with neutral pH water that has low conductivity. Ideally, distilled de-ionized water is used, but de-ionized water may be hard to obtain outside a research laboratory. Fortunately, many bottled waters are acceptably pure. The measurement process is straightforward, and is described in the textbox labeled "@Home Biochar/Testing pH and TDS."

---

**@HOME BIOCHAR**
**Testing pH and TDS**

**What You'll Need:**

- A source of de-ionized water.

- Generally, bottled water can be used. That's because bottled water is basically purified tap water with small amounts of salts added for "flavor." One brand in particular –Aquafina®–is especially suitable because it's essentially bottled de-ionized water.

- pH paper or a pH meter.

- Conductivity or TDS meter. Inexpensive handheld meters are readily available in the range US$20–$30.

**What to Do:**

- Measure the starting pH and TDS of the water.

- Create a slurry by mixing 1 part pure biochar for 10 parts water by weight.

- Depending on the density of the biochar, the biochar may take some time to become wet and release entrapped air.

- Mix or shake the slurry, and allow it to settle for 10 minutes.
  **NOTE**: If the mixing and settling cycle is too short, floating biochar may influence the TDS measurement.

- Measure the pH and TDS.

---

If the initial measurement reflects extremely high TDS, dilutions should be made to estimate the calculated undiluted TDS level being created in the soil water. The actual TDS level in the soil is what matters to the plant, not the range on the TDS meter. So, do the dilutions, multiply the measured TDS by the dilution factor to predict the undiluted TDS in the soil, and make sure the plant will be in a soil environment that enables it to thrive.

Many biochars are difficult to wet for a number of reasons. The biochar may have (a) elevated levels of condensed **hydrophobic** oils and tars, (b) a significant fraction of torrefied wood, or (c) a significant fraction of micropores, requiring water vapor to migrate into and condense in the pores to "wet them out."

The first two conditions do not provide the long-lasting benefits associated with biochar, although they may provide short-term benefit. Hydrophobic oils and tars are dissolved from the biochar by soil water, providing extra food for microbe proliferation. Once the microbes consume the tars, they die back and nothing of lasting benefit to the soil or the plants has been accomplished. Torrefied wood is not biochar, and likely breaks down in the soil over time.

---

**@HOME BIOCHAR**

**An Easy Way to Accelerate "Wetting"**
A simple method of accelerated biochar "wetting" borrows from home canning.

**What You'll Need:**

- A pint canning jar, with lid.

- A saucepan with lid large enough to enclose the entire jar, filled with a shallow depth of water (sufficient to surround the jar in steam).

**What to Do:**

- Make a slurry of 10% (by weight) dry biochar and water (using de-ionized water) and put it in the canning jar.

- Put the jar, with the lid on loosely, into the saucepan.

- Heat the water, bringing it to a boil.

- Cover the pan.

- Boil for 30 minutes.

- Remove from heat and cool.

**What to Look For:**
Upon cooling, the microporous biochars will sink and the less desirable hydrophobic biochars will continue to float, giving you a visual and measurable partitioning of the biochar components. Now you can measure the TDS and pH of the wetted biochar slurry to gain insight on the likely impact after the biochar is added to the soil.

---

On the other hand, micropores are highly desirable. One way to ascertain if significant micropores are present is to heat the biochar slurry close to the boiling point of water, which promotes the migration of the water vapor into the pores. The presence of desirable micropores is indicated if the biochar gives off many tiny bubbles, then sinks. If the water picks up an oily sheen or turns the color of tea, that indicates the presence and release of hydrophobic oils and tars discussed above.

A simple at-home method of accelerated "wetting" of biochar is suggested in the textbox labeled "@Home Biochar/An Easy Way to Accelerate 'Wetting'."

### Final Check: The Soil-Biochar Blend

The above-described initial pH and TDS measurements on a biochar-water slurry will indicate how much of a given biochar can be added to a given soil. As a final check, the actual proposed soil-biochar blend can be prepared and tested for pH and TDS in the same way.

To do this final testing, the biochar-water slurry is created, and a sample of the target soil is then simply added to it. However, for any proposed soil-biochar blend, the pH and TDS are tested at "saturation," where the slurry contains as little water as possible that still fully covers the soil and biochar solids—since the soil in the field will not typically have a significant excess of free water (because of runoff, seepage, and evaporation), except during rare rainfall or flooding events. Measuring soil properties at saturation are standard analytical methods used by soil scientists, and it is anticipated that similar standard methods relating to biochar will be adopted in the future.

For the soil-biochar ratio being tested, these final pH and TDS tests measure the conditions that will actually be created in the soil. If the pH is unacceptable or the TDS increase is excessive, the biochar should not be added to the soil in the tested proportions. Either a lower biochar load—or a different biochar altogether—should be tested and utilized.

### Cation Exchange Capacity (CEC) and Adsorption Capacity

Although CEC and adsorption capacity are considered crucial to predicting how a particular biochar will impact the soil, it is difficult to measure them analytically and to understand their precise roles in the soil. (Many atoms occur in nature with either a positive or a negative charge. A cation is a positively charged ion, and a negatively charged ion is an anion.)

Conceptually:

- CEC is the extent to which biochar can exchange ions. Generally, CEC is a benefit in soil: the higher the CEC, the more resistant the soil is to leaching fertilizer and the more nutrients that will be retained and become available to plant roots.

- Adsorption capacity is the extent to which a biochar has **activated carbon** properties. The higher the adsorption capacity, the better the biochar will retain moisture and soluble organic matter, in addition to its capacity to remove any organic toxicity from the soil due to residual pesticides.

Because many biochars exhibit significant and measurable amounts of CEC and adsorption capacity, these properties may well lie at the heart of the uniquely and dynamically beneficial role of biochar in the soil.

## Measuring Cation Exchange Capacity (CEC)

The CEC of a biochar is measured in a three-step sequence. First, all cations in the sample are converted to one cation form. Next, these new cations are displaced with another cation. Finally, the displaced cations are quantified.

Here is a typical procedure used by a commercial analytical laboratory to measure CEC:

- Shake a sample of dried char with sodium acetate solution, then drain or centrifuge to remove excess solution. Repeat two more times.

- Shake that converted sample with 2-propanol three times, each followed by draining or centrifuging. This alcohol rinse removes excess cations that are not bound to the char.

- Shake the sodium-loaded char with ammonia acetate solution three times, each followed by draining or centrifuging. This displaces the sodium cations into the solution.

- Measure the total solution from the three ammonia acetate rinses for sodium level and calculate CEC in milli-equivalents per 100 grams of dry starting char.

There are two notable challenges in gauging CEC and its role in soil. First, CEC is not a very common analytical test—exact procedures vary from lab to lab. Moreover, biochar testing protocols have not yet had sufficient time to fully evolve. Better and more standardized CEC testing methods, specific for biochar, are anticipated in the future.

Second, predicting the role of CEC in a specific biochar is complicated by the development of additional CEC within soil over time. It is therefore likely that measuring the CEC of a char is a temporary snapshot that does not, by itself, predict additional soil CEC that may later develop.

### Adsorption Capacity (AC)

Adsorption capacity (AC), like CEC, is under-appreciated and poorly understood in biochar. One characteristic of the adsorption capacity phenomenon in chars is shown in Figure 8.3, where a sequence of chars, carbonized over a range of **Heat Treatment Temperatures** (HTT), shows a dramatic variation of measured **BET** surface area (BET is a method for measuring surface area).

The phenomenon shown in Figure 8.3 has been confirmed for many chars and always occurs. Although individual chars will exhibit a different surface area at any given temperature, this characteristic rise and fall is highly reproducible. Because surface area and adsorption capacity are properties of the char itself, adsorption capacity is determined when the char is created and is unlikely to further develop after the char is added to soils. Moreover, the adsorption capacity of a char can deteriorate over time; foreign matter might either occupy the adsorption sites or physically block access to the adsorption capacity by coating the outside of the char particles. Therefore, as a practical matter, the adsorption capacity of a freshly made char represents the upper ceiling of adsorption capacity for the life of that char.

In terms of soil dynamics, it is believed that adsorption capacity of a biochar contributes the bulk of its moisture retention capacity and most of its capacity to buffer soluble organic compounds. These characteristics may be pivotal in stimulating microbial populations in the soil by stabilizing the minimum moisture and carbon source levels in the soil and elevating microbial survival rates during times of drought and shortages of other soluble carbon sources.

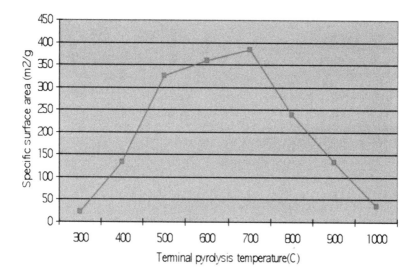

Fig. 8.3    Variation of Char BET Surface Area with HTT

Source: JIANG Shenxue, *Training Manual of Bamboo Charcoal for Producers and Consumers*. Bamboo Engineering Research Center, Nanjing Forestry University, May 2004. http://terrapreta.bioenergylists. org/files/TrainingManual.pdf. Accessed April 2, 2010.

## *Measuring Adsorption Capacity*

Adsorption capacity is measured by "challenging" the char with a known substance, usually an organic vapor, and measuring the extent of uptake of the challenge gas under controlled conditions. The test is not a routine analysis. In fact, several analytical methods used to measure adsorption capacity in other areas have been (or could be) usefully adapted for biochar. However, none of these methods are ideal or considered standard for testing biochar specifically, because of varying accuracy, applicability, or practical availability.

On the other hand, and perhaps surprisingly, the home practitioner can rather readily perform a useful "challenge gas" test to gauge adsorption capacity. It takes some practice, and it helps if you obtain a sample of activated carbon to use as a standard control reference. Small quantities of activated carbon are available at pet supply stores, since it is used in home aquarium filters.

---

### @HOME BIOCHAR

### MEASURING ADSORPTION CAPACITY – 1

### Approach

The approach is to prepare a very dry sample of the candidate char, and then "challenge" it to adsorb a known vapor source. Drying the char is critical, because adsorbed water will mask the observed adsorption capacity. The drying method described previously for "oven dry" biochar is used at a recommended temperature around 200°C.

### What You'll Need:

- Scale

- Container with a sealed lid

- Empty, clean and dry tomato paste can, with a small hole drilled into the bottom.

- "Challenge" gas, R134a (1,1,1,2 tetra-fluoro-ethane). This gas is a refrigerant used in auto air conditioners, and may be obtained from any auto supply store in 12-ounce cans.

- R134a dispensing device, with a metering valve and supply tubing. Modify the dispensing device by cutting the far end of its flexible hose and screwing into that open end an inflation needle used to inflate soccer and basketballs.

- Insertion meat thermometer (optional)

- Sample of biochar to be tested.

- Sample of activated carbon to use as a reference standard (available at a store selling home aquarium supplies).

**@HOME BIOCHAR**

MEASURING ADSORPTION CAPACITY – 2

**What To Do:**

1. Prior to drying, the candidate char should be crushed and sieved to yield a coarse granular material, with granules between 1 and 5 mm in diameter.
2. Dry the candidate char to approximately 200°C.
3. Cool the char in a container with a sealed lid to avoid uptake of atmospheric moisture.
4. Fill a weighed, clean, dry tomato paste can about half way with the dried char and weigh it again.
5. Using the dispensing device, slowly inject the "challenge" gas, R134a, through the hole in the can.
   **Note:** As the R134a gas is admitted into the char, some R134a will be adsorbed and the heat of adsorption will be released—the container may get warm to the touch.
6. Continue to slowly add the challenge gas until the char stops adsorbing it. Shake the can periodically to mix the char contents; this assists the equilibration process.
7. Adding the R134a may continue until the temperature of char returns to the starting temperature, since the excess R134a will enter as a cold vapor and eventually cool the char mass. A simple insertion meat thermometer may improve the accuracy of determining the endpoint of the R134a addition.
8. When completed, weigh the can containing the char and adsorbed R134a.
9. Calculate the fraction of weight increase caused by injecting the R134a gas as follows:

$$\frac{[\text{weight of can+char+adsorbed gas}] - [\text{weight of can+char}]}{[\text{weight of can+char}] - [\text{weight of can}]}$$

**@HOME BIOCHAR**

MEASURING ADSORPTION CAPACITY – 3

**What to Look For:**
Chars with good adsorption capacities show a noticeable temperature rise when R134a is added, and significant weight gain, such as 10% or more of the weight of the original char, when the sample temperature is near ambient. Chars with low adsorption capacities (0%–4%) will show little temperature rise during R134a addition and essentially no weight gain due to the adsorption of R134a. In contrast, the adsorption test conducted on activated carbon should yield very high percentage increases in weight and a substantial temperature rise during R134a addition. The differences become obvious with a little practice.

Good biochars will have between 20% and 40% of the weight gain of activated carbon. If the biochar has less than 10% of the weight gain, then the adsorption capacity is low; and any soil to which that biochar is added will have little of the benefits attributed to adsorption capacity.

*Notes:*
The results obtained by this ambient-temperature method are not directly comparable with the Gravimetric Adsorption Capacity Scan (GACS) results obtained at 100°C, as shown in Figure 8.4. Adsorption results at typical ambient temperatures are on the order of twice the levels observed at the 100–125°C range.

Other challenge gases may be used, including butane and propane—even the gas used to refill butane lighters. These gases are lighter and create less weight gain in a char sample than R134a.

For the adsorption capacity results shown in Figure 8.4, the specific procedure used was the Gravimetric Adsorption Capacity Scan (GACS). The GACS assay measures all the adsorption behavior of chars and activated carbons over a wide range of adsorption conditions. For the purposes of comparing chars, it is sufficient to subject chars to the same adsorption conditions and measure the extent of adsorption. The standard conditions were the weight percent uptake of R134a (1,1,1,2 tetra-fluoro-ethane, the refrigerant used in automobile air conditioners) by a dried sample of char at 100°C.

Figure 8.4 shows the CEC and the adsorption capacity of 11 chars and 2 wood samples. CEC data is shown at 10% of the measured CEC level to allow a common y-axis for both CEC in units of meq/100 grams and adsorption capacity in units of weight percent R134a at 100°C.

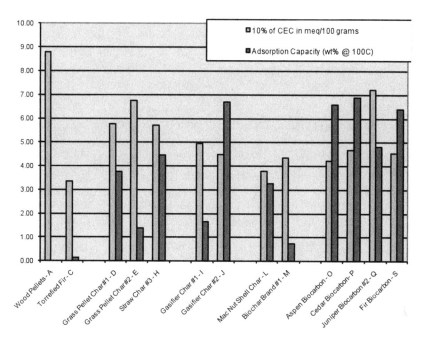

Fig. 8.4    CEC and Adsorption Capacity of Selected Chars

Source: Hugh McLaughlin, Paul S. Anderson, Frank E. Shields and Thomas B. Reed, "All Biochars are Not Created Equal, and How to Tell Them Apart," Version 2 (October 2009), Figure 8. (http://cees.colorado.edu/biochar_characterization.html).

There is significant variation of both CEC and adsorption capacity in the 11 chars and 2 woods. All samples tested showed good levels of CEC, but considering how few samples there are, no conclusions should be drawn about what may or may not lead to CEC in a char.

As for adsorption capacity, Figure 8.4 shows more dramatic trends, with the two pre-carbonization materials (wood pellets and torrefied fir) having little or no adsorption capacity—as would be expected from the trend of the low-temperature side in Figure 8.3. Overall, the adsorption capacity of the chars in Figure 8.4 seems to reflect the specifics of different carbonization processes more than the specific starting material. This also might be expected, considering the carbonization process creates the internal structures in the starting biomass as the volatiles are driven off and the solid char is formed. Also, of the two **gasifier** chars tested, Gasifier Char #1 used woody biomass as the fuel for gasification and represents a wood-gasifier char, whereas Gasifier Char #2 was residual char from a char-gasifier. Among the chars shown in Figure 8.4, letters H, L, O, P, Q and S were produced via the same carbonization process, and all had uniformly elevated levels of adsorption capacity.

## Additional Biochar Testing

Additional tests for soil and plant compatibility are the "germination test" and the "worm avoidance test," which are discussed in the chapter of this book titled "Gauging the Impact of Biochar: Simple Tests for Farmers and Gardeners."

## CONCLUSION

Any biochar can and should be tested prior to addition to the soil. Some tests characterize the biochar and allow predictions of its relative performance in the soil. Other tests alert the user to undesirable soil consequences, including pH changes and elevated TDS, that may result from adding the biochar and lead to poor crop growing conditions. Since the tests are easy to perform and it is highly desirable to know the consequences to different biochar characteristics before adding the biochar to the soil, do the tests first, consider the test result implications, and proceed accordingly.

From every biochar added to soil, a sample should be taken and retained in case additional analytical testing is a needed. Relatively dry biochar in a sealed jar will store at ambient conditions for years without significant change. A pint jar of a biochar sample is absolutely indispensable in determining what went wrong, or right, with a given biochar application.

## KEY POINTS FROM THIS CHAPTER

- The term "biochar" embraces various charcoal products generated from various raw materials via various processes. Each particular biochar has unique characteristics.

- All biochars have physical attributes, constituent attributes, and soil-relevant attributes. Each attribute has a set of quality indicators.

- The quality of biochar can be informally determined by feel: Good biochar is light and rigid but easily crushed; finely grained; not greasy to the touch; and washes off with plain water.

- The four main constituents of biochar are:

  - *Moisture* – refers to the fraction of the biochar that consists of water and volatiles (organic solvents). Moisture adds little value to a biochar.

  - *Ash* – refers to the inorganic portion of biochar, and also adds little value to it

  - *Mobile matter* – the organic portion of biochar that can leach into the soil or be ingested by soil microbes.

  - *Resident matter* – the organic portion of biochar that will remain stable in the soil for a very long time. Resident matter is therefore generally more valuable in biochar than mobile matter.

- Biochar also possess important soil-relevant attributes that are pivotal for assessing how a particular biochar will impact the soil: specifically, levels of pH and total dissolved solids (TDS), cation exchange capacity (CEC), and adsorption capacity.

- The pH and TDS measurements indicate how much of a given biochar can be added to a given soil. Excessive TDS means that the soil contains too much salt, which has an adverse effect on most plants. Soil pH is more critical. Many biochars have a "liming effect" that would not be beneficial for alkaline soils.

- Cation exchange capacity (CEC) and adsorption capacity are difficult to measure and their precise roles in the soil poorly understood. Generally, the higher the CEC, the more nutrients that will be retained and become available to plant roots.

- Adsorption capacity is a function of the internal surface area within the graphene plates in a biochar. The greater the surface area, the higher the adsorption capacity, and the better a biochar will retain moisture and soluble organic matter. These characteristics may be pivotal in stimulating microbial populations in the soil.

- Any biochar can and should be tested before adding it to the soil.

# Part III
## Producing Biochar

"Energy market forecasts...did not foresee the rapid development of gas-powered generation through integrated gasification combined cycle (IGCC) plants and it is very possible that similar new energy options will arrive in future. An example of one such promising technology, Biochar...a charcoal-like material produced by heating biomass with minimal oxygen (pyrolysis)...The Biochar systems need to be developed on a meaningful scale to determine better their true sequestration potential."

—*Tony Blair, Former UK Prime Minister*

Chapter 9

# Biochar Production Fundamentals

**Paul Taylor, PhD**
Biochar consultant,
Biocharbooks.org

**Jim Mason**
Director
ALL Power Labs, Director

## IN THIS CHAPTER YOU WILL LEARN:

- The importance of employing low-emission methods of producing biochar, and of thoughtfully researching and applying them.

- The fundamentals of small-scale biochar production so you can choose a suitable method and operate it safely.

- The stages and different types of pyrolysis.

- The different methods of low-tech, small-scale biochar production, including some examples.

- Other production-related considerations: safely cooling your biochar, yields, and direction of pyrolysis gas take-off.

- A Biochar Experimenter's Kit that allows exploring the basic production methods discussed in this chapter.

- The importance of cleanly burning pyrolysis gases, and a design for clean combustion of flares and retorts.

# INTRODUCTION

Authors of previous chapters have explained why they are excited about biochar, what it is, why it is good for the soil, and how to test and characterize it. Having read this far you may be eager to get your hands on some biochar and incorporate it into your own garden or farm.

This chapter is intended to explore—and also refresh—the fundamental concepts, methods, and devices for producing biochar. A firm grasp of the fundamentals will help you choose a suitable, environmentally responsible way to make your own biochar, and apply it safely.

The next four chapters (10 through 13) offer more detailed primers on biochar production, in various ascending categories from small, inexpensive, low-tech backyard biochar devices, through community and small farm-scale production, to commercial production.

The importance of "best practice" bears emphasizing, since there is always a broader context to individual activity. Internet research will reveal numerous methods, with various standards, for producing biochar. Unfamiliarity with fundamental principles can lead to adopting primitive approaches that are quite inefficient and polluting. Multiplied by millions, the cumulative adverse result would be an ironic inversion of the green "strength in numbers" appeal of the biochar movement.

## RESEARCH, GOOD SENSE, AND SAFETY

This and the following chapters are not instruction manuals for building and operating any device. Before constructing and operating a biochar maker, consult the resources in this book and on the web for more details, keeping in mind the principles outlined in these chapters. Your thoughtfulness and active participation are essential to the success of these designs and their safe operation.

Safety is paramount.

There are important safety considerations for constructing and properly operating devices involving fire, heat, and emitted gases. In particular, take care to stay out of any smoke generated, as the gases from a pyrolysis unit can be very different from a common campfire. Always operate in a well-ventilated environment, away from people and any potential fire dangers. Wear gloves to avoid being burned, or cut on sharp edges. Have an ample supply of water handy to deal with potential skin burns or fire.

Never attempt to make biochar in a completely sealed vessel. In making biochar, gases will be generated—and they must be allowed to leave the vessel. Tightly sealed vessels will become pressurized and can suddenly fail, explode, and cause injury. Although retorts (discussed below and in Chapter 10) are closed vessels, they are not completely sealed; they have ports of sufficient size to allow the generated gases to exit and burn. Moreover, emitted gases should be fully burned in excess air to avoid products of incomplete combustion (PICs), which are noxious pollutants that typically show up as unwelcome smoke (discussed below).

## SOURCES OF BIOCHAR AND BIOCHAR MAKERS

For those who want to try biochar, but not produce it, unfortunately it is not yet readily available at the garden store. You might be able to find small manufacturers on the internet. This market will surely develop, but in the meantime, lump wood charcoal, which can be purchased for grilling food, can be applied as biochar. Make sure that you test it first, using the simple test procedures outlined in Chapter 14. (Some charcoal "briquettes" are made of powdered coal, and may contain additives harmful to soil and plants).

Similarly, biochar-making devices cannot be easily purchased. The most available are small **gasifier** stoves—known as Top-Lit Updraft gasifiers, or TLUDs—that allow, or can be adapted for, making biochar. These devices are covered in Chapter 11, and information is given there on purchasing and costs. Other devices can be found through the resources at the end of the book. Biochar Engineering in Colorado, USA, for example, makes a larger TLUD for higher-volume batch biochar making.

If you are interested in experimenting with the multiple modes of biochar production discussed below, with close control of process parameters, you might want to look at the "Biochar Experimenter's Kit (BEK)" from ALL Power Labs in Berkeley, CA.

There is also a growing collection of designs and biochar-making reports on the Bioenergy Lists website, www.biochar.bioenergylists.org, managed by Tom Miles. We encourage you to look at the offerings there, as well as the website for this book, since the design options and understanding of desired performance characteristics will grow rapidly as the field develops.

## TERMINOLOGY

There are several parallel terms for the processes of biomass thermal decomposition as well as terms for the starting materials and end-products produced. Since some of these terms overlap, or are used interchangeably, it will be beneficial to refresh them here for this and following chapters on production techniques.

**Biochar** is charcoal made for incorporation into soils.

**Charcoal** is the solid, carbon-rich residue left when biomass is heated in an environment with limited oxygen. Generally, charcoal is intended for use as fuel, but if made under suitable conditions from non-contaminated starting material, and crushed into small pieces for mixing in the soil, it is biochar.

**Biomass** refers to living or once-living material, which is the **feedstock** (starting material) for making biochar. Wood is the preferred feedstock for making lump charcoal for fuel, and since the backyard biochar maker will likely use scrap wood or woody plant material, we will often for convenience use the term "wood", but mean other feedstock as well. Nearly all reasonably dry organic materials, such as bark, nutshells, crop residues, and even manure, can be used as feedstock in appropriate devices. These less dense or granular feedstocks produce small-grained char, which is desired for biochar, though not preferred for fuel charcoal.

**Pyrolysis** (from Greek roots *pyr* "fire" and *lysis* "loosening") refers to the thermal decomposition (breakdown under heat) of biomass into a carbon-rich solid residue (char), gases, and liquids.

**Carbonization** emphasizes the carbon enrichment, as opposed to the "breakdown", aspect of pyrolysis. "Carbonization" will often be used interchangeably with "pyrolysis" in discussing low-tech biochar making. Pyrolysis and carbonization are discussed in detail in Chapter 6.

**Torrefaction** refers to a mild, early stage of pyrolysis, between complete drying of the feedstock and full pyrolysis.

**Char** is a general term for the solid product arising from thermal decomposition (pyrolysis) of any organic material.

**Temperatures** in this chapter are expressed in degrees Celsius and convert to Fahrenheit as follows:

°C = °F  |  100 = 212  |  300 = 572  |  400 = 752  |  500 = 932  |  600 = 1112

## THE ART OF COOKING

Pyrolysis and carbonization play roles in familiar kitchen activities such as baking, roasting, toasting, and caramelizing. Generally, kitchen pyrolysis is in the mild form of torrefaction, and usually only at the surface of the food. (Sometimes the process goes too far, resulting in charred toast or worse!) When dried foods such as coffee and nuts are roasted, the entire food is transformed, resulting in modified color, flavors, and other properties.

As in everyday cooking, when wood or other biomass is heated, it is transformed into a material with new properties, as described in Chapter 6. And also similarly to cooking, success in biochar making requires close attention to the stages, timing and temperature of the procedure.

## STAGES OF PYROLYSIS IN BIOCHAR MAKING

When biomass is heated the energy of the heat progressively breaks the molecular bonds in the biomass, with the volatile portions coming off as various gases and the fixed carbon lattice being left behind as charcoal. Many of the volatile products condense to liquids when they cool.

If condensation occurs in external air, the volatile organic compounds (VOCs) show up as smoke; on surfaces they form liquids of various viscosities from "wood vinegar" to tars. The honeycomb-like structure of the residual charcoal reflects the carbon-to-carbon structural backbone of the original biomass, with the more weakly bonded volatile molecules removed.

Figure 9.1 shows a weight loss curve for biomass heated in a steady manner from room temperature to 600°C (1112°F). This illustrates that pyrolysis occurs in consecutive stages. Different gaseous organic and inorganic emissions are produced at each stage. For practical biochar making it is important to become familiar with these stages and their emissions. The resultant products and amounts will vary depending on the composition of the biomass, the rate of heating, and the specific pyrolysis process employed—as discussed further below.

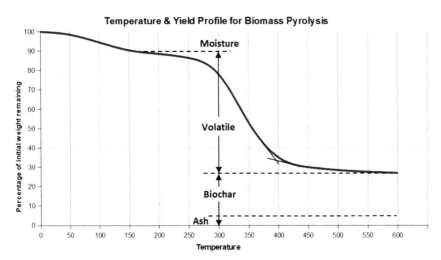

Fig. 9.1 Weight loss of biomass as it is heated

### Stage 1: Drying

Wood, and vegetation generally, consists of four main components: cellulose, hemicellulose, lignin, and water. "Seasoned" wood contains 12–19% of **adsorbed** water, held as molecules on the cellulose/lignin structure. "Unseasoned" or freshly cut wood contains additional bulk or liquid water and has total water content of about 40 to 85% (expressed as a percentage of the **oven-dry** weight of the wood). *All* water must be driven off as vapor before carbonization can occur. Vaporizing water requires a lot of energy, so using the sun to dry the feedstock *before* carbonization greatly improves efficiency (discussed in Chapters 10 and 12).

During heating, as the temperature of the biomass rises towards and above the boiling point of water, it further dries and the vapors distill into a white steam. Vaporization of biomass moisture continues at temperatures up to 200°C (about 400°F), and in addition to water results in emissions of smaller amounts of methanol and other VOCs. These emissions comprise a substantial fraction of the weight-loss of biomass during heating, since water typically represents 20–30% of air-dry biomass (in the example in Figure 9.1 the particular biomass was already relatively dry).

### Stage 2: Endothermic (Low- temperature) Pyrolysis

As the biomass is further heated into the temperature range of 200-300°C, the chemical bonds within the constituents of the biomass begin to break. This process is **endothermic**—continued heat input is required to increase the temperature of the dry biomass and break the molecular bonds. Methanol, acetic acid, and other oxygenated VOCs are released during this stage, along with emissions of $CO_2$ and CO from the breakdown of hemicellulose and cellulose.

The liquid condensate portion of low temperature pyrolysis was historically called "wood vinegar" or "smoke water" and is currently used to make flavoring products like "liquid smoke." Depending on its concentration and specific temperature of production, it can also be used as a fungicide, has qualities that aid germination, and is a helpful conditioning agent for biochar (see Chapter 16).

This transition phase between drying and full pyrolysis is also known as torrefaction and results in complete drying of the biomass, a partial decomposition of the volatiles, and further weight and size reduction. The result is torrified ("roasted") biomass. Torrefaction is of current interest for densifying biomass for easier transport, and preparing biomass for direct substitution in coal-fired boilers.

> **ENDOTHERMIC VS EXOTHERMIC**
> *Endothermic:* describes a process or reaction that absorbs energy in the form of heat.
> *Exothermic:* describes a process or reaction that releases energy.

### Stage 3: Exothermic Pyrolysis

At a temperature around 300°C, the thermal decomposition of the biomass becomes more extreme and results in emissions of a combustible mixture of $H_2$, CO, $CH_4$, $CO_2$, other hydrocarbons, and tars. Pyrolysis can become exothermic because biomass contains oxygen within its structure, which when liberated starts energy-releasing oxidation reactions with the gases and char. These energy-releasing reactions create the heat required to break other chemical bonds in the biomass. In principle the process becomes self-sustaining, and continues on its own up to a temperature of about 400°C, when only an oxygen-depleted, carbon-enriched charcoal residue remains. However, heat is always lost from an imperfectly insulated vessel, so as a practical matter, further heat input is typically necessary to maintain and increase the temperature during the course of pyrolysis.

## Stage 4: Additional Carbonization

The charcoal remaining at the end of exothermic pyrolysis still contains appreciable amounts of volatile residues, along with the ash of the original wood. The ash content of the charcoal is usually around 1.5–5%, the volatiles may amount to 25–35% by weight, and the balance is fixed carbon at 60–70%.

Further heating is required to increase the fixed carbon content by driving off and decomposing more of the volatiles. In a retort, a temperature of 500°C gives a typical fixed carbon content of about 85% and a volatile content of about 12%. The yield of charcoal at this temperature is about 33% of the weight of the oven-dry feedstock (not counting the material fuel burned to drive the pyrolysis, which we will discuss later). Heating to an even higher 700°C can increase carbon content to over 90%, but reduces yield to below 30%.

In a traditional charcoal-making process such as an earth mound, or kiln, all of the above drying, torrefaction, and pyrolysis stages may occur simultaneously in different portions of the feedstock, resulting in product that may vary from only partially carbonized (**torrefied**) wood to completely burned ash. This difficulty of quality control and uniformity is another reason—in addition to emissions control—to seek better methods to make biochar. Generally, these improved methods will involve heating the feedstock in a reaction vessel or retort.

## TYPES OF PYROLYSIS PROCESSES

There are various pyrolysis methods being applied or developed for industrial settings, some of which are recent and novel, such as microwave conversion and hydrothermal pyrolysis. Here we outline only the main types, with reference to Table 9.1.

**Slow pyrolysis** is carried out in the absence of oxygen in a batch process, or with a slow auger feed, in kilns or retorts. In this type of pyrolysis, peak temperatures are relatively low, heating rates are relatively slow, and **residence times** of the char in the reaction are long. In fact, the term "biochar" was originally associated with this type of production, but has since been extended to include char products from other processes. The processes involved in slow pyrolysis are discussed in Chapter 6.

**Fast pyrolysis** turns finely ground feedstock into mostly bio-oils in a few seconds. However, there is also a more or less small portion of granular char residue. It is likely that there will be higher condensed volatiles present in the product, which will affect its performance and desirability as biochar for soil amendment. Fast pyrolysis is more likely to be used in commercial biochar/bio-oil producers, as discussed in Chapters 13.

**Gasification** typically refers to processes that include a combustion and reduction stage after drying and pyrolysis, so as to produce a synthetic flammable fuel consisting mostly of $H_2$ and CO. Gasification processes happen over a wide range of temperatures, often with the combustion and tar-cracking happening above 1000°C. The resulting gas can be used in thermal applications, or (with appropriate refinement and controls) to run engines, or as a feedstock for conversion to liquid fuels, chemicals and fertilizers. Biochar from gasification is the underlying method of the automated biochar process described in Chapter 12.

Recent development of small gasifier biomass stoves for third-world application has led to an interest in the potential of biochar production from small-scale gasifiers. The small TLUD gasifiers described in Chapter 11 operate at a lower temperature range, as shown in Table 9.1.

**Carbonization** is the term emphasizing the carbon-enrichment aspect of pyrolysis. The term is often applied to the traditional and commercial methods of charcoal manufacture, which fall in the slow-pyrolysis category. As already mentioned, in traditional charcoal making the temperature range is often below 400°C, making a volatile-rich charcoal, which is suited for fuel. Industrial retorts, with their increased insulation and efficiency, are more likely to operate at 500-600°C. Chapter 10 provides a primer on pyrolysis, traditional charcoal production, and biochar making in low-tech, small-scale retorts.

| Mode | Temp °C | Residence Time | Heating Rate | Char % | Liquid % | Gas % |
|---|---|---|---|---|---|---|
| **Carbonization** | <400 –600 | Very Long Hrs to days | Slow | 5-35 | | |
| **Slow Pyrolysis** | 450 –650 | Very Long Min. to days | 1-100°C/m | 35 | 30 | 35 |
| **Fast Pyrolysis** | 400 –500 | Short, seconds | Very Fast | 12 | 75 | 13 |
| **Gasification** | >800 | Long | Fast | 10 | 5 | 85 |
| **TLUD Gasifier** | 500 –750 | Minutes | Moderate | 20 | 0 | 80 |

Table 9.1 Typical Product Yields (Dry Wood Basis) from Modes of Pyrolysis

Source: Extended from A. V. Bridgewater "Thermal Conversion of Biomass and Waste."

## METHODS OF HEATING TO MAKE BIOCHAR

There are three methods of heating to initiate pyrolysis and maintain high temperatures during carbonization. These methods also vary as to whether oxygen is present (oxic pyrolysis) or oxygen is absent (anoxic pyrolysis), which influences the particular characteristics of the resulting biochar. The three methods are:

*Method 1. Direct Combustion (Oxic Pyrolysis):*

Part of the raw material in the reactor is burned with limited air to create hot gases which pass through and heat the remaining biomass.

*Method 2. Indirect Heating (Anoxic Pyrolysis):*

The reactor (**retort**) is heated from the outside and no air enters the reactor. Heat transfers through the reactor vessel walls into and through the biomass.

*Method 3. Heating with Re-circulated Sweep Gas:*

Part of the pyrolysis vapors are burned in an external combustion chamber and the hot gases are directed into the reactor, where they make direct contact with the raw material.

These three methods of heating to make biochar, and some examples, are discussed next, but only as they relate to low-tech backyard or small-farm scale production.

## METHOD 1. DIRECT COMBUSTION
## – TRADITIONAL METHODS AND NEW TLUD METHODS
*Traditional Methods and Limitations*

In this method, the heat for carbonization comes from burning a portion of the biomass feedstock in a limited air environment. The process can be called auto-thermal carbonization (or auto-thermal pyrolysis). This is essentially the method of a controlled open fire, a traditional earth mound kiln, or large masonry or metal kilns (such as beehive kilns, the Missouri Kiln, and TPI metal kiln), as described in parts of Chapters 2 and 10. It is also a method that can be found promoted on the internet using variations of burning in partially closed drums.

The problem with this method is that in order to preserve the created charcoal, air must be limited, which results in products of incomplete combustion. PICs, including methane and other hydrocarbons, have large greenhouse effects. Many of these PICs condense as soon as they cool in the atmosphere, creating copious smoke—not welcomed by your neighbor, and generally illegal in many communities in the developed world, and increasingly illegal in the developing world.

Nonetheless, this is the method by which most fuel charcoal is made in developing countries. Without care and expertise in the art, this method can be very inefficient, with yields as low as 5%.

It is not ideal for making biochar since, as mentioned above, there is often poor control of temperature within the reaction space, both in regard to uniformity and duration of treatment.

In traditional kilns or poorly controlled drums, pyrolysis temperatures may be well under 400°C in some portions of the feedstock, resulting in char that has not been depleted of volatiles. As pointed out by Hugh McLaughlin in Chapters 6 through 8, such chars will probably be suboptimum as biochar for application to soil because they generally are low in the desired biochar property of high adsorption capacity and the associate benefits of nutrient and water retention.

*Top-Lit UpDraft Gasifiers*

There is one very accessible, low-tech method of internal heating that results in clean combustion and, according to preliminary tests, produces biochar with high adsorption capacity. **Top-Lit Updraft Gasifiers (TLUDs)** burn cleanly because the biomass is lit from above and the pyrolysis gases, formed in a space of limited air, are allowed to rise away from the biomass to a region where sufficient secondary air is admitted, resulting in their complete combustion. (See Chapter 10 for a description of why top-lighting fuel makes for a clean burn, and see Chapter 11 for a detailed discussion of TLUDs and how to make basic devices.) TLUD biochar devices only operate properly on feedstock that has been processed into uniform, small pieces, such as dry wood chips, pellets, briquette pieces, shells of peanuts and walnuts, or seeds such as Jatropha seeds and cherry pits.

## METHOD 2. INDIRECT HEATING – RETORTS

Modern commercial charcoal making uses a vessel (a retort) to enclose the wood, which does not allow air to be admitted. This results in higher yield and more control over the process, as well as emissions.

In a retort, heat is supplied from outside the vessel. This dries the wood and raises its temperature to the point where pyrolysis starts. When pyrolysis gases are emitted, they exit into a combustion zone outside the retort, where they can be burned completely in excess air. The heat generated is used to maintain the pyrolysis. There are ingenious ways to do this, ranging from simple (see Figure 9.2) to more sophisticated, which are discussed in Chapter 10; additional ways can also be found online or in the available literature on charcoal production, some listed at the end of this chapter. In an efficient system only a portion of the available heat is needed to drive the pyrolysis, leaving excess heat to dry feedstock, or initiate further pyrolysis, or be harnessed for other purposes according to your ingenuity.

A stainless steel clothes dryer drum (outer) provides lots of secondary air through its holes, and is a good size to contain a 20-liter paint bucket as the retort. The retort is filled with wood and turned upside down on a metal plate. Wood fuel burned in the space around the outside of the retort initiates pyrolysis. Pyrolysis gases escape between the retort can and the plate, burning in a ring of fire that helps maintain the pyrolysis.

Fig. 9.2 Folke Günther-Style Inverted Drum Retort

# PHOENIX RISING

- Human scaled for 1 person
- Output must justify the input

---

- Metal shell of washing machine
- Lined with fire brick
- Compact method
- Produces useful amount of char
- Contains and stores the heat
- No need to top up fuel during burn

Simple parts

Double drum retort

Fig. 9.3  Phoenix Kiln
Developed by Project 540 from salvaged parts. Photos: Ben Speirs

*Project 540 Phoenix Kiln*

Next, we illustrate some of the principles of the retort method with a design developed by the Biochar 540 team out of recycled materials. This is an adaptation of the Folke Günther[1] inverted drum technique described in Figure 9.2 and in Chapter 10.

Project 540's focus is to prove that emissions from small biochar kilns can be controlled to best-practice standards, while still using simple designs, accessible materials, simple cues for checking emissions, and basic or no instrumentation.[2]

A metal shell of a washing machine is lined with firebrick (which happened to fit snugly) to make a well-insulated kiln (see Figure 9.3). The retort is made of two standard 20-liter (5-gallon) drums, each opened at one end (it could be a single taller drum), resting on a metal plate.

After the drums are filled with wood pieces or other feedstock, they are stacked on top of each other, open ends up, and the top drum is closed with a flat metal plate. The two drums and the plate are then wired together, so the whole structure can be flipped upside down, and lowered into the kiln to sit on bricks as shown in Figure 9.3. Scrap-wood fuel is placed inside the kiln, around the drums, and lit. The firebrick lid is placed on the kiln, followed by the stovepipe or chimney.

Once pyrolysis commences, gases will escape and ignite in a ring of fire around the bottom rim of each drum, providing heat to support the pyrolysis. A hole in the bottom of the kiln combined with the draw of the chimney allows ample air for complete combustion of the gases. Once pyrolysis ends, the fire extinguishes, and the weight of the drums is sufficient to seal out air while the char cools. This compact design contains and stores the heat, and efficiently transfers it into the retort, so that there is no need to add more fuel during the burn. It produces about 30 liters of biochar—a useful amount.

## METHOD 3. HEATING WITH RE-CIRCULATED GAS

As the size of the retort increases, retort designs suffer increasing problems of poor heat transfer, and thus slow biochar making. Both raw biomass and charcoal are good insulators, so it can often take hours or days for the externally applied heat to fully complete pyrolysis in the interior of the retort. This problem can be overcome by circulating combusted gases, which are almost oxygen-free, through the retort. The hot gases can then make direct contact with all pieces of the feedstock and significantly increase the heat transfer rate to the material. Once pyrolysis is occurring, the pyrolysis gases are combusted and recirculated.

The challenge in recirculating the combustion gases back through the retort is the resulting dilution of the flammable pyrolysis gases with the $CO_2$ and $H_2O$ in the combustion gases. The amount of combustion gases fed back through the reactor bed must be limited and adjusted to maintain gas flammability.

---

[1] http://www.holon.se/folke/carbon/simplechar/simplechar.shtml
[2] Moxham G., P. Taylor, P. Gibson, and J. Seed. "Project 540: Low-emission, Low Cost Biochar Kilns for Small Farms and Villages." Asia Pacific Biochar Conference, 2009.

In practice, this requires some method to actively vary the proportion of combustion gases recirculated, and change this percentage as the pyrolysis gas composition changes over the various stages of biochar making.

One of the main goals of the Biochar Experimenters Kit, discussed below, has been to develop a method to achieve this control of sweep gas recirculation, and demonstrate the significant impact sweep gas can have on heat transfer rate in a retort-type reactor.

## HYBRID DESIGNS
### Adam-Retort
The Adam-Retort, described in Chapters 4 and 10, is a 3 cubic-meter retort designed to operate in two phases. In phase 1, some of the exhaust gases from the firebox are swept through the feedstock to speed the heating and drying, and exit the retort from the phase 1 chimney. Once pyrolysis is well underway and the gas becomes combustible, the phase 1 chimney is closed and the gases are diverted to the firebox. Now the Adam-Retort is operating as an indirectly heated retort.

The Adam-Retort was chosen as a proven design to meet the objective of Project 540—specifically, to develop a low emission, low-cost biochar kiln for small farms and communities. The 3 cubic-meter retort with large top lid can be conveniently loaded with feedstock by a bucket loader, and makes 350 kg of charcoal in a daylong session. After considering the charcoal making methods in the literature, one comes away with appreciation for the ingenuity, simplicity, and effectiveness of the Adam-Retort.

### Hybrid Gasifier-Retort
Simple designs are being explored to combine a biochar-making gasifier and a retort. Combusted gases from the gasifier can pass through the feedstock to efficiently dry it and heat it. Once the pyrolysis gases become combustible, they can be fed back to continue heating the retort to maintain the pyrolysis. These designs will be updated on this book's website.

## MORE CONSIDERATIONS

### COOLING THE CHARCOAL
Once all the material undergoing pyrolysis has arrived at the final temperature, it should be allowed to cool without access to air. Care should be taken that charcoal is totally cooled, and sealed before any untended storage. Once your char is cool it is ready for any further treatment as biochar. (Conditioning of biochar is discussed in detail in Chapter 15.) The surest way to preserve all your hard-gained biochar for your garden is to thoroughly soak the cooled biochar with water or your favorite compost tea.

A further word of caution is warranted. Fresh charcoal is very active, with a low self-ignition temperature, and oxidative reactions can raise its temperature back to red-hot. The higher the temperature at which charcoal is created, the lower the volatile content and the higher its reactivity. Storing the char in an open container, or with a lid that allows air leaks, could lead to its auto-ignition. Small amounts of air or even water applied to hot charcoal can send it quickly into combustion. At the surface of hot charcoal, water can be reduced to hydrogen and carbon monoxide (the water-gas reaction), which can easily "whoosh" back at you if there is a spark or ember to light it. Be careful of scalding or blowback when pouring water onto char. First, let it cool without access to air.

## A QUESTION OF YIELDS
The yield of charcoal is the weight of the final charcoal (cold and dry, not soaked), divided by the weight of the starting material. Whether some of the biomass is burned inside the kiln (to provide direct heating), or external to the retort (indirect heating), it is lost to making biochar. Therefore, in comparing yields, the output weight of the char should be compared with the weight of all dry feedstock consumed in the process, including the feedstock consumed as fuel to drive the pyrolysis. The net yield for a retort that is externally heated by burning wood (or other biomass) is then the weight of the final charcoal divided by the starting weights of the feedstock placed inside the retort plus all the fuel used in heating it.

Efficiently designed commercial retorts can yield about 33% char relative to wood placed in the retort. However, the yield is less when the fuel consumed to heat the retort is used in the accounting. The fuel used may be quite substantial in primitive drum retorts with scanty insulation and poor fire management. The actual net yield may easily be less than the net yield from a simple TLUD gasifier char maker, which is typically about 20%.

Yields will be affected by several factors, which can be thoughtfully managed, including:

1.  Dryness of the feedstock.
2.  The effectiveness of heat-retaining insulation or heat shields in a TLUD or retort design.
3.  The efficiency with which heat from heating fuel, and also from combustion of pyrolysis gases, are fed back into a retort.
4.  The highest treatment temperature (and related volatile content as discussed above).
5.  The amount of redeposition of volatiles into the charcoal (discussed below).

## BIOCHAR CHARACTERISTICS

The characteristics of biochar will vary widely depending not only on the feedstock but also on the pyrolysis procedure used. Biochar characteristics are discussed in detail by Hugh McLaughlin in Chapters 6 through 8.

The combination of characteristics often desired—high adsorption capacity, high cation exchange capacity, and high percentage of stable (non-volatile) carbon—seem to be optimized when the char is produced in the temperature range of 500°C to 600°C. Much can be learned by following the process of pyrolysis with a woodstove or chimney thermometer, a thermocouple, or an infrared thermometer.

## DIRECTION OF GAS TAKE-OFF

In addition to the method of heating, another potentially important variation in reactor design is the manner and direction in which the gases liberated through pyrolysis are removed from the reactor. Pyrolysis gases can be removed away from the made char, or passed through the made char on their way out of the reactor (as in a TLUD).

Pryolysis gases that pass back through char, or have a long residence time with the char, can initiate secondary carbonization reactions and also condense on the char, altering the characteristics of the resulting biochar. These secondary reactions and redeposition factors are often used to increase yields of fuel charcoal. Less understood at the moment are impacts they will have, positive or negative, on biochar performance in the soil.

Low-temperature pyrolysis condensates (i.e. wood vinegar) are often claimed to have positive benefits when reapplied in small amounts to char, and are not unlike the substances which give barbecued food its distinctive flavor. However, it is also known that condensates from higher-temperature pyrolysis can contain polycyclic aromatic hydrocarbons (PAHs), many of which are carcinogenic. Thus the impact and desirability of the secondary reactions may depend on the temperature of pyrolysis, or other factors not currently understood. This is one of many areas of current research and debate in the biochar community.

## MANY DESIGNS IN ONE

### BIOCHAR EXPERIMENTER'S KIT (BEK)

The BEK (Biochar Experimenter's Kit), from ALL Power Labs in Berkeley California, is an open-source design aimed at the researcher or enthusiast wanting more precise control over biochar-making conditions. (See Figure 9.4.)

The goal of the BEK is to provide a single flexible reactor that can run all the slow pyrolysis process modes described above: direct combustion, indirect combustion (retort), and heating with re-circulated gas (sweep gas heat transfer). A mixer box lets the user choose between these different modes, or mix them in desired combinations.

The user can control highest treatment temperature, temperature ramp rate, and residence time, with instrument ports and thermocouples provided to allow monitoring the results.

Clean combustion is ensured across all the different modes via a swirl burner with propane assist and silicone nitride "always on" lighting elements. More detail on this clean combustion system follows in the next section.

The BEK can be run in either batch or continuous feed process, via included augers and fuel level control. There is also an optional bio-oil condensing and collecting solution for those wanting to explore pyrolysis oils.

ALL Power Labs provides open-source CAD files and instructions for you to build your own BEK. They also provide sheet metal kits you can weld together, or completed machines that arrive ready to run. See www.bekbiochar.com for more details.

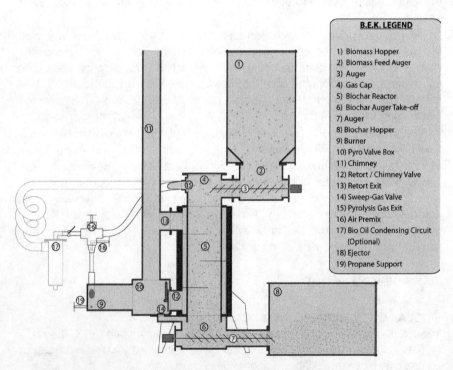

**B.E.K. LEGEND**

1) Biomass Hopper
2) Biomass Feed Auger
3) Auger
4) Gas Cap
5) Biochar Reactor
6) Biochar Auger Take-off
7) Auger
8) Biochar Hopper
9) Burner
10) Pyro Valve Box
11) Chimney
12) Retort / Chimney Valve
13) Retort Exit
14) Sweep-Gas Valve
15) Pyrolysis Gas Exit
16) Air Premix
17) Bio Oil Condensing Circuit (Optional)
18) Ejector
19) Propane Support

Fig. 9.4 Biochar Experiments Kit (the BEK) Multi-mode Pyrolyzer Reactor

Source: ALL Power Labs

## CLEAN COMBUSTION

With most biochar reactors, achieving clean and consistent combustion is a challenge. The consequences of not doing so will be a smoky mess, often accompanied by angry neighbors, a visit from the local fire department, and an early end to your biochar-making activities.

When building your own pyrolysis reactor, it is important to understand you are building something with the ability to produce an amount of smoke exponentially larger than a typical campfire. In retorts, the first phase of pyrolysis produces large amounts of steam, as moisture is being vaporized out of the biomass. If released, it will appear to be white smoke. When pyrolysis proper begins around 200°C, the early-produced pyrolysis gases will not have enough energy density to combust on their own. If released unburned, they will produce profuse amounts of creamy smoke with an unpleasant, toxic, acrid character. (Chapter 10 describes an Adam-Retort with an added condenser to trap these VOCs, resulting in clean air, and an additional product: smoke water or wood vinegar.)

Likely the easiest way to cleanly and completely combust the gases of biochar making is to use a TLUD-type design. The TLUD pyrolysis front is limited to a small layer of the fuel, so it does not dry all the fuel before pyrolysis can occur. Also, because the TLUD integrates the combustor into the basic reactor, you do not need to design and build a separate gas pumping, mixing, and flaring solution. However, if you want to work with other reactor types like retorts or sweep gas units, or have additional control of your unit, you could find yourself needing to build a flaring system.

One system to consider for this is the swirl combustion system developed by ALL Power Labs (APL) (see Figure 9.5). This is an integrated gas pumping, mixing, and burning system that works well with the tarry gases of varying energy density that are typical of biochar reactors. The system is based on a swirl combustor rather than a typical linear burner. The swirl burner provides a much more stable flare than a linear burner, as the swirl is constantly bringing the flame back on itself. Premixing the fuel and air before the swirl burner ensures complete combustion and clean emissions and further enhances flame stability.

Gas drive is provided by an "ejector-venturi" or "eductor," using a small jet of high-pressure air to pull the gases out of the reactor. Pumping hot tarry gases with common fans and blowers is a notoriously difficult problem. The motors get too hot and burn up, and the tarry gases foul the bearings and other moving parts. The "ejector-venturi" eliminates all these moving parts and sensitive components. It is a very useful method for pumping difficult gases, though at the cost of needing compressed air to operate.

The ALL Power Labs gas drive, mixer, and burner system can be built with typical plumbing parts from any hardware store, some scrap metal, and minor metal fabrication.

The APL system also incorporates a propane feed to augment gas quality as needed, insuring the complete combustion of the low energy gases at the beginning and end of a run.

Hot element glow igniters are used for "always on" ignition, relieving the operator from always holding a lighting torch in hand. Silicon nitride igniters are recommended as they will survive in full combustion temperatures.

Finally, APL details a puff lid solution and encourages its use so any sudden detonations inside a retort vessel are safely released without damage to reactor or operator.

Fig. 9.5 APL Swirl Combustion System

The APL flare system under fire

Ejector-Venturi gas pumping assembly

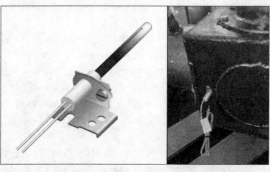

Silicon Nitride Lighting element (left) and installed (middle).
APL puff lid for pressure release inside pyrolysis reactor (right).

## CONCLUSION

The technology of biochar production is in the early days of development, with many lessons left to learn. As well as the commercial development underway, many refined techniques are being developed by the book's authors and others—perhaps you! The book's website, shown at the bottom of each page, will continue to gather and update the best of these techniques as an evergreen resource.

## REFERENCES FOR BIOCHAR AND CHARCOAL MAKING

http://www.biochar.bioenergylists.org/.

*Biochar for Environmental Management: Science and Technology* (Earthscan, 2009), edited by J. Lehmann and S. Joseph.

*Simple technologies for charcoal making.* FAO Forestry Paper - 4, 1987

*Charcoal Production, Marketing, and Use.* July 1961 No. 2213.

*Industrial Charcoal Production*, FAO Paper, June 2008, Zagreb, Croatia.

*Charcoal Production with Reduced Emissions.* P.J. Reumerman and B. Frederiks. 12th European Conference on Biomass for Energy, Industry and Climate Protection, Amsterdam, 2002.

*Industrial Production of Charcoal.* Morten Gronli, SINTEF Energy Research, N-7465 Trondheim, Norway.

*Review of Technologies for the Production and Use of Charcoal.* Daniel M. Kammen & Debra J. Lew, 2005. Renewable and Appropriate Energy Laboratory Report.

*Volatile organic emissions from the distillation and pyrolysis of vegetation.* J. P. Greenberg, H. Friedli, A. B. Guenther, D. Hanson, P. Harley, and T. Karl. National Center for Atmospheric Research, Boulder, Colorado, 80307-3000, USA.

Chapter 10

# Biochar Production:
# From Colliers to Retorts

## Peter Hirst

*[Peter Hirst's earlier chapter in this book, "From Blacksmith to Biochar: The Essence of Community," describes how he left the corporate world and settled on Cape Cod, Massachusetts to become at first a village blacksmith and then a biochar producer and community builder. That chapter lends perspective to the basic production information set out in this one.]*

**IN THIS CHAPTER YOU WILL LEARN:**

- The similar historical roots of, and methods for, producing charcoal and biochar.

- An easy explanation of pyrolysis—the basis of all charcoal and biochar production.

- The crucial differences between making charcoal and making biochar.

- Descriptions of various modern, community-sized "retorts"—scalable, clean-burning, yet low-tech devices that are relatively easy to build and are well suited for permanent practice in producing biochar.

- Practical information for aspiring retort builders and biochar producers.

"Light a wooden match and watch it burn. At the end of the burn, the wood in the matchstick will be completely burned and blackened. Congratulations! You have just produced your first biochar."

## INTRODUCTION

The production of charcoal and biochar have a common root. Before fossil coal emerged during the eighteenth century's Industrial Revolution, the word "coal" meant charcoal—the black fuel made from wood. The ancient methods for making charcoal were dirty, dangerous, and environmentally unfriendly.

Nevertheless, the essentials of low-tech production of charcoal and biochar are the same, and set the stage for later advances. This chapter discusses those principles, basics, and advances, and offers practical information for aspiring biochar makers.

## HOW EARLY COLLIERS MADE CHARCOAL

The basis of all charcoal and biochar production is **pyrolysis**: essentially, breaking wood down into its chemical constituents by heat, with little or no oxygen. The early **colliers**—the artisans who made charcoal—had none of today's pyrolysis technology: no cylindrical gasifiers, no steel **retort** vessels, no high temperature refractories. Instead, they had piles of wood, and plenty of leaves and mud. From that, they built temporary charcoal kilns that supplied the iron furnaces, glass factories, and brick plants of early America.

The collier would assemble his **feedstock**—cords of seasoned hardwood, uniformly cut and split—into a circular pile of sticks leaning inward teepee-style. More layers of sticks were added until a mound perhaps fifteen feet (4 to 5 meters) across and half as high had been constructed. In the center of the mound, the collier would leave an open space a foot or two across to serve as a chimney during the burn.

The mound would be covered in a coating of leaves, followed by a thick coating of moist soil or mud. This mud would harden like clay as the burn progressed, forming a temporary oven, or kiln, enclosing the entire mound of wood. A single hole was left in the center of the mud mound, at its apex, as the chimney vent. At ground level, other smaller vents would be left in the mound; these allowed the collier to regulate the air entering the mound in order to sustain the burn.

The collier would ignite the mound at its center by dropping smoldering tinder through the top vent. He carefully limited the air entering the mound throughout the burn; if he let in too much air, the whole mound would be consumed by fire—yielding only ash and no charcoal. Too little, and the burn would be smothered completely. Indicators of a good burn were a steady, voluminous, thick stream of smoke pouring from the center vent, and a uniform lukewarm mound surface.

This smoke-and-stench-producing, smoldering burn went on for many days, even weeks.

The collier tended and monitored the mound continually throughout, making constant adjustments for temperature, rate and quality of smoke production, and leaks. This work was replete with dirt, discomfort, and danger. If the mound developed a leak—and it often did—someone had to climb the smoldering, belching mound to fix it. Occasionally, a worker fell through the shell and into the kiln, sometimes to his death.

At the end of the burn, as indicated by the reduction and then absence of smoke, the collier and his crew would dig out the remains of the fire—the charcoal—with hand tools.

This is essentially how charcoal is still produced in much of the world, including rural parts of the United States and Europe. In more developed regions, the temporary mud mounds have merely been replaced by more durable kilns made of masonry, or sometimes steel. The Missouri kiln, the New Hampshire kiln, and the beehive kiln are all variations on the same basic technology: a slow, low-temperature, low-oxygen burn in an enclosed structure.

In many parts of the world, the charcoal-making industry is unregulated. It produces heavy pollutants, often engulfing entire communities in a permanent pall of acrid, poisonous smoke. The health of everyone nearby suffers.

In the United States, clean air regulations now require afterburners to destroy the smoke and reduce pollutants. These devices, usually fired by natural gas or propane (both fossil fuels), burn off the gases emitted by pyrolysis (**pyroligneous** gases) into the atmosphere. But this wastes the heat and potential by-products of those gases—and the energy of the fossil fuel as well.

## MAKING CHARCOAL AND BIOCHAR: SIMILAR, BUT DIFFERENT

The traditional charcoal-making method does not produce good biochar. Good biochar has high porosity, extensive microstructure, and **adsorption capacity** that enable beneficial interactions between microbes, nutrients, and water in the soil. In traditional charcoal making, the low temperatures and long residence time of the smoke in the feedstock usually results in the opposite; any microstructure and adsorption capacity tends to be saturated with condensed tars, and is therefore unavailable to the microbes, nutrients, and water in the soil. [Dr. Hugh McLaughlin discusses biochar properties and principles in more depth in his chapters titled "What *Is* Biochar?", "How Biochar Helps the Soil," and "Characterizing Biochars: Attributes, Indicators, and At-Home Tests."]

Char made this traditional way essentially clogs its own pores. However, the practices of traditional charcoal making do offer potential techniques for making modern biochars, and those methods will be reviewed next.

## THE FUNDAMENTALS OF WOOD GASIFICATION IN OPEN BURNS

### Overview on Open Burns

The open burn is a basic, low-tech method for making char, which is useful for understanding the fundamentals of pyrolysis and char making.

But first, a strong caution. Although open burns can produce good quantities of biochar, they are not efficient or environmentally friendly, and should not be used as an ongoing production method. Open burning is explained here only for educational purposes or as the first step in the transition away from historic practices: the open burn methods described in this chapter, although somewhat more time and labor-intensive, are cleaner than the old farm bonfire. A single, small open burn of *one* of the types described here is sufficient to educate, and more is neither suggested nor advocated.

## INTRODUCTION TO OPEN BURN BIOCHAR: LIGHT A MATCH

The first step in the experiment with pyrolysis is to simply light a match and watch it burn. Use wooden kitchen matches, and hold them with a tool (pliers or tweezers will do), so that you can watch the entire match burn without making char of your fingertips.

For your first burn, hold the lighted match horizontally and observe the process as the flame progresses along the match. You will notice three major zones in the structure of your little fire: the flame itself, the unburned fresh wood, and the blackened, burned wood. At the end of the burn, the wood in the matchstick will be completely burned and blackened.

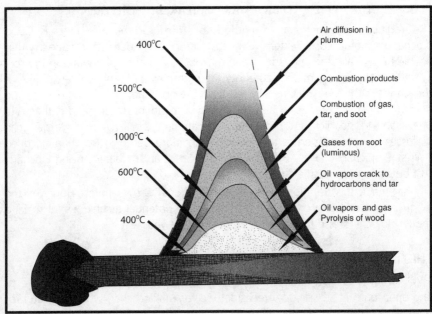

Adapted from Tom Reed

Fig. 10.1 Pyrolosis, Gasification and Combustion in a Flaming Match
Source: ALL Power Labs, Jess Hobbs

Congratulations! You have just produced your first biochar. That little blackened stick represents almost half the carbon atoms that were in the original match. Crumble it in your fingers. Then brush or rinse the residue off your fingers. If your fingers come clean without soap, further congratulations are due, for you have also just made your first *good* biochar. The powder washes off cleanly because it contains almost no greasy residue; it's mostly pure carbon with clean, open pores and decent adsorption.

Light a second match, and this time, observe more closely. Look for additional details in the structure and the progress of the flame. First look for that transition zone between the fresh wood and the char, noting how the wood turns brown and then black as the smoke is driven off and the char is left behind. Notice especially that the *wood itself is not burning.* It is not the wood that is glowing with the light and heat of fire. It's the flame hovering just above the wood. You can see this separation of flame and fuel even more clearly in a candle flame.

What these first matches tell us is that in order to burn, wood must first be pyrolyzed—that is, it must first be heated to give off gases, which then combust in the air just above the wood. It is the heat of this combustion which causes the wood to continue to pyrolyze, adding more gas to the flame, and so on until the wood has completely pyrolyzed and the flame goes out, leaving the char behind.

Also notice the flame itself. It has several interesting details. You may notice that the flame is not uniform, but seems to have small, brief flares branching off from it in different directions, sometimes even straight down. These are little jets of gas being aimed in different directions by irregularities—pockets and small openings—in the wooden stick.

Sometimes you may see smoke accompanying the flame. This will generally occur at the leading edge of the flame. This is pyrolysis gas that is escaping to the air without igniting, where it cools and condenses into particulate smoke. If you turn the match vertically—that is, with the burned end up—you will also notice a couple of important things. First, any smoke being produced in the horizontal position disappears. That is because the leading edge of the flame, where the pyrolysis gas is produced, is now under the flame, so that all the gases rise directly into the burning flame where they cannot escape combustion. This is a key point. If you turn the match the other way, so that the fresh wood is above the flame, the opposite happens. The fresh wood above the flame now heats up and the gases rise away from the flame before igniting, resulting in smoke.

Finally, note the formation of the char. Even though that char may be engulfed in the flame, it is not consumed. That is because the flame is consuming all the oxygen around the char, preventing the char itself from oxidizing, and it takes a higher temperature to gasify the char.

These three phenomena—the advance of the heat along the wood, the consumption of all of the smoke, and the preservation of the char from burning—are the key elements and goals of every one of the "oxic" (oxygen present) char production methods and units we will be discussing. Corresponding processes also apply in the "anoxic" (oxygen absent) or retort processes.

## THE PIT OR TRENCH BURN

The most easily executed open burn method is the pit or trench fire. Simply dig a trench or pit big enough to contain all of the material to be burned. Start off small, with a fire you can easily manage, and after a little practice, work your way up to what you need to get rid of your accumulated brush. As you load the pit, put the thickest stuff on the bottom and smaller and smaller material as you build up.

This is the opposite of what you're likely used to. To make a campfire or bonfire, we usually have learned to build a small fire down low and add bigger fuel on top of that. This is fine if the goal is simply to burn as much as you can as fast as you can. The problem is, the fresh wood above the flame cooks, producing pyrolysis gases that rise away from the fire and produce lots of smoke.

In producing biochar, however, the goal is to burn as clean as we can and keep as much char as possible. So we do it upside down. We are still going to light the small stuff first, so that the heat can build up as it reaches the bigger material, but we want it to burn from the top down. In this way, the gas that is produced from the fresh wood below as it heats up passes directly into the hot flame above it and ignites, burning very cleanly and very hot.

As the wood below ignites, the flames tend to consume all of the available oxygen, so the char at the upper levels remains in an oxygen-free environment, preventing it from being immediately consumed. Once the fresh wood is fully charred, however, the flames will go out and the hot pile of coals will oxidize and heat, and eventually be reduced to ash. To prevent this from happening, and to preserve the char, you must bury it.

Take the soil you removed when digging the pit and bury the hot coals, completely and tightly. Remember that just like in the traditional charcoal mound, any air let in at this point will consume the char. After a few days (or hours if the initial experiment is small) the buried char will be cooled enough not to re-ignite on exposure to the air, and may be dug up.

## THE REED PILE

This variation of the open burn is named after Dr. Tom Reed, a respected combustion scientist who teaches this extremely effective, low-tech method despite spending his career developing much higher-tech processes.

Unlike the trench burn, the Reed Pile method uses a little water rather than a lot of soil to quench the flame and preserve the char. It can be done on flat ground in an area safe from spreading the fire.

Judicious application of a fine mist accomplishes three important objectives:

1.    More char is preserved.
2.    Time is saved, since the char is cooled as soon as the flame goes out.
3.    There is no chance of re-igniting, since at the end of the burn, the char should be doused completely rather than hidden under dirt.

To try the Reed Pile, here's what to do (and again, start small):

•    Have an ordinary garden hose at the ready, with the nozzle set to deliver a fine mist

•    Build your woodpile with some small stuff on top

•    Light the pile at the top, and stand by with the hose

•    When any white ash appears on the black char, sprinkle it lightly with the mist as the fire descends, being careful to douse only the char without soaking any of the unburned material or dousing the fire itself

Only a small amount of water is needed. This is because char needs a much higher temperature to sustain combustion than the original wood did, and it only takes a misting of water to keep it under that temperature. You may need a few repetitions to become adept at dousing the char while the fire rages on.

### SUMMARY OF OPEN BURN CONCEPTS

Having mastered one or more of these open burn processes, you will gain an intuitive as well as intellectual understanding of the role and behavior of fire in biochar production. Open burns, while not recommended for long-term production, are important tools for observing and understanding the four key processes of most low-tech char production methods:

•    Inducing pyrolysis by progressive application of heat

•    The pyrolysis process itself, during which the wood breaks down into gases and char

•    Consuming the pyrolysis gases for clean emissions and in many cases, to maintain the reaction

•    Preserving the char from further combustion by excluding oxygen or cooling the char

These elements are common to all low-tech methods and technologies.

Fig. 10.2 Open Burn
Making charcoal at the Jack Daniel distillery, Lynchburg,Tennessee

## SCALABLE PYROLYSIS DEVICES

This section describes the construction and operation of some simple devices that better control the key processes just described, and are thus suitable for more permanent practice in producing biochar.

### The TLUD

One popular small pyrolysis device is a gasifier, specifically the top-lit updraft gasifier, or TLUD (pronounced "Tee-lud"). This unique configuration is covered in detail in the next chapter of this book, titled "Making Biochar in Small Gasifier Cookstoves and Heaters," and is briefly mentioned here to acknowledge its importance. [Before embarking on any biochar production experiments it makes sense to read that chapter, and select an approach that suits your circumstances and environment, such as urban versus rural setting.] The remainder of this section will concentrate on another scalable approach to making biochar—the retort method.

### The Retort

The retort differs from the open burn and the TLUD in one fundamental respect: in a retort, the feedstock is entirely contained and heated within an enclosed chamber or vessel (the retort), where neither flame nor oxygen can enter. This is "anoxic" pyrolysis (no oxygen in the area of the pyrolysis); the other two methods are oxic.

More specifically, in open burns, the four key elements discussed above occur in the same space, while in a retort they are physically separated. The processes that *require* oxygen—applying initial heat to induce pyrolysis and the combustion of pyrolysis gases—are separated from the pyrolysis and char preservation processes, which must *exclude* oxygen, by a layer of steel. The feedstock is heated in an enclosed chamber, or retort, and its pyrolysis gases escape to be burned entirely outside that chamber. Pyrolysis on the inside, fire and heat generation on the outside.

### *Throw Another Can on the Fire: The Rudimentary Retort*

Perhaps the simplest of all retort designs consists of nothing more than an enclosed can or barrel resting on a grate on or near an open flame. The container needs just enough vents to release pyrolysis gases while limiting the entry of air during heating and cool-down.

After heating up for an hour or two, this crude retort produces impressive quantities of pyrolysis gas. The setup is not efficient, however, since it does not use the heat of pyrolysis to assist in heating the retort. Nevertheless, the basic features of a continuous pyrolysis process are there: a strong gas flame is produced, and the residue left behind is char.

## The 55/30: a Simple Closed Retort

The double barrel or inverted drum retort is popular with biochar enthusiasts. A typical configuration, the "55/30," consists of a 55-gallon (about 200 liters) outer drum containing the fire around a 30-gallon (about 100 liters) inner drum acting as the enclosed retort.

A 30-gallon barrel, open at one end and standing with the open end down on a flat surface, makes a simple and serviceable closed retort. If you fill the 30-gallon barrel with wood, upend it inside a 55-gallon drum open at the top, you have a closed retort inside an outer shell, with a couple inches of space between the walls of the outer and inner barrels. With suitable air openings in the outer drum, this creates a combustion space around the retort; fill the space with fuel and ignite it, and there you have it—the simple closed retort pyrolysis system. This concept can be executed in various sizes, down to a quart-sized juice can inside a gallon-sized vegetable can.

To build a more refined 55/30 yourself, you can follow these steps:

- Find a 55-gallon drum with a removable lid.

- Cut a hole in the lid and fit it with a flange that holds about 4 feet of 6-inch diameter stovepipe. This provides about the right amount of chimney that induces draft, to draw in both primary and secondary air. This facilitates a clean, hot burn throughout the cycle.

- Drill six or eight 11/4- to 2-inch holes (3–5 cm), evenly spaced, all around the 55-gallon drum just above the closed bottom. This admits "primary" air not only to fire the initial raw starter fuel wood, but once gases begin escaping from the inner drum, provides air for combusting the pyrolysis gas as well.

- To assure complete combustion of the escaping gases, provide additional, "secondary" air by drilling a series of ½ inch holes, evenly spaced, around the perimeter of the outer drum, but at the highest point, just under the upper rim.

- The final assembly is completed by installing the lid and stack on top.

While not necessary, we boost heat retention and efficiency by wrapping a layer of alumina silicate refractory blanket insulation around the middle of the outer drum, being careful not to cover either the primary air vents at the bottom or the secondary air vents at the top. We then cover this insulation with thin sheet metal. [If you do this, be careful to choose a refractory material capable of taking flaming heat. Do *not* use fiberglass insulation, which contains resins that decompose into acrid vapors when heated. Also be aware that the higher temperature reached by an insulated drum may lead to earlier burnout of the drum. A longer lasting combustion chamber and retort can be built out of recycled stainless steel vessels.]

When assembled, the unit is now configured as a closed retort inside a larger barrel, with a space of a few inches between the outer and inner barrels. To operate the unit, the starter fuel is packed into this space, with the larger material underneath and the fine kindling and tinder material at the very top. Just like the open burns, this starter charge is lit at the top while the unit is open. When a strong, uniform flame front has taken hold around the top surface of the charge, the lid is replaced and the stack put in place. The starter charge burns from the top down, cleanly and efficiently, directing the maximum amount of energy into the closed inner retort.

When the feedstock in the inner retort reaches pyrolysis temperature, the pyrolysis gases are forced out under the rim into the combustion space in the outer barrel. As long as there are burning embers in the combustion space, the gases ignite there and provide heat to maintain pyrolysis for the remainder of the burn. When the gas combustion ends, pyrolysis is complete, and after the retort cools, the char inside may be emptied.

A demonstration of this simple retort can be seen on the web at:
http://www.youtube.com/watch?v=RXMUmby8PpU

Although the unit used in that demonstration, nicknamed "The Tin Man," is slightly larger than a 55/30, it is identical in configuration, principle, and operation.

## SCALING UP AND THE CONCEPT OF MULTIPLE DRUM RETORTS
The 55/30 is too small for large-scale use. At 20 to 25 pounds (10 kg) of quality biochar per batch, over 800 batches would be needed to achieve an optimal soil concentration of, say, 10 tons per acre (25 tons per hectare). If operated to produce 50 batches per year (about one per week), then in one year, the 55/30 would produce enough biochar to bring about a sixteenth of an acre—perhaps 3,000 square feet (300 square meters)—up to that concentration.

The 55/30 is therefore better suited for the single household that can dedicate some time to building top quality soil in a good-sized garden plot. For more serious operations like ours—for market gardeners and small farmers—we had to scale up.

### Enter the Shotgun
Looking for a unit with higher capacity and reduced labor per unit of production, but without significantly more complicated technology or operation, we created the double barrel "Shotgun" design, with two 55-gallon drums inside a single outer chamber made from a stretched US-standard 275-gallon (1000-liter) residential fuel-oil tank. We stretched the tank by splitting two of them not quite in half, and then welding the two larger sections together. [The same could be accomplished by splitting a single tank in half and welding inserts to stretch the 42 inch dimension to about 56 inches, which would accommodate two 55-gallon retorts side by side.]

The top of the Shotgun is made from the cut-off ends of the tanks, also welded back together to form a slightly larger oval. The main tank is drilled with primary and secondary air holes, just like the 55/30, and can also be wrapped in a layer of refractory blanket insulation. We fit the lid with a 6-inch stack over each of the barrels.

To fill the Shotgun, the outer unit is tipped onto its side and the two loaded 55s, one at a time, are slid in. Then the entire unit is tipped upright for firing. This design almost quadruples the capacity of the 55/30. The Shotgun is bigger and heavier than the 55/30, and not easily operated by one person, although with practice it can be. However, a team of two can easily operate and transport it.

We have burned the Shotgun just as hot, clean, and efficiently as the 55/30, and it produces about 75 pounds of char per batch, in less than twice the burn time of the smaller 55/30. The Shotgun has taken its place alongside the 55/30 as the second in our line of community biochar units.

Before we move on the largest of our community-sized units—the Adam- Retort —we next offer some important practical considerations that apply no matter the unit scale, and arguably become even more important in operating larger units.

## PRACTICAL CONSIDERATIONS

### FEEDSTOCK PROPERTIES

#### Feedstock Type
Wood is by far the most productive and accommodating feedstock. In various parts of the world, however, other biomass products are so plentiful that they command primary interest as char stocks: for example, **bagasse**, corn stover, rice hulls, and coconut coir.

Three density-related factors favor wood over these agricultural feedstocks, especially for small units. First, most agricultural products have low density—that is, they take up a lot of room for the mass of carbon they contain. In practice, this translates into more burn cycles, more repetitions of loading and unloading, and more work for a given yield of char. Second, in a closed retort system, the lower the density of the feedstock, the less total gas is given off and the less likely a complete pyrolysis will result. (One might suppose that less density would make it easier to achieve pyrolysis, but that has not been our experience.) Third, less density also means more airspace, and we believe that less-dense materials may act as insulators against heat penetration. We have in fact observed this in the larger Adam-Retort, and also at times with the 55/30.

## Feedstock Size

A second vital feedstock factor is the size and shape of the individual feedstock pieces, particularly in smaller units. If the smallest or thinnest particle dimension is too small, the material will pack so tightly that no gas can circulate and heat will not penetrate to the center of the charge. If the individual pieces are too large, there will be plenty of circulation, but heat will not penetrate to the center of each piece.

We have found that the best feedstock thickness (thinnest dimension, or diameter in the case of round stock) for the 55/30 is about ½ inch to 2 ½ inches (1 cm to 6 cm). A few pieces in each charge may be larger or smaller, but it is advisable to have at least 90% of the feedstock within these limits. These limits will also vary with different species of wood. Finding the optimal balance between particle size and shape for your unit and feedstock requires some experimentation.

## Feedstock Moisture

A third critical factor is feedstock moisture content: generally, the drier the better. Evaporating moisture out of feedstock is the single biggest energy requirement, and hindrance, when heating feedstock to the desired pyrolysis temperature.

This is because to dry the feedstock, the water in it has to be taken from ambient temperature to boiling point, and then the water has to be evaporated. Water has a higher heat capacity than almost any other substance: it takes two or three times more energy to heat a given mass of water through a desired number of degrees than the same mass of dry wood. On top of that, it takes between seven and eight times more energy to boil that quantity of water at 100°C than it does to heat it from room temperature to 100°C.

Don't waste any more energy on drying material than you have to. Let the sun and wind air-dry it for you. This means getting at least six months ahead of your feedstock needs in order to allow time for air drying, but this investment will pay off in improved results.

Generally, the preferred feedstock is limb wood that has been air-dried for about six months. In addition, the feedstock surface should not have gotten wet too recently before the burn; best practice is to keep all feedstock under loose cover.

## Hold the Chips

The combination of material density, particle size, and moisture bring us to the special question of wood chips.

Wood chips are ubiquitous. Everybody seems to have them, and wants to char them. Our advice on wood chips is "don't." Stop making them, stop thinking about them. Why? Because in small-scale retorts, chips present problems that are difficult to overcome.

Specifically:

- Wood chips are so small they pack into a dense mass inside the closed retort. Little or no gas can circulate between the chips, so the only heat penetration is by conduction through them. This is like trying to pyrolyze a solid block of wood.

- Wood chips are difficult to dry. Unlike stacked limb wood, virtually no air circulates through a pile of wood chips to help dry them. Even under cover, they have been known to stand for years without drying more than an inch or so below the surface of the pile.

- Finally, making wood chips is more expensive and consumes more energy than preparing limb wood. A decent wood chipper can run into the thousands of dollars, and is expensive to run compared with a chain saw, which is essentially all that is needed to prepare limb wood.

Everywhere we go, new biochar enthusiasts greet us with a passion for learning, and boast about unlimited supplies of wood chips. They are disappointed when they learn how much effort goes into converting any significant amount of this "abundant resource" into decent char in a low-tech retort. Wood chips are a practical fuel only for large thermal installations specifically designed to process and pyrolyze cheap raw chips. [Because of their small and uniform size, wood chips are a fuel of choice in small TLUDs, as discussed in the next chapter, although particular efforts must be taken to ensure that the chips are dry enough for the intended use.]

## ANCILLARY TASKS AND EQUIPMENT

All char production involves ancillary tasks. These tasks become increasingly important as production volumes increase, and should be reconsidered and reevaluated with every increase in scale.

These ancillary tasks are divided into three general categories:

- Feedstock management (pre-production)

- Char handling (post-production)

- Conditioning biochar (post-production)

### Feedstock Management

Proper feedstock preparation is of paramount concern, but the equipment and machinery needed to handle the feedstock is also important. This presents a challenge to balance environmental- and cost-related desires for less technology and less energy-intensive practices against the desire for efficiency and volume of production. Significant amounts of char can be produced without mechanization, but only you can decide whether this is practical for your own operation.

To load the 55/30, about 100 pounds (45 kg) of wood feedstock is typically required. Since the 30-gallon can is about 30 inches (75 cm) tall, the most efficient way to do this is with fairly straight sticks just under 30 inches in length. This makes it easiest to upend the unit for loading without spilling the charge. Breaking these sticks across your knee can get old in a hurry, so usually a saw or a sharp ax is required. Even then, breaking or sawing 100 sticks for a single batch can be wearing, so it won't be long before you consider the practical advantages of using a power saw that can cut many sticks to the desired length at a single pass.

In addition, your year's worth of biochar, say half a ton from 50 burns, will require the equivalent of a cord (3.6 cubic meters) or two of feedstock. Spread out over a year, you may need no more than a wheelbarrow or garden cart to move this amount around. If you get into quantities larger than a cord, you will find some mechanization helpful, say a trailer behind a garden tractor.

In order to preserve all the work that you have put into collecting and preparing your feedstock, you will also want to keep it dry, as previously stated. For a cord or two, a temporary loose cover, such as a well-secured tarp, may suffice. For larger quantities, you should consider a more permanent cover, such as a well-ventilated plastic hoop house, or high tunnel, as commonly used for greenhouses. Just about any feedstock but wood chips will dry out and stay dry under such cover.

### Handling Finished Char

Many people have the impression that handling fresh char is a dirty, dusty job. This is not necessarily so. Since biochar will be used as a soil amendment rather than fuel, there is absolutely no problem with getting it wet—this actually helps keep the dust down, and prevents product from blowing away in the breeze.

Sometimes, wetting will be necessary to cool a hot or even burning charge when opening the retort. Don't hesitate to do this. Just be careful to avoid the hot steam that may billow up. In fact, for safety and convenience, a ready source of at least low-pressure water should be considered an integral part of your biochar operation.

### Sizing the Char

With smaller quantities of char, reducing it to a proper finished particle size will partly take care of itself. Good char is extremely brittle and will begin to break down with any handling. To complete processing, simply push a roller or drive a vehicle over it. A couple of passes does it.

Sizing biochar is not a precision operation. The char doesn't have to be crushed particularly fine, and the pieces don't have to be of uniform size. Less than one-half inch (1 cm) is good, and if some of the product is a little larger, that is not a problem. It will break down physically in the soil soon enough, particularly where there is significant frost or freezing action or mechanical impact such as annual tilling.

## Conditioning or Charging the Char

Before biochar is introduced to the soil, it should first be mixed with an organic medium—compost, **compost tea**, or the like. This is because in its raw, unsaturated state, biochar's most endearing chemical property—adsorption—will tend to make it compete with your plants for soil nutrients, microorganisms, and water until it is saturated and begins to make those benefits available to the plants. [For more about conditioning biochar, see the chapter titled "Conditioning Biochar for Application to Soils."]

The most common method of conditioning the char before applying it to soil is by mixing it with compost. This can be done in small batches, in the same way a mason mixes mortar: in a trough or wheelbarrow, using shovel and hoe. Experience shows, however, that this can be the most physically difficult process in preparing char; it takes a lot of work to get a consistent, thorough mix. As you move up the production scale, you may want to do what the mason also does for larger quantities—use a portable mechanized concrete mixer.

## A Final Word on Machinery and Equipment

As previously suggested, up to the level of the Shotgun—which produces about 75 pounds of char per batch—most or all tasks relating to feedstock management and char handling and preparation can be done manually or with common tools and small machines. Here is a helpful rule of thumb: expect that the level of technology and mechanization you already apply to cultivating your land will be appropriate for adding biochar to it. This will change if you plan to produce more biochar than you need for the land that you work yourself.

## THE ADAM-RETORT: LOW TECH COMES OF AGE

When we started building devices to produce biochar, we tried to build whatever we needed by using or modifying off-the-shelf components. The initiative to scale up collided with that founding principle—or so it seemed until we learned of the Adam-Retort.

Christoph Adam, an engineer from Germany, developed the Adam-Retort (also called the Improved Charcoal Production System) in 2004 in Auroville, India. Long before then, Chris had recognized the widespread dependence in certain countries on charcoal fuel in general and on traditional production methods in particular, and had sought to provide a more environmentally sound system.

Fig. 10.3 Steel Adam-Retort

## Building the Adam-Retort

The original Adam-Retort is a stationary masonry unit with few movable parts, such as the lid and the flat steel plates, which are used to block the chimneys and air vents at various stages of operation. The unit is simple, elegant, and ingenious—yet easy to build. The materials cost around US$1,000–5,000 (ranging from recycled materials to high quality firebrick and steel); construction entails a week of labor for several people, including a bricklayer.

However, the Adam-Retort's technology has several unique and subtle design features that only a full set of plans will disclose. Biochar enthusiasts are urged not to attempt a project on the scale of the Adam-Retort without comprehensive plans for a proven design, and to follow the plans closely. The royalty fees are trivial compared to the expense of learning time and mistakes that will be avoided. In addition, there is a significant learning curve to becoming proficient in firing a 3 cubic meter (100 cubic feet/almost 4 cubic yard) retort, which releases megawatt hours of heat during an 8-hour or longer pyrolysis cycle.

For our own operation, we wanted to roll out a production unit immediately, but also wanted to make it transportable. Therefore, we jumped ahead to a prototype steel unit. In August 2009, the first Adam-Retort in North America went into production.

## Operating the Adam-Retort

In operation, the Adam-Retort is similar to the 55/30: an initial charge of starter wood is used to bring the feedstock up to pyrolysis temperature. Once enough moisture has evaporated to produce relatively dry pyrolysis gases, they are directed into the firebox to sustain the remainder of the pyrolysis. Secondary air performs the same critical function as in the smaller units, allowing for complete combustion of the excess pyrolysis gases in an afterburner to maintain a clean exhaust.

The Adam-Retort loads from the top, and takes close to a cord of wood per batch. To minimize loading time, we prepare our feedstock in sizes that can be handled by the 1/3 cubic yard (250 liter) bucket on our tractor. We can do this in about 15 minutes if we keep up with feedstock preparation, which is ever more critical as we increase the scale of production.

Feedstock selection and size makes less of a difference with the Adam-Retort than our smaller units. It can handle an impressive range of feedstock sizes and types, and does this best when a variety is included in each batch. We have tested it with just about every form of feedstock we could find, and it handles them all. Deciduous limb wood continues to be our mainstay, but we have loaded it with various combinations of pine, kiln-dried lumber, woody vines, corn stover, and large wood chips known as "hog fuel."

Some stocks, such as uniform pieces of kiln-dried lumber cutoffs, have pushed the unit to its limits, because the individual feedstock pieces will all reach pyrolysis temperature at about the same time. Therefore, uniform loads tend to have a very sharp peak of pyrolysis gas and heat production. This can overload the capacity of the secondary air to completely combust all that fuel. We've learned a lot about mixing feedstock to flatten out the heat curve and release gas in stages.

The amount and type of starter fuel for the Adam Retort's firebox can also vary. We've had best results with deciduous stove wood, especially black locust split to about two to four inches thick.

We've also experimented with wet feedstock, and it's taken as much as 16 hours of startup before pyrolysis kicked-in. With reasonably dry wood, we usually get a good, hot, and pure gas flame in the combustion channel after about 5 hours. From there, pyrolysis is completed in about 4 more hours. Just like our smaller units, the Adam-Retort simply goes out when pyrolysis is done. Then, we close it up, let it cool well below ignition temperature, and empty it. Sometimes this can all be done in as little as 3 or 4 hours.

For unloading, as with the smaller units, it's important to keep running water on hand. The char always needs misting to keep dust down, and sometimes remaining hot spots can approach combustion temperatures. That said, we've never experienced a sudden flare up, or been caught off guard by a hot charge, although as should be expected around fire and hot materials, utmost care and vigilance is a must to avoid physical injury.

Many newly introduced to the Adam-Retort are worried about climbing into a bin of charcoal to shovel out 600 pounds of char, but—somewhat surprisingly— unloading the unit is usually clean and expeditious with the right amount of dampening and the right tools. We use wide manure forks, flat-nosed shovels, brooms and dustpans. The most suitable unloading tools will vary depending on the feedstock and the particle size of the end product. Like many of the processes described in this chapter, this one can be customized and refined via experimentation and personal preference.

To mechanize unloading and handling, we've experimented with a leaf vacuum. Good char is very light and brittle, and early experiments with a small vacuum have been very successful in unloading the retort and pulverizing the char in one step. In fact, we intend to develop this into a system that will collect the char from the retort, pulverize it, wet it, and blow it into a storage bin. Mounting a small orifice or nozzle in the wall of the vacuum unit so that it delivers a fine spray as the char moves through the system would get the job done in one pass.

The final step in preparing the char from the Adam-Retort, as with our smaller retorts, is mixing it, usually with good compost. The optimal way to achieve a good homogeneous mixture is to use a mechanized cement mixer. After this final step, you'll have prepared and conditioned up to 750 pounds (350 kg) of char per Adam-Retort batch. Your yield will of course vary and improve with experimentation.

### Advances on the Steel Adam-Retort

The Adam-Retort represents an impressive advance in cleaning up traditional charcoal making. Chris Adam estimates that his masonry retort reduces pollutants by 75 percent from conventional kilns. The steel Mobile Adam-Retort positioned us to develop more advanced exhaust cleaning and energy conversion mechanisms.

During the first phase of the burn cycle, the feedstock is primarily being dried and brought slowly up to pyrolysis temperature, and the exhaust stream is a bright white plume, indicating that it is largely water vapor. Nonetheless, to the casual observer the exhaust stream looks and smells like smoke. For aesthetic purposes if nothing else, we began work to capture this stream and minimize if not eliminate the smoky discharge. We did this by replacing the phase 1 chimney with a condenser and a blower (see picture), which draws the entire drying stream through a 100 square-foot (9 square-meter) shell and tube condenser, where it is cooled, dried, and directed into the firebox instead of the atmosphere. In this process, we typically recover over 40 gallons (150 liters) of aqueous **wood vinegar** as well as a few gallons of heavy wood tars and oils. Without the recovery condenser, all of this material would have been discharged into the air.

Fig 10.4 Mobile Adam-Retort with Condenser

The water circulating through the condenser is also circulated to an air-water heat exchanger, essentially like a car radiator, where it provides a steady stream of hot air throughout the burn cycle. We have estimated that we recover between 1 and 5 therms (30 to 150 kWh) of energy or about 1 to 5 percent of the available heat of pyrolysis (the energy content of 1 chord of wood is about 200 therms or 6 megawatt hours, about 50 percent of which is released as excess heat during pyrolysis). In addition, we can tap into this cooled gas stream for the combustible gas it provides, and are developing applications to use this gas as feedstock dryer or generator fuel.

Another important advance in the Steel Adam-Retort is its system of valves to control circulation of the hot exhaust gases and the pyrolysis gases. This is useful for several purposes, including:

- Bypassing the combustion chamber to regulate temperature and clean up the secondary burn.

- Augmenting the drying process.

- Providing fuel gas both to the combustion channel and for auxiliary uses.

Our goal is to attain zero visual emissions, and we're getting there. The Steel Adam-Retort's valve system, combined with two secondary air feeds, makes the burn cycle extremely clean. In fact, for most of the burn cycle, we regularly meet this standard and in best cases approach 100 percent emission control.

The final advantage of the Steel Adam-Retort is transportability. Our most recent version is permanently mounted on an auto transport trailer adapted for this purpose. This allows us to travel far and wide not only to do contract work for a variety of property owners, but also to provide training and education in biochar production all around our region.

## CONCLUSION

With modest effort, individual- and community-scale biochar production is accessible to all. Charcoal is not biochar, but many charcoal-making practices can be adapted for biochar production.

Simple biochar-making devices can be built from commonly available materials. However, like the early collier, simple low-tech designs mean that in order to produce good biochar, the biochar maker must understand the properties of the biomass and the pyrolysis process, and must carefully attend to the details.

Hopefully, this chapter has offered guiding principles to that end.

Chapter 11

# Making Biochar in Small Gasifier Cookstoves and Heaters

Paul S. Anderson, PhD ("Dr. TLUD")


**IN THIS CHAPTER YOU WILL LEARN:**

- The process of pyrolysis, which creates biochar.

- The various types and sizes of TLUDs with picture gallery.

- How "Top-Lit Updraft" pyrolytic gasifier cookstoves (TLUDs) can be used, adapted, or built (including do-it-yourself projects) to produce biochar.

- How to make your own TLUD from scrap cans.

- The opportunities to participate in a worldwide initiative, and where to find additional resources.


"TLUD pyrolytic gasifiers are convenient sources of biochar, and can be easily constructed and operated for small-scale production. The basic TLUD technology is 'open source'. Everyone has the opportunity (and is encouraged) to advance the designs."

# INTRODUCTION

In general, traditional wood-burning cookstoves and small biomass fires leave behind mainly ash and little, if any, charcoal. This is because excess air is available to burn all the char to ash. However, new cookstoves and small heaters have been developed to utilize the principles of gasifiers, which require controlled and limited air, thus allowing char to be formed and preserved.

This chapter is among the first writings to focus on using pyrolytic gasifier cookstoves to produce biochar. This chapter also contains an "Additional Resources" section at the end with web links to specific topics.

## MICRO-GASIFICATION

When any dry **biomass** fuel (such as wood) is burning, the visible flame is actually produced by the combustion of liberated gases. These flaming gases yield heat that continues to convert the fuel into its component **pyrolytic gases**, plus char and eventually ash. In a normal fire, these related processes occur together in the spaces between the pieces of fuel. Most people looking at a fire assume that the flames originate from the solid fuel, when in fact they are entirely associated with the combustion of released gases.

A **"gasifier"** is a device that physically separates where the component gases are generated from where they are ultimately used—or more precisely, separates the gas-*making* processes of **pyrolysis** and **char-gasification** from the gas-*using* processes of combustion or storage (for example by condensation) for later use.

Large-system gasification has been in use for nearly two centuries (for example, gasification of coal or biomass to produce fuel gas or electricity), but very small-scale gasification (called **"micro-gasification"**) was not practical or commercially available until 2003 and 2007, with the advent of **Top-Lit UpDraft** (TLUD, pronounced "*Tee*-lud") and Anderson Variation UpDraft (AVUD) technologies, respectively. This chapter centers on the TLUD technology.

The name "Top-Lit Updraft" denotes two key characteristics:

* The fire is ignited at the top of a column of biomass fuel, and the active zone of pyrolysis (the "pyrolysis front") progressively moves downward through the stationary biomass.

* A limited (or controlled) amount of primary combustion air flows upward through the column of biomass fuel from an entry point at the bottom of the fuel chamber.

These general characteristics are depicted in Figure 11.1.

## THE ADVENT OF MICRO-GASIFICATION

In 2003, Dr. Thomas B. Reed's Woodgas Campstove was introduced to the market. This campstove utilizes the TLUD gasification technology that Dr. Reed conceived and developed in laboratory prototypes in 1985 and that Paal Wendelbo independently developed in the 1990s.

In 2007, Chip Energy began making and selling the Biomass Grill. The Chip Energy products utilize AVUD gasification technology,[12] first developed in 2004 by Dr. Paul S. Anderson and taken to commercial production in collaboration with Paul W. Wever in 2007.

From their inception, TLUD devices have been primarily intended as biomass-burning stoves for cooking, with the heat for cooking generated by secondary combustion of the pyrolytic gases. Therefore TLUD gasification technology and products have only been developed on a small scale, primarily for kitchen use in developing societies.

Until the recent surge of interest in biochar, the potentially valuable char-making capabilities of TLUD devices attracted sparse attention. The notable exception is Dr. Ronal Larson, who since the 1990s has been a prominent advocate of producing charcoal from TLUDs; his advocacy has inspired subsequent development efforts.

Biochar production is now drawing ever-increasing interest and, consequently, the technology is dynamically changing. New and more refined variations of micro-gasification (such as semi-gasifiers and alternative air flows) will continue to surface in the years ahead.

## TLUD GASIFIERS FOR PRODUCING BIOCHAR

TLUD pyrolytic stoves and biochar makers are convenient gasifier sources of biochar. TLUDs can be easily constructed and operated for small-scale production.

### Characteristics of TLUD Technology

Among the types of gasifiers, TLUDs are unique for two reasons. First, TLUDs operate in an "oxic batch mode." This means that a batch of fuel is pyrolyzed by direct heat from its own combustion of the gases it produces. In other words, the fuel is auto-pyrolyzed. Second, virtually all of the biomass is pyrolyzed and transformed to charcoal before appreciable char-gasification occurs. These qualities can be tremendously beneficial for producing biochar when the device is tended manually, because no fuel needs to be added or char removed during the pyrolysis phase.

---

[12] AVUD (Anderson Variation UpDraft) is a variation of an updraft gasifier. AVUDs operate in a continuous mode in which feedstock enters the fuel chamber from the top and is subjected to heat rising from the bottom where limited amounts of air (from tuyeres or tubes) sustain sufficient flaming (oxic) pyrolysis to provide the needed heat. The pyrolyzed materials are extracted from below the air entry level, allowing the column of biomass to move downward, making space for additional fuel to enter at the top. The created gases exit near the top to be combusted or collected.

Moreover, the transition between the two gasification phases—pyrolysis and char-gasification—is readily identifiable. During pyrolysis, the characteristic flame of secondary combustion is yellow-orange (from burning tarry gases), and changes during char-gasification to a smaller, bluish flame, indicating that char-gas, including carbon monoxide, is burning.

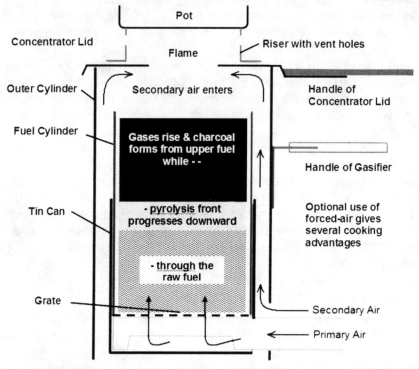

Fig. 11.1   Vertical Section of the "Champion" TLUD Gasifier (2008)

In TLUD gasifiers the fuel is stationary, moving only slightly by the effect of shrinkage as it is pyrolyzed. As depicted in Figure 11.1, a hot "pyrolysis front" moves downward through the fuel, converting the biomass to charcoal as it proceeds. The air supply to the pyrolysis front (primary air) is limited and controlled by the flow rate so that only a portion of the liberated gases are combusted, generating just enough heat to sustain the pyrolysis and carbonization. As the pyrolysis front moves downward, the upward-moving gas mixture has virtually no remaining oxygen to oxidize the char—thus the char is preserved.

Because of the presence of oxygen and flame, this method of pyrolysis has been called "flaming pyrolysis" (actually, better described as "glowing pyrolysis" since the primary air supply is limited to prevent excess flaming). In contrast, the method known as **retort** pyrolysis" obtains the necessary heat for pyrolysis from *outside* its oxygen-deprived feedstock container, with consequent differences in the biochar produced.

In a typical TLUD, the pyrolysis front moves downward at a rate of 5 to 20 mm (.2 to .8 inch) per minute, depending on the nature of the fuel and the flow rate of available primary air. As shown in Figure 11.1, "primary air" refers to the air that enters from the bottom and moves upward through the fuel. Since the rate of heat generation is determined by the amount of available oxygen, the progression of the pyrolysis front is partially controllable by regulating the primary airflow.

Increased airflow (provided by the force of a fan or by the draft of a tall riser or chimney) will result not only in faster processing, but also in higher temperatures in the pyrolysis zone, which impacts the characteristics of the biochar produced.

Above the pyrolysis front, the created char accumulates, and hot, oxygen-depleted air rises and draws the created pyrolytic gases upward to the secondary combustion zone. There, additional (secondary) air is provided, and the pyrolytic gases are fully burned in a separate and very clean flame. This secondary combustion, with full burning, is important because pyrolytic gases contain tarry, long-chain hydrocarbons that form thick smoke if not fully burned.

### The Champion TLUD Gasifier

Prominent—if not unique—among TLUD gasifiers, the version named "Champion" is designed so that the fuel canister or "reactor" (the main body of the gasifier) can be easily removed after pyrolysis is completed. With this feature, hot char can be readily removed from the device, collected into a separate container (a "snuffer box"), and easily extinguished.

The snuffer box does not have to be elaborate. It can be as simple as a clay pot with a plate to cover it. The vessel must, however, be fireproof and nearly airtight to starve (smother) the hot char of any access to oxygen. If the hot char is not removed from the reactor and air is not excluded, it will be char-gasified down to only ash, leaving no charcoal. Sprinkling water onto the hot charcoal will extinguish it more quickly.

The ability to easily remove hot char from the Champion and save it for an alternate use is a major attraction for biochar makers. (For further information on the Champion and other TLUDs, see the "Additional Resources" box at the end of this chapter.)

## VARIATIONS OF TLUD PYROLYTIC GASIFIERS

TLUD technology has numerous variations (including the Champion version just described), each with a unique history and intended application. Most of them, however, do not facilitate salvaging biochar because they are designed to utilize the char-gasification and char-gas combustion process—which ultimately destroys the char—in order to deliver maximum heat from the fuel.

## GOVERNING CONCEPTS

When reading this section on TLUD types and variations, it will be helpful to keep the following in mind:

- Because all of the products described below utilize TLUD pyrolytic gasification, they all create charcoal as an outcome of controlled airflows. This gasification/ combustion technology distinguishes the TLUD group of products from traditional fuel-controlled biomass cookstoves that do not produce charcoal very well.

- As noted, many of these TLUD devices are not designed to preserve charcoal after pyrolysis; however, they could be altered slightly for that purpose. In a cookstove, for example, a simple, independent pot support (a tripod or a supported grate) can keep the weight of the cooking pot off the device, permitting easier removal of the fuel canister for saving the biochar after pyrolyzing each batch of fuel.

- Some devices have been optimized for specific fuels, making them exceptional in some situations but less appropriate in others. In general, however, TLUDs can use a wide variety of feedstocks. The fuel pieces are usually small (for example, pellets, chips, briquettes, or pucks). Well-dried feedstocks are recommended, as TLUDs have less stable secondary combustion with wet fuels due to the additional moisture in the volatilized wood gases.

- Some developers (Belonio, Reddy, Karve, Anderson, Donnelly, and others) have many more designs and models than are mentioned here. Those designs might be better alternatives in certain applications. The best design is often the one that can be fabricated out of locally available materials by local labor resources.

- The basic TLUD technology is "open source" (not protected by patents or copyrights). There are countless variations and improvements, and probably more yet to be discovered. Everyone has the opportunity (and is encouraged) to advance the designs.

---

### HOW THIS SECTION IS ORGANIZED
Picture pages are located at the end of this chapter.

- The information on TLUD variations contained in this section is supplemented with Picture Pages (PP) that contain annotated photos. The Picture Pages are organized according to airflow characteristics and then by size.

- References to specific Picture Page sections (A through F) and specifically numbered photos will be denoted as PP: Section "X" or PP: "X1".

---

### TLUDS: MAIN CONSIDERATIONS

The various types of TLUDs can be categorized according to the following main considerations relating to biochar production (*not* cooking):

1. Refueling the fuel chamber
2. Ease of removing biochar
3. Manner of air control
4. Availability for purchase, ease of manufacture, and cost
5. Size of gasifiers

### *1. Refueling the Fuel Chamber*

A process sequence common to all true TLUDs—small or large—includes burning fuel in batches and, after the fuel is carbonized, removing (dumping out) the charcoal to save the biochar. The ease of, and methods for, doing this will be influenced by the size of the device. As used in this chapter, the terms "small" and "large" are defined as follows:

Small: For operation by one person as a cookstove, typically with fuel capacity up to 10 liters (2.5 gallons).

Large: For use by one or more "fire-tenders," typically with fuel capacity from 20 liters (5 gallons) up to barrel and tank sizes (discussed below after small units, and shown in PP: Section E).

Several factors significantly impact refueling TLUD fuel chambers. First, once the pyrolysis front has been established and is progressing downward, small amounts of raw fuel can be added on top of the charcoal created. The rising heat, in the absence of oxygen, will dry, then **torrify**, and finally pyrolyze that fuel, just as in a retort. The generated gases move upward into the secondary combustion zone. Adding too much new raw fuel at one time can produce excessive moisture or an overwhelming volume of pyrolytic gases, either of which will seriously disrupt secondary combustion. Certain TLUD models, such as forced air (FA) designs, facilitate adding fuel during operation because they have wider openings at the top (PP: Section A).

Second, if not manually interrupted and extinguished, the pyrolysis front will proceed downward until pyrolysis ends—the point of maximized biochar production. After that, char-gasification begins. Any attempt to generate additional char from pyrolysis of new biomass added on top of the created biochar is offset by the char consumed below as it undergoes char-gasification to ash. In addition, char-gasification with sufficient airflow is akin to creating a forge in the bottom of the TLUD, and such high heat can shorten the life of the device.

Third, for at least a few minutes after dumping the hot charcoal, the TLUD fuel chamber can remain too hot for immediate refueling (because the new fuel might ignite at the bottom of the chamber). A short disruption is acceptable for producing biochar, but not for continuous cooking in a TLUD cookstove. If more cooking time is required than can be obtained from one cycle of pyrolysis, it makes sense to have a second loaded fuel canister standing by. When one TLUD is finishing pyrolysis of its fuel, the standby fuel canister can be ignited and inserted to continue cooking while the first one is removed, dumped, and refueled when cool.

## 2. Ease of Removing Biochar

Very few cookstove-size units are designed to permit char (biochar) removal. The exceptions are noted in the textbox labeled "Cookstove Units Intended for Removing Biochar." However, as previously noted, forced air (FA) models (discussed in detail below) have larger top openings that facilitate hot char removal by cautiously inverting the unit and dumping the char directly into a snuffer box.

> Cookstove Units Intended
> For Removing Biochar
>
> • Juntos B  PP: A7
>
> • Champion models
>   PP: B1, B2, and C1
>
> • Flanagan  PP: C2

In other TLUD cookstove units, char removal can often be accomplished with care, though it may not be very convenient. Many do not have handles, are relatively heavy, and have cooking pots supported on top of them. These obstacles can usually be remedied by providing separate cooking-pot support and handles for the stove, which together allow the TLUD unit to be moved and emptied of char at the end of its pyrolysis cycle.

Some units are intentionally designed *not* to permit charcoal removal, to avoid the safety risks in handling red-hot charcoal (examples: Oorja – PP: A-3, Navagni – PP: D4).

## 3. Air Control

For a TLUD device to function, air must move upward. It can move by natural draft (ND) or by manually or mechanically forced air (FA). Very limited work has been done to design a single unit that can be operated either way. The author is working on such a unit—a cross between the Juntos B and the Champion models—which will be reported online (see this book's website, http://www.TheBiocharRevolution. com).

### Forced Air (FA)

Forced air devices rely on mechanical or manual power to drive a fan or blower to create the necessary airflow, usually by "positive pressure." Surprisingly little energy is needed to create the necessary draft. There are several ways to create the draft, some of which are shown in PP: Section A.

- *Integrated fan or blower* attached to the unit; convenient, but costs more. (Reed, Oorja, Biolite, Magh, Belonio; PP: A1–6)

- *Separate fan or blower* that can be switched between multiple TLUD units or even different models. Sample electrical and manual fans and blowers for this draft method (including muffin fans and even a standard hair dryer) are shown in PP: F9. (FA-capable units include the Juntos B, PP: A7, as well as units B1, B2, E2–E4 and F10.)

| FA Methods of Creating Draft |
| --- |
| • Integrated Fan/Blower PP: A1–A6 |
| • Separate Fan/Blower Juntos B (PP: A7); B1, B2, E2–E4, F10) |

- *Induction blower*, which creates low pressure inside the TLUD to draw in the primary air and provide secondary air. (Not yet seen in the smallest TLUDs, but used in larger units, PP: E6)

The disadvantages of forced air devices include additional cost, maintenance, batteries, and the need for uninterrupted electric or manual power. The advantages include a significant increase in control of the heat and emissions. In an era that prizes convenience, people want features that support clean and easy operation; therefore the prospects for advances in forced air designs are good.

### Natural Draft (ND)

Natural draft occurs because hot air is less dense and rises, leaving a partial vacuum behind it, into which cooler air then moves. When hot gases are channeled up a heated chimney, natural draft is created and sustained; the strength of the draft depends on the size and characteristics of the chimney. This chimney effect is why smoke from a fireplace goes up the chimney instead of out into the room.

Natural draft TLUD units can be divided into three categories:

- *Units with risers:* Risers are essentially short chimneys between the gasifier and the pot in cookstoves (as in the Champion models). See PP: Section B.

- *Units with true chimneys:* Chimneys are the best-known source of natural draft. Chimneys draw from the point of a stove's application (that is, its intended use of the heat produced, as in cooking). See PP: Section C. The Anderson TLUD design (the original Champion) depicted in PP: C1 has both a riser and a chimney.

  Chimneys can draw virtually all of the emissions from the room. Therefore, stoves with chimneys can be installed indoors where permitted by local regulations.

- *Units without risers or chimneys* rely on the height of the stove itself to generate updraft, and thus have weaker flames, which might be desired in certain applications (see PP: Section D).

## 4. Availability, Ease of Manufacture, and Cost

Small and easily carried units (up to 5- or 6-liter capacity) are good for use as cookstoves. Especially appropriate for use in households in the least developed societies, these stoves can produce a pound (half-kilogram) of biochar per day (one study in Kenya showed an average of 1.5 kg/day of char from family cooking). Considering that over 30% of the world's population cooks with biomass, biochar production could aggregate to hundreds of millions of tons per year. [See Chapter 18 titled "Climate Change Mitigation Using Thinly Distributed Feedstock."]

The options for obtaining a biochar-producing TLUD gasifier are to purchase a commercial unit or to make one. They can be purchased from several suppliers for less than US$35, and may cost literally nothing if made from scrap steel cans.

The purchase options are limited, and consist mostly of forced air designs—many of which are not for sale in North America. At least three manufactured designs are available in India; these can be purchased from the U.S. allowing an extra US$100 for shipping. (Note: Wherever this chapter or the Picture Pages refer to purchase price, that information is believed current as of August 2010.)

The other option is a DIY (do it yourself) effort. These TLUD stove designs are so simple that hundreds of people have made their own devices using mainly tin cans and duct parts from hardware stores. Fortunately, many people have shared their designs on the internet, and a few have provided detailed construction information. (See below and PP: Section F for more DIY information.)

Because of their generally small size and batch-fueled operation, TLUD pyrolytic gasifiers do not justify the expense of automated fuel and biochar handling, even as the sizes increase to a medium range.

## 5. Size of Gasifiers – *Larger TLUD Pyrolytic Gasifiers*

Four reasons for making larger TLUD pyrolyzers are:

1. The need for more heat for institutional and restaurant cooking
2. The need or desire for longer operating times between changing batches of fuel (especially when using less-dense fuels)
3. The need or desire to use larger pieces of fuel
4. The desire to produce larger batches of biochar

During the brief 25-year history of TLUD technology, efforts with large devices have been made almost entirely during the three-year period preceding this writing, except for the "Pyroneer" experiments by Alex English of Ontario, Canada. English displayed his experiments in India in 2000, but did not pursue them further until 2009, when he produced the largest known TLUD. This device has a capacity of 600 liters (PP: E6), is 42 inches (1.1 meters) in diameter, and is 6 feet in height (1.8 m). It uses a blower to induce draft and to feed the combustible gases into an existing furnace for heating large greenhouses.

The greenhouse operators use the biochar created in their potting soils. This research will help determine the maximum size of TLUDs and whether they can compete with other char-producing gasification technologies.

| Large TLUDs |
| --- |
| • Largest known – PP: E6 |
| • Use of oil drums ≤ 200 liters (55 gallons) – PP: E3–E5 |
| • TLUDS with 20-liter (5-gallon) capacity – PP: E1, E2 |

Except for an initiative by John and Charles Anglin to pasteurize milk in Uganda, known efforts to use 200-liter (55-gallon) and smaller oil drums as TLUDs have essentially been biochar-producing experiments, with minimal interest in using the heat (PP: E3–E5). Success in these experiments is relative, depending on the pre-defined goals, available time, and available resources (including money) of the experimenters.

So far, only the 20-liter (5-gallon) size TLUD devices are attracting much attention. Units developed by Art Donnelly and Paul Anderson are shown in Picture Pages E1 and E2 (note that Anderson's pictured unit is actually a 10-gallon device). [Also see the Seattle Biochar Working Group (SeaChar.org) website: http://seachar. org/wordpress/?p=176.] Donnelly and others of the SeaChar group have initiated a cookstove project in Costa Rica where many cooks prefer that size of unit. In the coffee plantations there, tree pruning yields an abundance of appropriately sized biomass fuel that would otherwise be open-burned. Anderson is working with the producers of the StoveTec 60-L institutional stove to offer an alternative model incorporating 5-gallon TLUDs that can produce biochar.

## DO-IT-YOURSELF TLUDS FOR PRODUCING BIOCHAR

### DIY OVERVIEW
There are many remarkably simple ways to build TLUD pyrolytic gasifiers as biochar production units (without the added complexity of applications to utilize the heat). Moreover, the performance of these units is generally unaffected by variations in materials and designs. (PP: Section F)

### Fundamentals of Building TLUDs

#### Fuel Chamber
The initial consideration in designing, constructing, and operating a DIY TLUD is selecting the fuel chamber, which is typically metal, cylindrical, and taller than it is wide. Its size may vary as greatly as the readily available containers, whether small tin cans or barrels or tanks.

Smaller sizes allow char to be easily recovered because the TLUD may simply be tipped over to dump its yield. Larger DIY units may require extraction of char through a door at or near the bottom of the fuel chamber, although this char-recovery option is uncommon and relatively more difficult.

*Airflow*

There are two flows of air in a TLUD that need regulation to optimize the efficiency of operation and biochar yield of the unit.

1. *Primary Air*
   Primary air refers to the airflow that enters under the fuel and moves upward through the fuel chamber. Here are two simple ways to enable primary airflow:

   a. Holes in the bottom of the fuel chamber effectively create a grate that retains the fuel while allowing air to enter. For primary air to reach the holes, the fuel container must be elevated using an air base or simple supports, as shown in PP: F2–F5, as well as in E1 and E3 (the pictures for Donnelly's and Anderson's Barrel units).

      Helpful Tip: At the end of the pyrolysis stage, the primary airflow can be slowed and nearly halted by removing the supports under the fuel cylinder or by otherwise closing the air entry about the base. This partial sealing of the unit helps to extinguish the char, but does not seal it well enough from oxygen to prevent oxidation of the char. As previously noted, the hot char should be placed into a snuffer box with a well-fitting lid.

   b. Hole(s) in the side of the fuel chamber, near its bottom, may also be used admit primary air to the fuel. However, if the fuel chamber is large, introducing primary air through holes around the perimeter may permit a "dead zone" of limited pyrolysis to develop due to insufficient oxygen penetrating to the center of the fuel.

      Helpful Tip: Occupying the center of the bottom with a "filler" object, such as an empty inverted metal can or a pile of previously made cold charcoal, can alleviate this problem. To avoid the problem altogether, in a fuel chamber more than 6 inches (150 mm) in diameter, use one larger side hole with a grate just above it inside the chamber. The grate elevates the fuel to allow a more evenly distributed circulation of air under it (PP: E5 and F7). A single side hole allows easy control of the primary airflow for either natural draft or forced air configurations (PP: B1, B2, E4, and F10.)

2. *Secondary Air*
   Secondary air must enter and mix well with rising gases for clean combustion. Here are some options for introducing secondary air into the unit:

   a. Install a burner segment with side holes in a chimney, above a tight lid (PP: E2 and F8).

   b. Gap entry under a concentrator disk, which may be just a hole in a lid (PP: D1, D3, E3, F3, F4, and F10).

   c. Forced air (rather than natural draft) through holes in the top of the reactor, with the air rising between the walls of a two-walled unit (PP: A1 – A5, A7, and F10).

Sustaining the flow of both primary and secondary air is a function of the TLUD's draft mechanism, which as noted previously is either natural or forced. Natural draft (ND) requires a chimney or other vertical riser sufficient to generate a draft (PP: F3, F8). Forced air (FA) systems use fans to blow air or, less commonly, pull it (PP: E6).

3. *Concentrator Disk*
   A concentrator disk is a metal disk or lid with a centered hole, typically 2 to 4 inches in diameter, which fits snugly over the end of the fuel chamber. This concentrates and therefore speeds the flow of gas and produces a more stable and clean burn. A concentrator disk is utilized in many of the shown TLUDs (PP: B1-B3, C1, D1, D3, D1-E4, F3, and F4.)

4. *Chimney or Riser*
   As already mentioned, draft is created with a riser or chimney. For cooking units, the riser is a metal cylinder between the fuel chamber and the pot. For DIY units constructed solely for producing biochar, the riser is typically a taller chimney centered above the concentrator hole. In either case, the riser or chimney can rest on top of the concentrator disk or concentrator lid (PP: B1–B3, F3, F4–riser not shown, and F8)

**SINGLE-WALLED TLUD-ND**
Single-walled, natural draft TLUDs are the simplest DIY units to build and operate. The basics are simply a fuel container, a lid with a concentrator hole, and a metal chimney.

The web offers many simple designs, such as the "1G Toucan TLUD" (http://terrapreta.bioenergylists.org/content/1g-toucan-tlud-biochar)

If you search the web for "TLUD stove", you will get dozens of leads to instructions and videos of TLUDs in action.

For DIY enthusiasts who want to build a single-walled TLUD, the next part of this section offers step-by-step construction notes for building a TLUD char maker or stove from just two recycled metal cans. (This is NOT the same as the "1G Toucan TLUD" design by Dr. Hugh McLaughlin.)

## BUILDING A SINGLE-WALLED TLUD

### What You'll Need

*   Two empty clean steel cans (such as large *tin* food cans, but *not* aluminum), both with one end cut out. The cans may be either the same size, or one slightly smaller in diameter than the other.

*   Something to make air holes in the can, such as a "church key" type can opener, a screwdriver or small punch, a drill, or a DIY punch.
    (See PP: F6 for an example of a DIY punch.)

*   Tin snips to cut out the concentrator hole.

### What to Do

Step 1.   *Primary Air*
          Select the smaller can (or either can if the same size) as the fuel chamber. Punch or drill numerous primary air holes uniformly spaced in the bottom as shown in PP: F1, F2, F5, and F6

Step 2.   *Secondary Air*
          On the same can as in Step 1, punch or drill numerous secondary air holes in the sides of the fuel chamber, as near the open top as possible. Alternately, with tin snips, you can cut a series of small triangles out of the open top edge—about the size hole that a "church key" can opener makes, leaving a small section of the top edge between each cut-out. If the cans are the same size, choose the second technique and bend the triangular flaps inwards, but only slightly.

Step 3.   *The Concentrator Disk and Chimney/Riser*
          Punch or drill a hole in the center of the other can—large enough to insert the tin snips. Use the tin snips to cut a circular hole about one-half the diameter of the can top. This can functions as the concentrator disk and chimney/riser. The second can sits on the first can, concentrator disk down, to form the TLUD. (If the cans are the same size, the slightly bent-in tabs of the bottom can slip inside the bottom rim of the top can.)

Step 4.   *Configuration for Cooking (optional)*
          If you want to cook with the TLUD, the top can acts as a riser to direct the flames underneath an independently supported pot. The cooking pot must not seal the top of the riser, otherwise unburned wood gases will come pouring out of the secondary air inlets of the lower can. (Do not attempt to support the pot on the riser due to the instability of this simple two can stack.)

Step 5.     *Heat Protection (Optional)*
Since all surfaces become dangerously hot during operation, consider attaching handles to the fuel cylinder and to the chimney/pot holder for ease of handling during operation (PP: B2). Whether you add handles or not, wear gloves whenever handling tin can TLUDs—between the potentially hot surfaces and the sharp edges, gloves help avoid many small but irritating cuts and burns.

Step 6.     *Setting up the TLUD*
The lower can needs to sit on a fireproof surface, such as rock or concrete, with the bottom slightly above the surface to allow primary air to enter. (Note the nails at the bottom of the Toucan in PP: F4). If the surface is slightly uneven, then no additional spacing is needed. The bottom tin can should be made stable enough for the top can to sit on it without being held in place. (Note: This configuration is NOT intended for cooking or water heating because of its instability.)

Step 7.     *Lighting the TLUD*
Fill the fuel chamber about three-quarters full of dry fuel pieces (try what you have available, but make sure it is dry and small enough, such as wood chips or pellets). Light the top of the fuel with some tinder or soaking a bit of fuel in alcohol (not gasoline) and placing the soaked fuel on the top of the dry fuel (do not pour the alcohol on the top of the fuel—it will just drain to the bottom and the TLUD will not burn correctly). Once the top of the fuel catches on fire (effectively immediately if alcohol is used to start the fire), place and center the concentrator end of the upper can on the top of the fuel chamber. Initially, the flames will reside on the top of the fuel, but shortly the flames will rise and be located at the top of the fuel chamber, where the secondary air enters—with the secondary combustion flames rising through the concentrator disk and up the inside of the top can.

Step 8.     *Ending the TLUD Burn*
When the "pyrolysis front" reaches the bottom of the fuel chamber, all the fuel has been converted to char. The bottom of the lower tin can will be very hot and a red glow can usually be seen beneath the fuel chamber. The flames will decrease and turn from the characteristically yellow flames of wood gas combustion to the more blue flames of char gas burning. As this time, the top can is removed and the fuel chamber is dumped into a snuffer box or other airtight container to smother the char gasification and save the char.

---

## BE SAFE: TLUDs ARE NOT TOYS!

- All surfaces of the unit become hot enough to cause severe burns.
- Fresh char is hot! Tipping hot char out of the fuel chamber may be hazardous.
- As with any combustion device, especially during its first use, fumes may be hazardous and should not be inhaled.
- Wear gloves—it is much easier than explaining why you were silly enough not to.

### Double-Walled DIY TLUDs: Pre-heating Secondary Air

This unit type and its construction options are covered in the *TLUD Handbook*, available online at: www.bioenergylists.org/tludhandbookdraft-1. Examples of double-walled units include the following:

- Champion models (PP: B1 and B2); for construction information, see "Additional Resources" at the end of this chapter.

- Peko Pe (PP: D1); for construction information, see "Additional Resources."

- Diermair (PP: E4).

- Refuse-bin DIY unit as shown in PP: F8 and F10.

## CHARACTERIZATION OF TLUD CHARS

TLUD pyrolytic gasifiers utilize oxic (oxygen and flame-present) pyrolysis to produce biochar with characteristics different from biochars produced by other methods or devices, such as retorts (which also can be done at home-scale) and **fast pyrolysis** (which requires a major capital investment). Moreover, the conditions under which TLUD devices are operated can influence biochar properties—especially **adsorption capacity**.

Research about biochars is just beginning and structured studies of carbonization conditions and resulting char properties are rare. The first detailed analyses of TLUD biochars were published in "All Biochars Are Not Created Equal" (2009), available online at http://www.biochar-international.org/node/1029. The data shown there were derived from tests with one biochar maker (a Champion TLUD cookstove) using one fuel (wood pellets) and operated only one time each using natural draft and forced air draft for the primary air supply.

Forced draft operation resulted in a higher temperature at the pyrolysis front than natural draft, and produced lower yields of char (14% versus 23%). As might be expected because of the higher temperature, the forced air char contained more ash and less mobile matter (carbon that can be volatized at 450°C) than natural draft char. The resident matter contents (carbon not volatized at 450°C) for TLUD chars were generally higher than chars produced in retorts.

Notably, the chars produced via forced air had almost triple the adsorption capacity of those produced via natural draft. This increase is offset by the lower weight yield with forced air production (as noted above), but taking that into account, forced air operation produced nearly double the adsorption capacity per kg of feedstock.

While these findings are still awaiting replication studies, they offer potentially valuable generalizations, with the conclusion that TLUD pyrolytic gasifiers produce biochar with characteristics that merit further consideration.

It should also be noted that when comparing the yields of charcoal produced by oxic processes (such as with TLUDs) and anoxic processes (such as by retorts), the external fuel utilized to sustain the anoxic pyrolysis needs to be included in the overall yield calculations. In small home retort experiments that are not carefully designed for efficient transfer of combustion heat into the retort, it is easy to burn (for example) as much fuel as feedstock being pyrolyzed, thus reducing the apparent overall yield by a factor of 2.

## OPPORTUNITIES TO PARTICIPATE

Much is known about the TLUD gasifiers, both as cookstoves and as biochar makers. However, much is still to be learned, and the field is wide open. There are opportunities for experimentation in both affluent and developing countries. This is especially true for the larger (20- to 200-liter) biochar makers, the sizes most likely to be suitable for the residential gardener, for small-scale research, and as part of a serious decentralized effort at climate mitigation using waste feedstock.

### THE AMATEUR SCIENTIST AND HOME GARDENER

As previously discussed, by altering the rate of primary airflow (and by using different raw biomass), the TLUD operator can alter the characteristics of the biochar produced. The home gardener or amateur scientist who takes and maintains careful notes can create numerous biochars and conduct comparative experiments on local soils with specific plant species. [In this regard, see Chapter 14 titled "Gauging the Impact of Biochar: Simple Tests for Farmers and Gardeners."]

Because the TLUD technology and device designs are freely shared, it encourages decentralized investigation of biochar impacts. Any interested person can keep abreast of the latest developments and actively participate online via several websites and listservs.

### CLIMATE MITIGATION AND THE DEVELOPING WORLD

The small size, low-tech construction and modest cost of TLUD cookstoves enables the poorest people to obtain household energy for cooking and space heating while also producing biochar. Aggregated over large numbers of possible users, large yields of biochar are possible in developing countries. This would enable substantial soil benefits and carbon dioxide offsets. Larger barrel and tank-sized units can produce more char and be adapted to produce useful heat and power in both the developing and affluent world.

In this way, TLUD technology enables "distributed biochar production." Such a "low tech- low capital" approach—with implementation on a massive scale—could well have more cumulative, and more immediate, impact than standard, centralized channels of production through proprietary processes, which need profit for motivation and move slowly to gear up and improve. Certainly, however, "distributed" programs must be in step with sustainable biomass procurement practices.

## CONCLUSION

Biochar can play a dynamic role in the future of the planet and its inhabitants. It is hoped that this chapter and its DIY roadmap provide a small nudge in the right direction.

## KEY POINTS FROM THIS CHAPTER

- A "gasifier" separates the pyrolyzing processes that produce gas from the processes that use gas, such as combustion, condensation, or release to the environment.

- TLUDs can use a wide variety of feedstocks and can be easily constructed and operated for small-scale biochar production, including do-it-yourself devices.

- Because TLUD cookstoves are small, low-tech, and low-cost, even the poorest people can obtain household energy for cooking and heating while also producing biochar. If individual biochar yields are aggregated over millions of users in developing countries, substantial soil benefits and carbon dioxide offsets can be achieved.

- Basic TLUD technology is "open source" (not protected by patents or copyrights). Everyone has the opportunity to advance TLUD designs.

- Research about TLUDs and about biochar in general is relatively scant. Home gardeners and amateur scientists can contribute by creating various biochars and conducting experiments.

## ADDITIONAL RESOURCES: TLUDS AND BEYOND

### CHAMPION AND PEKO PE TLUDS
Information about and construction details for Anderson's Champion TLUD gasifier and Wendelbo's "Peko Pe" TLUD gasifier, respectively, can be found on the internet at:
www.bioenergylists.org/andersontludconstruction
www.bioenergylists.org/wendelbopekope

### Champion in Action
This YouTube video provides information and a demonstration of the Champion TLUD in action: http://www.youtube.com/watch?v=SaeanoWZE7E (or search for "TLUD Gasifier Stove" at the YouTube website).

### OTHER TLUD TECHNOLOGY-RELATED REFERENCES
There are numerous additional references. Although they tend to focus on the cooking aspects of the TLUD technology, they are nevertheless informative about overall concepts.

### TLUD Cookstoves
An extremely good website dealing with all types of cookstoves, especially for developing countries: www.stoves.bioenergylists.org

### TLUD Emissions
"Carbon monoxide and particulate matter emissions from TLUD cookstoves": www.bioenergylists.org/andersontludcopm

### TLUD Handbook
For more on the history, construction, and operation of TLUDs, and additional references: TLUD Handbook: www.bioenergylists.org/tludhandbookdraft-1

### BIOMASS GASIFICATION
A broad overview of biomass gasification, not just cookstoves: www.bioenergylists.org/stovesdoc/Anderson/GasifierLAMNET.pdf

Dr. Reed/BEF: Website of Dr. Tom Reed and the Biomass Energy Foundation (BEF): www.woodgas.com
"Micro-gasification: What it is and why it works": www.hedon.info/docs/BP53-Anderson-14.pdf

### INTERNET SEARCHES
Internet searches on the names and topics associated with TLUDs will reveal additional and more current information.

### BIOCHAR DISCUSSION GROUPS
www.biochar.bioenergylists.org
stoves@listserv.repp.org
biochar@yahoogroups.com

## TLUD PICTURE PAGES

The following PICTURE PAGES (PP) contain many TLUD variations that supplement the material in Chapter 11, "Making Biochar in Small Gasifier Cookstoves and Heaters."

- The Picture Pages are organized according to airflow characteristics and then by size in sections A through F.

- In the chapter text, references to specific Picture Page sections and specifically numbered photos will be denoted as PP: Section "X" or PP: "X1". In the chapter there are also side boxes drawing attention to the locations of particular variations of TLUDs to aid the reader in correlating text and pictures.

- The information contained in this Appendix is current as of August 2010.

- All prices are in US Dollars.

- This collection of pictures can be found in color on the book's website, www.TheBiocharRevolution.

- All of these TLUDs are discussed (some in great detail) on the internet, especially at www.stoves.bioenergylists.org.

- Additional designs can be found by searching the internet using names or key words, such as TLUD.

## AUTHOR'S DISCLAIMER:

- These pages are not intended to be an authoritative nor an exhaustive review.

- Information is subject to change, and is not verified.

- The writer does not have experience with every design.

### STOVE CAMP AND CHAB CAMP FOR ADULT ENTHUSIASTS

Each summer, an annual "Stove Camp" is hosted at the Aprovecho Research Center in Cottage Grove, Oregon, USA. For a week, 20 to 40 serious adults gather to study, construct, and test cookstove designs of all types appropriate for developing societies. Stoves that make biochar are increasingly important at Stove Camp. The Champion TLUD earned its name when it won a clean combustion award at the 2005 Stove Camp.

Starting in 2010, another camp not limited to cookstoves will be held in Massachusetts, USA, focused on Combined Heat and Biochar (CHAB). Both Stove Camp and CHAB Camp registrations are open to all serious stove and biochar enthusiasts. These camps are not for kids!

## SECTION A. TLUD-FA Gasifier Cookstoves with Fans (FA=Forced Air)

### A-1 & A-2   Reed's WoodGas Campstoves

First commercialized in 2003, manufactured in India, and sold on the internet in the United States in 3 sizes for US$55, $80, and $190. All other designs of TLUD cookstoves with forced air have evolved, sometimes very indirectly, from the "Pyroneer" work of Dr. Thomas B. Reed.

### A-3   Oorja

A project of BP (British Petroleum) in India 2005-09; now by First Energy in India. Designed by gasification experts at the India Institute of Science in Bangalore, led by Dr. H. S. Mukunda. Created specifically to burn biomass pellets and NOT to make biochar. Subsidized retail price approx. US$18. More than 400,000 units produced.

### A-4   Biolite Campstove

By Alex Drummond and Jonathan Cedar. Prototypes only. Blower, attached to the side, is powered by a thermal electric generator (TEG) that uses the heat created by the device to make electrical power.

## SECTION A. (Cont.) TLUD-FA Gasifier Cookstoves with Fans (FA=Forced Air)

### A-5    Magh Stove

One of many innovative designs by Dr. Sai Bhaskar Reddy of Hyderabad, India. Shows that the stove body can be made of ceramic or even mud.

### A-6    Rice Husk TLUD Gasifier

One of many groundbreaking TLUD designs by Alexis Belonio, a Rolex Award winner in 2008. Manufacturing has started in Indonesia and Vietnam. These stoves produce blue flames, associated with the rice husk fuel and superior designs of gas combustion.

### A-7    Juntos B

Designed by Dr. Paul S. Anderson in 2004 to replicate the Reed WoodGas Campstove. Complete DIY (Do It Yourself) instructions for making and operating the "Juntos B" TLUD-FA can be found at: www.bioenergylists.org/stovesdoc/Anderson/GasifierLAMNET.pdf.

**SECTION B. TLUD-ND Gasifier Cookstoves with Riser (ND = Natural draft)**

In natural draft TLUD gasifiers, a short riser (chimney) below the pot dramatically improves the airflows.

**B-1    Anderson's Champion TLUD**

Manufactured in India by Servals Automation. The stainless steel unit (shown), plus a second fuel chamber, sells for US$32.

See Figure 11.1 for diagram explanation of the champion design.

Units B- 1 and B-2 have double walls (can-inside-can).

**B-2    DIY "Refugee" Champion TLUD-ND**

Made from three metal cans (numbered).

The "concentrator disk" (or lid), common to all Champion designs, is shown here as hand-crafted from a single piece of sheet metal.

1.    Riser attached to concentrator lid.

2.    Fuel chamber with primary air inlet tube at bottom.

3.    Outer heat shield with handle and hole around primary air inlet tube for secondary air, which is channeled between the two cans.

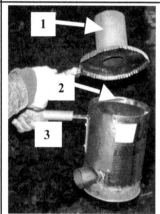

**B-3    Agni TLUD (2006) by ARTI (India)**

Based on Anderson's earliest Champion designs, including a very tall riser.  A tall riser (or a chimney) is especially important at elevations over 1,000 meters (3,000 feet) above sea level. US$58 each.

This unit has single-wall construction.

| | |
|---|---|
| **SECTION C. TLUD-ND Gasifier Cookstoves with Chimney (ND = Natural draft)** | |
| A chimney enhances natural draft and can expel emissions to the outside. | |

**C-1    Anderson "Champion" TLUD Design**

Won a clean emissions award and earned the name of "Champion" at Stove Camp 2005. This unit includes a riser below the pot (which might not be necessary) as well as a chimney. It was built and operated in Bolivia at 2,600 meters elevation. TLUDs with chimneys and stove bodies can be used for room heating in cold climates.

**C-2    Flanagan's Two-pot TLUD with Chimney**

Prototype with unknown production in China. Designed to make biochar.

**C-3    Daxu TLUD**

Won a stove design and low- emissions contest in China in 2007. Reported production cost over US$100, but was heavily subsidized to families, and now discontinued. (Note: Comparatively little information is available from China, where there also are several "semi-gasifier", non-TLUD cookstoves that may or may not produce biochar.)

**C-4    Chip Energy Biomass Grill**

Can operate initially as a TLUD-ND with chimney, and then convert to operate with continuous feed of chip-type fuel from the fuel hopper (upper right of unit). Price: US$300 excluding the lower auger for biochar removal ($100 extra). (Note: This unit is too heavy for tipping to dump the biochar.)

| SECTION D. TLUD-ND GASIFIER COOKSTOVES WITHOUT RISERS OR CHIMNEYS | |
| --- | --- |
| TLUD operation without risers, chimneys or fans is possible, but the flames tend to be less strong. Fuel types and local cooking preferences are important factors in acceptance of these stoves. | |
| **D-1    Peko Pe (means "No Problem")**<br><br>Developed in Uganda in the 1990s by "Pyroneer" Paal Wendelbo, independent of the work by Thomas Reed.  Includes the "concentrator disk" that is also a key element in the Champion TLUDs.  Early success faded, but interest has increased since 2008.  Complete instructions are on the internet. |  |
| **D-2    Sampada Gasifier Stove by ARTI in India**<br><br>US$24 per unit. |  |
| **D-3    Char-baby TLUD**<br><br>By Art Donnelly of SeaChar in Seattle, WA (USA).  Includes the concentrator disk developed by Wendelbo and Anderson. |  |
| **D-4    Navagni TLUD**<br><br>A product of Qpre of Bangalore, India, which has an office in the United States. |  |

## SECTION E.   LARGER TLUD BIOCHAR MAKERS

Because of the recent (2009) start to making biochar in large TLUD devices, a significant number of additional designs and true innovations can be expected in the next few years.

### E-1   SeaChar Cookstove and Biochar Maker

SeaChar cookstove and biochar maker using a 5-gallon (20 liter) fuel container inside an outer corrigated wall. Designed by Art Donnelly of SeaChar in Seattle for a project in Costa Rica. Primary air enters through the Altoids door into the attached air base and continues upwards through holes in the bottom of the bucket with the fuel.

### E-2   "Biochar Can"

The "Biochar Can" design uses a metal single-walled generic trash can of any common size (shown is 10 gallon, 40 liter size). Shown here with lateral entry of primary air near the bottom (requires a small grate to allow the air to enter under the fuel).  A combustor (duct expander with lateral holes) is between the lid and the chimney.  A lateral "T" chimney inlet is optional, but useful.

### E-3   Biochar Barrel

The "Biochar Barrel" design has been used for different barrel sizes up to 55-gallon (200 liter) standard oil barrels. Anderson's unit, at right, has an "air base" that facilitates additing forced air to alter the characteristics of the biochar, and  a concentrator lid that is elevated by two bars for entry of secondary air. Draft can be adjusted by any of the following:  (1) height and diameter of chimney; (2)  lateral inlet on chimney (shown); (3) change the gap under the concentrator lid, or have no gap but use a combustor (simple one is shown in the Biochar Can E-2 above, but better ones can be made to include forced secondary air); (4) regulating the primary air inlet.

| SECTION E. (Cont.) LARGER TLUD BIOCHAR MAKERS | |
|---|---|
| **E-4 Diermair TLUD**<br><br>Double-walled TLUD by Rob Diermair in the Niagara area of Ontario, Canada. |  |
| **E-5 Diermair TLUD (With Top Removed)**<br>Same as E-4 with top removed showing inner barrel with grate sitting above primary air inlet tube. Inner fuel chamber is resting on rods to support it above the floor of outer barrel. |  |
| **E-6 Alex English's Biochar Maker**<br>Alex English's biochar maker at Burt's Greenhouse in Ontario, Canada consists of a single-walled tank 1.8 meters high by 1.1 m diameter (6 ft by 42 inches). It utilizes a blower to induce the draft and propel the combustible gases into an existing large furnace for heating a greenhouse. The biochar can be a valuable ingredient in preparing potting soils, so the heat and biochar are both utilized. The best method(s) for removal of the biochar from such large devices are being studied. Description and video are on the internet. |  |

## SECTION F. Do-It-Yourself Fabrication of TLUDs for Biochar Production

McLaughlin and Anderson (and others) have made many very simple TLUD variations from tin cans of many sizes, shapes and combinations with basic hand-tools. Not all designs are practical, but all can be great learning experiences.

### F-1    Screwdriver holes in a small tin can

Examples of primary air holes made at the bottom of a TLUD fuel chamber.

As an alternative to what is shown, hole(s) in the sidewalls of the fuel chamber near its bottom may be used to admit primary air to the fuel, but a grate is needed inside if the diameter of the fuel chamber is large.

### F-2    Triangular holes by a "church key" can opener

Can opener can also be used to make the straight slots. Example shown is a Toucan by McLaughlin (PP: F4 below).

### F-3    "Willie One-Can"

**Riser for Natural Draft** (bracket)

**Concentrator disk** (long arrow) sits on indented metal of the top of the **secondary air holes** (short arrows).

**Fuel chamber** has holes in bottom for the primary air; hence, these TLUDs are raised on nails.

| SECTION F (cont.) Do-It-Yourself Fabrication of TLUDs for Biochar Production | |
|---|---|
| **F-4    McLaughlin's Toucan TLUD**<br><br>Made from two cans (pun intended) but normally utilizes a third can as a riser (not shown). This one-gallon size unit is one of the easiest small TLUD designs for DIY (Do It Yourself) biochar makers. Full instructions are on the internet. Note the nails to raise the fuel container to allow primary air to enter through the bottom. The thermometer is optional. |  |
| **F-5    Biochar can (30 gallons = 130 liters)**<br><br>Note the two metal bar supports under the unit. Simply resting the unit slightly off the ground in this fashion provides for under-grate passage of the primary airflow. |  |
| **F-6    Home-made DIY punch from pipe segment**<br><br>This punch was used to make holes in the "Biochar can" shown in F-5 above. | 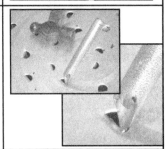 |
| **F-7    Grate in large fuel chamber**<br><br>The grate is seated on the indentations of the primary air inlet holes around the side of the can below the grate. | 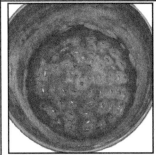 |

**SECTION F (cont.) Do-It-Yourself Fabrication of TLUDs for Biochar Production**

### F-8    Natural Draft (ND) Chimney

Examples of two chimneys on natural draft DIY units.

### F-9    Forced Air (FA) Fans and Blowers

A sampling of fans and blowers is pictured at left. From left to right, the display includes a squirrel-cage fan, one large and one small muffin fan, a hair dryer, and two hand-cranked blowers.

### F-10    Double-walled Refuse-bin DIY TLUD

At right are two pictures of the same, double-walled DIY TLUD with primary and secondary air ducts at the bottom of the unit. The first picture shows the unit with its larger concentrator disk resting beside it on the ground. The second picture shows the large concentrator disk properly installed, with a second (smaller) concentrator disk seated upon the larger disk.

Chapter 12

# Automated Biochar Production

**Jonah Levine**
Vice President of Technical Sales
Biochar Engineering Corporation

**Daniel Mulqueen**
Vice President of Research Engineering
Biochar Engineering Corporation

## IN THIS CHAPTER YOU WILL LEARN:

- About the continuous, automated production of biochar, including its upstream, production, and downstream phases.

- Design and operating considerations, procedures for choosing and handing raw materials and finished product, and tips for optimizing the process.

- How automated biochar production fits into a broader, sustainable ecosystem.

- Relevant issues and next steps for commercializing biochar production, including production cost and current price examples.

"For the biochar movement to fully take hold and deliver its promised global benefits, automated, commercial production is a must."

## INTRODUCTION

This chapter will examine one method for continuous, automated production of agricultural grade charcoal, or biochar. This method is broken down into three phases. The discussion of each phase includes relevant design and operating considerations, procedures for handing the raw materials and finished product, and tips for optimizing the process.

This chapter also describes the next steps for the commercial production of biochar.

### BASIC PROCESS: THE THREE PHASES

Successful biochar production is as much an engineering pursuit as a biological pursuit. As shown in Figure 12.1, it involves three phases: upstream, production, and downstream.

The three phases interact. The physical condition of the upstream feedstock will impact production requirements and will also impact the downstream product and its handling. A portion of the downstream output will be fed back upstream for processing and production, and the specifications for downstream products will place requirements on upstream products and processing. Those who can best align these three interconnected domains will reap the greatest rewards.

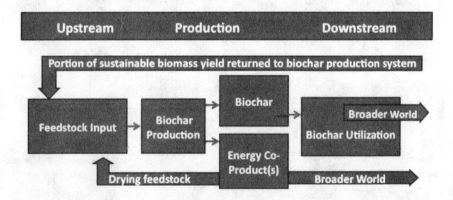

Fig. 12.1 Making Biochar: Upstream, Production, Downstream Phases

### UPSTREAM

The upstream portion shown in Figure 12.1 is feedstock input—the preparation and processing of biomass entering the system for conversion into biochar. Although many feedstock options exist, this chapter focuses on woody biomass feedstock.

## Choosing Feedstock

Choosing feedstock involves many factors, including sustainability, cost, and immediate and long-term availability. For example, in the State of Colorado (USA), **lodgepole** pine is a logical choice. The lodgepole pine has been under siege from the **mountain pine beetle**. The beetle kills the trees, and after more than ten years of infestation, the die-off of timber has been substantial—in some areas, the majority of trees standing are dead. Harvesting these dead trees for biochar makes good sense.

## Physical Condition of Feedstock

To enter a continuous and automated process, the feedstock should have relatively uniform physical characteristics. The physical characteristics of primary concern are feedstock particle size, density, and moisture content:

- Particle size should be uniform to ensure successful materials handling, and to standardize residence time behavior during thermal processing. Sorting screens—automated or non-automated—can help ensure consistent size.

- Particle density should be uniform so that the material heats uniformly.

- Moisture content should be uniform—and low—to ensure uniform energy availability for the **pyrolysis** reaction.

Uniform input will help ensure uniform output of biochar and biochar co-products. An example of a uniform feedstock is wood from one specific family of trees—such as *Pinaceae* (pine family)—chipped to a particle size of 0.5–1.25 inches (1–3 cm), with a moisture content range of 10% **dry basis** (for example: 8%–18%). (See Table 12.1 for definition of dry basis).

## Particle Size

Particle size of the feedstock affects downstream materials handling. Pyrolysis reduces the size of the particles. Hence, if the original feedstock is of small particle size (sometimes referred to as "fines"), the end biochar product will be even finer.

The pyrolysis process may produce dusty material as an end-product, which requires special handling. If this is a concern, start with larger original feedstock, or aggregate char dust into pellets, slurry, or other non-dusty product.

Dusty end products present logistical handling issues and health concerns for the people working around them. However, these concerns can be managed.

Standard operating procedures relating to dusty product should include:

- Eye protection

- Dust masks

- Deploying personnel upwind of biochar stockpiles

- Combining dusty product with a binder, such as compost or manure

| Table 12.1 | | | **SIMPLIFIED ENERGETICS OF DRYING** |
|---|---|---|---|

**DRY BASIS (db) and WET BASIS (wb)**

There are two standard methods for reporting the moisture (or water) content of a solid substance: "wet basis" and "dry basis." The scientific convention is to report moisture content of a wood sample on "oven-dry" basis—that is relative to the weight of the sample after drying in an oven set at $105°C$ for 24 hours.

| ITEM | VALUE | UNIT |
|---|---|---|
| Heat capacity of water | 4.2 | Joules/g/°C |
| Heat capacity of wood | 1.5 | Joules/g/°C |
| Heat of vaporization of water | 2,260 | Joules/g |

**EXAMPLE**

Let's consider 1 kg of wood with 30% water (wet basis) at $20°C$ that needs to be dried to 10% moisture (db).

We have to raise the temperature of 300g of water and 700g of wood to $100°C$ (an increase of $80°C$), and then evaporate 230g of water to get to 10% moisture db (70g remaining).

The energy needed to raise the 1kg of wet wood to $100°C$ =

$700 \times 1.5 \times 80 + 300 \times 4.2 \times 80 = 184,000$ Joules

Energy needed to evaporate 230g of water

$= 230[g] \times 2260 [j/g] = 519,800$ Joules

**TOTAL = 703,800 JOULES TO DRY 10% MOISTURE**

Another 158,200 Joules is required to dry to zero % moisture.

**FEEDSTOCK MOISTURE CALCULATIONS**

If:  $W$ = weight of wet wood

$D$ = weight of oven-dry wood

$M$ = moisture weight

$MC$ = moisture content (%)

Then:  $M = W - D$

$MC\ wb = M / W$ (%)

$MC\ db = M / D$ (%)

Wood typically reaches fiber saturation at around 28% moisture db.

Dry wood, from a construction standpoint, has less than 19% moisture db.

Fast moisture measurements can be taken in the field with an LED or conductivity moisture meter, which can cost as little as US$20.

**DEFINITION FOR NON-SCIENTISTS**

**Joule:** A unit of energy equal to the work done when a current of 1 ampere passes through a resistance of 1 ohm for 1 second.

In laymen's terms, 1 joule is the energy required to lift a small apple one meter against the Earth's gravity.

Charles Moyers and G. Baldwin, "Psychrometry, Evaporative Cooling, and Solids Drying," *Perry's Chemical Engineers Handbook*, ed. Don W. Green (New York: McGraw-Hill, 1997), 12.25-90.

US Department of Agriculture, *Dry Kiln Operator's Manual* – USDA Agricultural Handbook AH-188(2001). Available online at: www.fpl.fs.fed.us/documnts/usda/ah188/chapter01.pdf.

## Feedstock Moisture

High feedstock moisture is a challenge in production, and therefore feedstock should be managed to minimize moisture content. Preferred moisture content is about 10% dry basis (db). As feedstock moisture increases, the energy required to convert biomass into biochar also increases. From the experience of the authors, the energy available in a woodchip-driven gasification process is not sufficient to convert feedstock with moisture above 30% db, and in fact, the process throughput suffers significantly with moisture above 20% db. (For feedstock moisture calculations, see the sidebar to Table 12.1.)

Still, feedstock with moisture content above a target specification can be utilized if dried before entering the primary conversion reaction. External heat sources can accomplish this, although the cost of external heating would raise the cost of the overall process. Alternatively, heat from burning pyrolysis gases can be recycled to dry the feedstock before it enters the pyrolysis chamber.

The energy required to dry woody products equals the energy to heat the wood to drying temperature (100°C), plus the energy to heat the water in the wood to boiling point, plus the energy to vaporize that water. The related heat values are shown in Table 12.1.

## Pre-process Biomass Preparation

Simply choosing the right biomass feedstocks and storing them in the correct configuration can increase efficiency and thereby decrease cost, energy, and the labor needed to successfully produce biochar.

In particular, appropriate staging and handling of feedstock prior to production can help achieve the all-important goal of controlling and reducing feedstock moisture levels. For example, naturally available solar energy can aid in pre-drying the feedstock, given sufficient and appropriate storage conditions, materials handling, and time.

"Solar energy" need not be solar technology. It can be as simple as storing materials in a sunny location protected from precipitation. In a dry, sunny location, the top two to six inches (5 cm to 15 cm) of chipped material will be considerably dryer than the material deeper in the pile. Hence, maximizing its surface area relative to the volume can decrease the overall moisture of a given feedstock.

Questions to ask when designing pre-process facilities should include the following:

1. What is the total volume of material needed over what time interval and at what moisture content?

2. How can feedstock drying be incorporated into materials staging and sort yard conditions?

3. Are any products (individually or as a suite) commercially available to decrease costs and improve performance?

## Feedstock Handling

In planning how to handle feedstock material from its source to its entry into the production phase, the following factors should be considered:

- The distance from the feedstock source to the production site.

- The ability to create uniform density, size, and moisture content of the feedstock.

- The ability to stage and load the production system in a continuous fashion.

Project planners should bear in mind that materials handling equipment can require as much thought and cost—or more—as the biochar production equipment itself.

Equipment needed may include:

- Chippers, grinders, recyclers, or shredders

- Containers or trailers

- Hoppers and feed bins

- Dryers

- Conveyor loaders

- Mobile loaders (such as skid steer loaders)

## PRODUCTION

The production phase depicted in Figure 12.1 consists of (1) the actual process of converting raw biomass, such as wood chips, to a solid output (biochar), and (2) the associated liquids and gases that are driven off the original biomass during that conversion process. The proportion of solids, liquids, and gases will vary depending on the feedstock and on the biochar production technology used.

The conversion technology that generated the specific data for this chapter is a gasifier produced by Biochar Engineering Corporation, optimized to produce maximum biochar while putting by-product gases to use, and minimizing production of liquids. The approximate proportions of production output from input feedstock with 10% moisture db is 20% to 25% biochar solids and 75% to 80% vapors. (Vapors are approximately 95% gas and 5% liquid when cooled to room temperature.)

## Biomass Production as Part of a Sustainable Ecosystem

Figure 12.2 shows a simplified biochar production system within a broader, sustainable ecosystem. The system is a cycle: the biomass-to-biochar and energy co-product reaction is displayed from left to right in the figure, and the thermal energy feedback and biomass recycling runs from right to left. Distribution of the biochar to the soil supports biomass growth, which in turn stores solar energy and enables its return to the system as feedstock and energy for the production process.

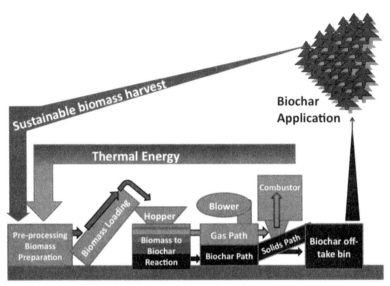

Fig. 12.2    Biomass Production within a Broader, Sustainable System

Fig. 12.3  Biochar Engineering Corporation Production Unit – May 2010
(Photo: James Fournier)

The following discussion of biomass preparation and the ensuing solid and gaseous product flows is standardized to 500 pounds (227 kg) of pine woodchips as input at 10% moisture (dry basis). Any figures given are approximate. Moreover, the information given here pertains to a fairly specific process; it could be configured in various other ways depending on particular circumstances and goals. For purposes of approximate conversion of weights and volumes in the discussion below, a kilogram is 2.2 pounds, or approximately 2 pounds; a US gallon is 3.8 liters; and a 55-gallon barrel can be equated to a 200-liter drum.

### Biomass Loading

Loading biomass into a continuous feed unit will generally require a choice between a lower technology and higher labor-cost approach, and a higher technology with lower labor-cost approach. This choice can be made based on location-specific labor costs versus available capital.

### Example: Low Technology, High Labor

An example of low technology processes and higher labor requirements is a team of workers filling and loading the hopper of the production phase reaction chamber with pitchforks, plastic trash cans, and a ladder.

A plastic 55-gallon (200-liter) trash can of pine woodchips at 10% moisture db weighs about 40–50 pounds. To load the production phase at 500 pounds per hour, approximately 10 cans need to be filled, lifted, and dumped into the hopper.

### Example: High Technology, Low Labor

An example of the lower labor-cost with higher technology approach is using a continuous-feed conveyor, with a small hopper on the low end, running up an incline to the hopper of the reaction chamber. (See the left-hand side of Figure 12.2.)

Feedstock loading rate is a major variable that can be regulated to allow control of the overall process. Ideally, variable-speed conveyors (Figure 12.4) at strategic points in the materials handling path can respond to system-wide feedback from monitors to regulate the continuous flow of feedstock by slowing down, speeding up, or even stopping for periods as required.

Fig. 12.4    Example of a Conveyor to Load and Move Biomass

In this regard, higher technology enables greater control and consistency when loading biomass into the production system. If the system is loaded manually, the feedstock will likely be dumped into the hopper all at once; for each 55-gallon trash can in our "low technology" example, this would result in a sudden feed of 40 pounds of chips in about 5 seconds. By comparison, the loading rate of a typical conveyor would be a uniform 8 pounds per minute or 0.13 pounds per second (0.06 kg/s).

### Hopper

The hopper receives feedstock from the loading process and feeds the reactor chamber, where biomass is transformed to biochar. A hopper should be steep enough to avoid feedstock backup due to "bridging," and large enough to accommodate the desired volume of material. A hopper may also have modifications to accommodate the loading apparatus and a lid to facilitate shutting down the reaction when desired during standard operations or for safety and emergency reasons.

### Biomass-to-Biochar Reaction

When biomass is sufficiently heated, it decomposes and releases gases (pyrolysis = decomposition by fire.) If this occurs in an environment with limited oxygen, then the end products are solids (char), gases (some of which are flammable), and liquids, all of which contain some of the energy derived from the original biomass. [The transformation of biomass to biochar is described more thoroughly elsewhere in this book; see, for example, the chapter titled "What *Is* Biochar?"]

The thermal energy (heat) for the biomass-biochar reaction can come from a source outside the biomass (making it an **endothermic** reaction). An example is putting bread into a toaster and using electrical energy to drive moisture out of the bread. If the bread is heated long enough it will blacken and release smoke. The biomass (the bread) is **carbonized** (scorched), and the pyrolysis gases driven off during that reaction are manifested as smoke.

If the flammable gases emitted via heating ignite, then the heat released into the biomass (an exothermic reaction) can continue the conversion process, just as a fire, once lit, will burn until its fuel is exhausted and converted to ash.

The energy contained in the wood, once thermally released, is more than sufficient to convert the mass to biochar and release vapors. The excess energy appears as heat. This self-sustaining **exothermic** reaction is known as **autopyrolysis**.

The particular continuous reaction process described in this chapter is initiated by a small amount of external energy from a propane torch. That reaction will continue for the duration of the production run, sustained by the energy supplied by the input biomass. In the case of an 8-hour run, 3 pounds of propane may be used to start the reaction process for 4,000 pounds of wood.

The process is as follows:

- Air, containing oxygen, enters the reactor above the feedstock, and is drawn down through the reaction zone. The reaction consumes the vast majority of oxygen present in the airflow as it converts the biomass to biochar.

- The converted product travels downward in the reactor in the presence of hot gases devoid of oxygen. At the time of conversion, the heat of the reaction causes the gases released to expand and move upward, away from the solid biochar.

- To move the gases downward on the designed gas path, a blower is needed. A design concern is the operational temperature range of a given blower and whether the blower will be pushing cool gases into the chamber or pulling hot gases out.

- The flow of air and gases, as well as gravity, will propel the biochar, but assistance from a mechanical screw or conveyor may be needed to move the biochar along the designed process path.

It is critical to move the solids out of reaction temperatures once the char is formed. Hot char left exposed to even a little oxygen will continue to convert into ash. Gasifiers optimize their production of energy by fully converting char to ash. In a biochar-optimized process, however, the char must be moved out of the reaction zone as soon as the conversion to biochar is complete.

Managing input rates, thermal conversion temperatures, movement of solids, and movement of gases—all within the operational limits of the feedstock material and the mechanical, electrical, and structural components—is critical to creating a working, continuous process.

## Gas Path

During conversion, biomass is transformed into solids and gases. The equipment should be designed so that gases are separated from the solids shortly after the transformation, which allows the liberated gases to flow away from the biochar.

If gases linger with the solids then they might either condense on the biochar, negatively affecting the **adsorption capacity** of the char, or condense on the process equipment. In the latter case, the liquids will at a minimum impede operation of the equipment, and could eventually clog it (requiring cleaning) or break it (requiring replacement).

The condensable portion of the separated gases can be captured as **bio-oils**. In the appropriate industrial setting, bio-oils can be combusted as is or further refined as biofuel and other valuable end products.

The separation and temperature management of gases should be carefully considered when designing the process and the equipment. The example shown in Figure 12.2 above uses a blower to move gases via an induced draft. Prior to exiting the process, the gases are burned in a combustor, which converts them to safer gases, to meet air quality standards. If 500 pounds (227 kg), 10% moisture db feedstock is processed, then at the end of the process, approximately 1.5 million BTU (440 kWh thermal) of thermal energy, in the form of producer gas, will be available for combustion. This thermal energy can be channeled for application to the upstream needs, downstream needs, or exogenous needs co-located with the biochar process.

### Biochar Solids

As described above, the biochar solids are the product created after thermal modification drives the liquids and gases out of the feedstock. Once the biochar is created, it should be moved out of the reaction space to prevent conversion of the char to ash by further gasification and oxidation reactions.

Once biomass is converted to biochar, the product becomes friable and light, and can be moved relatively easily by a screw conveyor to off-take or storage. The hot solids need to be cooled by various means, such as a water quench or storing in a non-insulated box that is sealed and free of oxygen. If high-temperature char contacts oxygen, combustion will ensue and valuable biochar will burn to ash.

In the continuous, automated process described in this chapter, 500 pounds of pine woodchip feedstock at 10% moisture db will produce approximately 125 pounds of biochar (or equivalently, 200 kg of pine woodchip will produce 50 kg of biochar). The bulk density of material will dictate the volume of space needed to store it. Biochar occupies about 1.3 the volume of the original biomass feedstock. Biochar chip that is on the order of 1.5 cm by 1.5 cm by 0.5 cm will fill a 55-gallon steel drum with 50 pounds of biochar in approximately 24 minutes (or equivalently, a 200 liter (l) barrel will hold 22 kg). Biochar dust that is on the order of 0.1-0.01 mm on each side will fill a 55-gallon steel drum with approximately 120 pounds in just less than 1 hour. (See Figure 12.5.)

Fig. 12.5  Steel Drum with Sealing Lid, and with Fine Biochar from Gasifier

## Automated Controls

Applying automated controls to the above process enables repetition and adjustment, thereby transforming otherwise discrete steps into a continuous, automated process. Such automation can and should be designed to control all of the following variables:

- Input rates

- Thermal conversion temperatures

- Volume of reaction within the reaction space

- Movement of solids in all stages

- Movement of gases in all stages

- System dynamics between these interlinked processes

To optimize the overall process and the end-products, and to avoid equipment wear and malfunction, all of these variables should be managed within the processing materials' operational limits. This requires measuring and monitoring temperatures, pressures, and flow rates at key points in the process to guide proper adjustments of variables under the operator's control.

Simple manual recording with a logbook is useful and important. However, automated recording by a data-logging computer allows feedback control so that needed run-time adjustments can be made in real time, and also provides stored data for later review and analysis. A well-designed control system and protocol will, over time, enable learning and improvements to optimize the entire automated process.

Automated continuous biochar production requires uniform feedstock going into the production process, and allows uniform and standardized products coming out. This is a benefit if the goal includes continuous thermal energy production but imposes a challenge if there is a requirement to deal with diverse feedstock. However, diverse feedstocks can be managed with suitable upstream resources and materials handling.

## Downstream

Both biochar and the energy co-produced during pyrolysis should be used. However, since biochar is the primary objective of the continuous, automated production method described here, the intended use of the biochar is the primary consideration in the design of this process.

For the example used here, one may expect 125 pounds per hour of biochar production. Over the course of an operating day of two 8-hour shifts, with ½ hour for start up in the morning and ½ hour for shut down in the evening, 15 hours of production can be expected. Given 15 hours of production at 125 pounds per hour, the weight of biochar produced will be 1,875 pounds, representing a volume of thirty-eight 55-gallon steel drums.

Packing the product in steel drums has several advantages. They hold enough to allow about 25 minutes between switching off-take barrels, without being too heavy to move once they are full of biochar. Moreover, steel drums are fireproof, and can be sealed. The challenge to using drums is their cost: one drum can cost US$40. If a drum holds 50 pounds of biochar, then that adds US$40 to the price per 50 pounds—on top of any margin cost on the container, the cost of production, any profit margin on the biochar, and any delivery costs.

Clearly, less costly containers will allow lower sale prices. Decreasing container cost can be as simple as using returnable barrels. For large purchases it may be cheaper to fill much larger containers (or super sacks), and move those containers with heavy equipment typically found in the agriculture and forestry industries.

For retail consumers, any type of durable, sealing container could be used. One inexpensive option is a simple, sealable 5-gallon pail. Of course, the char must be thoroughly cooled before putting it into non-metallic containers. One source for such 5-gallon containers charges US$7.50 each. Each would hold 5 pounds of char, enough to use in a few container pots or in a section of a backyard garden.

Adsorption is a desirable quality in char, because it helps keep nutrients and water consistently available in the soil. Non-conditioned char will initially adsorb water and nutrients from the growing media in which it is applied. If non-conditioned biochar is mixed with other nutrients (such as manure) prior to application, the properties of adsorption will benefit plants by decreasing the leaching of nutrients and water that would otherwise occur. In addition to the benefit of keeping nutrients and water where intended, mixing biochar with a nutrient can act as a binder, which will help keep the low-density biochar from blowing away.

## NEXT STEPS: MAKING THE BUSINESS CASE

For the biochar movement to fully take hold and deliver its promised global benefits, automated, commercial production is a must. However, the business case for biochar operations has yet to be widely proved.

In order to promote continuous automated systems, a long investment horizon is necessary. To confirm assumed benefits, establish best practices for production and application, and demonstrate market profitability, projects will need to extend for years. Moreover, if biochar businesses are to advance past the pilot testing phase, the revenues will have to exceed the costs—in most cases, by 30% or more.

In the meantime, pilot-scale testing must be conducted to gauge the viability of expanded and longer-term operations, and that will require investment. The equipment described in this chapter would require a minimum capital investment of approximately US$125,000 (2010). (See Figure 12.3.)

In one instance known to the authors, the equipment described in this chapter has made biochar for a production cost at or below $0.30/lb. Production cost will vary according to particular facts and circumstances, but this is a useful illustration. As for sales prices, the current price for biochar in the research market, as well as the retail market in the western United States, is generally between US$1.00–$2.50/lb (2010). At these prices, bulk purchases for biochar as an agricultural commodity are not likely. Over time, these prices will likely come down.

Most production cost is concentrated in two categories: labor and feedstock. If biochar is produced at a location where suitable feedstock is readily available as a waste product, and staff is locally available, the production cost can be less than one-half the $0.30/lb reported above.

Shipping and container costs are significant drivers of retail price. At a char production rate of about 100 lbs/hr, the cost of the container and the shipping are each about the same as the production cost plus overhead and profit. Thus, by producing and selling biochar in a local market, up to two-thirds of the consumer cost could be avoided.

Next steps require the production and application of biochar to **agroforestry**, seedling production, remediation, retail, and other potential outlets. In order to produce and utilize biochar to maximum effect, the production systems must function, the economics must be viable—and most importantly, every project will need a champion. You can be that champion!

Chapter 13

# Medium & Large Scale Production

## James Joyce BE Chem (Hons) MBA PhD
Principal Technologist
Black is Green Pty Ltd., Australia

### IN THIS CHAPTER YOU WILL LEARN:

- About the continuous, automated production of biochar, including its upstream, production, and downstream phases.

- Design and operating considerations, procedures for choosing and handing raw materials and finished product, and tips for optimizing the process.

- How automated biochar production fits into a broader, sustainable ecosystem.

- Relevant issues and next steps for commercializing biochar production, including production cost and current price examples.

"Mobile deployment—and local use—offer many commercial advantages."

# INTRODUCTION

Other chapters in this book discuss making char on a vey small (micro) scale, including production for at-home use. This chapter focuses on larger scale, commercial and industrial char production, describing and comparing the various current industrial processes and related apparatus. The medium- and large-scale processes discussed here are in many ways similar to large industrial thermal processes, including energy production at public utility-scale facilities. (The terms biochar, charcoal, and char will be used interchangeably in this chapter since the processes being harnessed for biochar production are developments of existing charcoal production methods.)

This chapter also outlines the relative merits of continuous systems over batch methods, and provides illustrations of continuous production processes.

First to be addressed, however, are the crucial safety considerations in char production.

## SAFETY MATTERS

Like most agricultural or industrial processes, biochar production presents a number of risks to the operators and general public. Anyone contemplating charcoal production must be familiar with these risks and the proper measures to minimize potential harm. The key risks are as follows.

### Toxic Gas Emissions
Charcoal production emits potentially harmful gases. The primary gas of concern is carbon monoxide. However, the other emitted gases are also potentially harmful, through both short- and long-term exposure. Equipment design plays a large role in the quantity and type of emissions. It is best to ensure that all char production equipment is operated in a well-ventilated location—not (for example) in the corner of a building.

### Explosion
Both the gases and char dust produced during pyrolysis can present explosion risks if improperly handled. Explosions causing equipment damage and injuries have occurred in pyrolysis plants where due care was not taken. Preventing gas and dust leaks, and avoiding the creation of explosive mixtures with air, are essential and primary precautions. Beyond that, explosion risks can be reduced by operating equipment in a well-ventilated location, maintaining good dust control measures, following operating procedures carefully, and being mindful of including safety features in equipment design (such as explosion vents).

## Spontaneous Combustion

Some unconditioned chars, especially those manufactured under anoxic conditions, can be **pyrophoric**—that is, prone to self-heating and combustion—in the presence of air or moisture. Spontaneous combustion risks are high during production and in postproduction handling, storage, and transport of such chars.

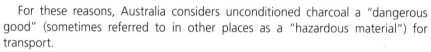

In addition, charcoal is a good insulator, retaining heat very well. The greater the quantity of charcoal, the longer its heat will be retained. A 44-gallon drum of charcoal, for example, can stay hot enough in the center to self-ignite days after it has been sealed.

For these reasons, Australia considers unconditioned charcoal a "dangerous good" (sometimes referred to in other places as a "hazardous material") for transport.

Carefully considered handling procedures are the best way to prevent a problem. Hot biochars should be immediately stabilized by dampening them to at least 25% moisture content, or blending them with significant proportions of moist composted matter or soil. Failing that, a suitable pre-transport holding time should be determined for a given production method and char.

## Burns

Pyrolysis processes inevitably involve heat. To protect against accidental burns, closed shoes, gloves, and safety glasses—at minimum—should be worn in the vicinity of the equipment. Fire-resistant cotton clothes with long sleeves and long pant legs are recommended. Fire extinguishing equipment should be at hand, as well as access to cool water for dousing hot char, and cooling burns.

## Dust Irritation

Charcoal dust is an irritant to eyes, lungs, and skin, and has negative short-term and long-term health effects. Some individuals will be more sensitive than others. At the very least, anyone handling dry char should wear gloves, safety glasses, and a suitable dust mask.

## CONTINUOUS AUTOMATED CHAR PRODUCTION

Historically, most charcoal has been produced in batches—typically in pits, mounds, kilns, or retorts. Some industrial retort designs have been modified to allow them to operate in a semi-batch or semi-continuous manner, to maximize production. Fundamentally, however, the modified designs are still batch devices.

Basic batch retorts and kilns are simple low-cost devices, often used for small-scale manufacture of biochar. These concepts are not suited to larger production scales because operating them is labor intensive, and their productivity is low compared with the alternatives.

Ultimately, the best way to get the most production from a given amount of equipment and labor is to operate continuously. For char production this means continuously feeding wood (or other materials) into one end while continuously discharging char from the other end. Table 13.1 offers an example comparing batch versus continuous production.

| Metric | Batch System | Continuous System |
|---|---|---|
| Load/Feed Rate | $2m^3 = 1$ ton | $2m^3 = 1$ ton/hour |
| Light up/run up to temperature | 2–8 hours | 1 hour (start of day) |
| Cool off/shut down time | 4–24 hours | 1 hour (end of day) |
| Discharge char | 0.5–1 hour | Continuous |
| Yield (dry basis) | 5–20% | 20–33% |
| Char produced @ 20%/25% yield | 200kg in 10–48 hrs ~ 100-200kg/day | 250kg/hour ~ 1.5–5.5 tons/day |

Table 13.1 Char Production: Batch Versus Continuous System

There are five key features that distinguish continuous char producers from batch systems:

1. *Productivity.* Continuous processes can typically produce 10 times more char per day than the same-sized batch unit, primarily because the time required for cooling the char is separated from the feeding process.

2. *Yield.* As Table 13.1 suggests, with rare exceptions, the charcoal yield from continuous systems (at 20%–33% on dry matter basis) is higher than batch systems (5%–20%). This is partly because of the inevitable unevenness in a "batch burn" and partly because in continuous systems, thermal loss is reduced since the equipment is not cycled back and forth from cold to hot. Continuous systems stay hot, while batch systems require additional thermal input at each start-up to ramp up to pyrolysis temperature. This additional energy is supplied by burning off as much as 20% of the starting biomass.

3. *Monitoring and Control.* Continuous systems are easier to monitor and control than batch systems. Operators can get nearly immediate feedback from any change they make, and thereby minimize their need to contend with continuously evolving batch process conditions.

4.  *Automation.* Continuous systems lend themselves more readily to automation than batch systems. This is because their controls are required to maintain constant conditions—such as temperature. In contrast, the control settings in a batch system need to follow a programmed series of events, which can require substantial adjustment from batch to batch if there are differences in feedstock characteristics.

5.  *Emissions.* Emission control is easier to implement in continuous systems, because the exhaust gas is not subject to the wide range of compositional changes that occur during a "batch burn." Typically, a batch burn has a smoky initial phase. This smoke is not very flammable, rapidly clogs filtering devices, and hence is difficult to clean from the exhaust. In continuous systems, the "smoke" components (a mixture of water vapor, tars, and soot) are blended with flammable gases that aid in destroying the smoke in flue gas re-burn or thermal oxidizer systems.

## INDUSTRIAL THERMAL PROCESSES

Continuous biochar production processes share the same concepts as used in industrial thermal processes. In both cases, feedstock is fed in continuously and the end-product is discharged continuously. In broad terms, these shared concepts can be classified as described below.

### LINEAR HEARTH SYSTEMS

The linear hearth is widely used in industry, for applications as diverse as cooking biscuits and making metal slabs. Linear hearths may be configured to transport the feed material in a vertical or horizontal path through an insulated chamber containing burners or some other form of heating. Horizontal linear hearths are sometimes referred to as "tunnel retorts."

In both vertical and horizontal units, the feedstock is progressively heated, dried, and charred as it passes from one end of hearth to the other. In horizontal units, multiple separate chambers are often used to allow the off-gases in the chamber headspaces (generated from different stages) to be recycled or recovered for different uses. For example, off-gases:

*   Can be recovered for use in producing pyrolysis oil or **wood vinegar**.

*   Can be recycled for feedstock drying, in the hearth or externally.

*   Can be recycled and burned to provide the heat required to roast (char) the feedstock.

Linear hearth systems allow ready control of the feedstock's time-temperature history. On the other hand, all feedstock particles, small and large, are exposed to essentially the same external time-temperature conditions. Therefore, the extent of charring will vary for different-sized particles.

In addition, linear hearths often exhibit relatively hot and cold zones—that is, uneven heating effects—which can affect product quality.

Most horizontal linear hearth systems require a separate fuel or energy source for start-up. Some vertical linear hearth systems simply use dry feed material as the starter fuel.

The key distinguishing feature of the different linear hearths is how the feedstock is transported into the unit. In some cases, the feed flows by gravity (for example, traditional hearth-type gasifier designs). In others, the feed is pushed or conveyed. Many systems use rails, carts, or metal conveyor devices.

Some designs can be operated at a slightly negative pressure relative to atmosphere. This enhances operator safety by eliminating the prevailing risk of carbon monoxide poisoning in systems that operate at ambient pressure or above.

Other prominent considerations relating to linear hearths are as follows:

- The footprint of horizontal linear hearths is relatively large compared with vertical hearths and other continuous processes.

- Where gravity is relied on to move feedstock through the unit (as in fixed-bed pyrolyzers or gasifiers), the equipment is often sensitive to feedstock size, density, and shape.

- Use of conveyor mechanisms presents the greatest engineering challenges, because they must operate in a harsh temperature environment.

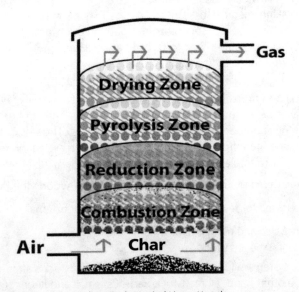

Fig. 13.1    Example of Small- to Medium-Scale Vertical Linear Hearth:
A Traditional Standard Updraft Gasifier.
*Note:* Usually operated to yield ash, not char.
For biochar production the air ratio is altered.

Source: Adapted from: ALL Power Labs, Jessica Hobbs.

Fig. 13.2    Examples of Large-Scale Vertical Linear Hearths

The Continuous Carbonization System          The Lambiotte Retort
Source: Adam + Partner.                                       Source: Lambiotte & Co.

## ROTARY HEARTH RETORTS

Rotary hearth retorts convey the feedstock through a vertical path. In this sense, they are like a vertical linear hearth with mechanical assistance, or a horizontal linear hearth "wrapped around in a spiral." Just as in a linear hearth, the feedstock is progressively heated and charred. In most designs, the feedstock enters the top of the hearth and is heated by hot gases emitted from the charring process in the lower sections. At the feed end, the rising heat is used to dry the incoming feedstock. As with linear hearths, off-gases from the pyrolysis stage may be recycled back and burned to improve the thermal efficiency. An early implementation of a vertical rotary hearth was the Herreshoff design, often used to make metallurgical coke and activated carbon.

In rotary hearth systems, as in linear hearth systems, the time-temperature history of the feedstock is readily controlled. However, in contrast to linear systems, some rotary systems are capable of varying the time-temperature history of small particles versus large particles, promoting product consistency and enhanced yield. The rotary action also helps to mitigate the effects of any uneven temperature regions in the units—a common problem (as previously noted) with linear systems.

Rotary hearths usually incorporate airflow and hearth pressure control to maintain a slightly negative pressure, which minimizes fugitive emissions. Rotary hearths also can add steam to activate or regenerate activated carbon. Some rotary hearth systems require a separate fuel or energy source for start-up. The natural path of the heat up through the unit lends itself to self-starting, by combustion of a dry starter feed in the lower section.

Among rotary hearth designs, the key difference is how feedstock is transported. In some cases, the feedstock is transported by moving rakes (driven from a central shaft or at the outer wall); in others, feedstock is transported by moving floors. Floor designs also vary.

Generally, the footprint of vertical rotary hearths is the smallest of any of the industrial processes. Some vertical rotary hearths are compact enough to mobilize on trucks (see Figure 13.3).

The native emissions from air blown, hearth-type pyrolysis units are up to 30 vol% carbon monoxide, 15% methane, and 5% other hydrocarbons, plus soot and entrained dust from the feed. These are typically scrubbed by a combination of particulate removal cyclones and a re-burner or thermal oxidizer. Sometimes wet scrubbers are used, but these create a liquid effluent stream that presents a disposal issue.

Fig. 13.3  Examples of Rotary Hearths

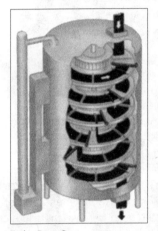

Turbo Dryer®                          Mobile Rotary Hearth.

Source: Wyssmont Company.          Source: Black is Green Pty Ltd, Australia

## ROTARY DRUM FURNACES

Rotary drum furnaces are another very common technology from the chemical and food process industry, where they are used in applications spanning sugar drying to cement making. Rotary drums are also commonly used to regenerate activated carbons by roasting them at temperatures up to 1,000°C in the presence of air or steam.

Rotary drums can be challenging to implement for the following reasons:

- The large rotating drum requires solid foundations and does not lend itself readily to being made gas-tight.

- Industrial implementations of rotary drum pyrolyzers sometimes have problems with odor emission. For biochar production, as previously suggested, the drums can be run at a negative pressure to eliminate emissions.

- Dust losses from the drum into the exhaust gases can affect yields and emissions. In practice, capture devices return char dust to the product. However, these capture devices can have problems when wet feedstocks are used, because the increased tar and moisture content is more likely to cause the dust to cake on the devices, especially when the furnace is started cold.

The native emissions from rotary drums are similar to those for air-blown hearths, and are handled in a similar manner.

**ENTRAINED FLOW AND FLUIDIZED BED PYROLYSERS** (Fast pyrolysis process)
In entrained flow systems, the feed is metered into a high-velocity gas stream (see Figure 13.4 for an example). This requires careful preparation of the feedstock. The metering imparts evenness in the feed, which results in very consistent charring. The feedstock to entrained flow and fluidized bed pyrolysis is exposed to **fast pyrolysis** conditions, with **residence times** measured in seconds or minutes rather than hours.

These systems are sophisticated and therefore technically challenging to design and implement. Hence, they are typically used at the "high end" of the char production sector for large industrial fixed installations that process more than 200 tons/day of feedstock and have sophisticated process and emission controls.

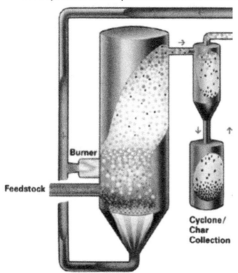

Fig. 13.4   Example of Fluidized Bed Pyrolyzer: Dynamotive Fluid Bed

Source: Dynamotive Energy Systems Corporation.

## MOBILE PYROLYZERS

Mobile biochar equipment allows the equipment to be transported to the biomass rather than transporting the biomass to a centralized plant. Mobile deployment—and local use—offer many commercial advantages, such as:

- Ready access to seasonal biomass feedstocks.

- Moving to new locations whenever feedstocks are temporarily exhausted or rendered unusable by wet weather.

- The ability to undertake short-term waste disposal/remediation tasks.

- Avoiding the overhead costs associated with establishing and maintaining a fixed site.

- Less complicated local permitting.

The most commonly mobilized industrial pyrolysis technologies are the rotary hearth and the rotary drum. Batch kilns and horizontal linear hearths have also been installed on trucks and trailers. (See Figure 13.5 for examples.)

Fig. 13.5  Examples of Mobile and Relocatable Pyrolyzers
Source: Black is Green Pty Ltd, Australia.

Table 13.2 Differences Between Scales of Biochar Production

| FEATURE | MICRO TO SMALL SCALE DEVICES | SMALL TO MEDIUM SCALE FACILITIES | LARGE TO MEGA SCALE PLANTS |
|---|---|---|---|
| Implementation cost | Very low costs per unit, but requires a very large number of units to have large impact. | Investment is comparatively small and can be staged. Investment in site infrastructure is often less. | Usually lower on a "per ton processed" basis, but requires a very large upfront investment. |
| Implementation timeframe | Weeks or days | Months | Years |
| Environmental performance | Generally poor except for recent innovations (such as TLUD) with emphasis on low emissions. | Varies from poor to good. | Usually better than small to medium scale because of higher energy efficiencies and better emissions controls. |
| Electrical energy export efficiency (electrical energy exported/biomass energy in) | Most do not generate electricity. | Many projects do not generate electricity. Those that do operate in the efficiency range of 5–10%. | Typically 10–20% (~50% of the energy input leaves again in the biochar) |
| Overall thermal efficiency (useful energy released) | 50–60 % is considered good. Better when extra expenditures are made. | Can be as high as 65%. | Can be as high as 80% if heat is used for municipal heating. |
| Feedstock access | Typically utilizes the best of the locally available, easiest collected, and lowest cost biomass. | Can be very flexible to feedstock availability. | Can easily be "stranded" by changes in feedstock availability or pricing within the economically viable transport radius. |

## VERY LARGE-SCALE BIOCHAR AND ENERGY PRODUCTION

Very large-scale biochar and energy production can be defined as an operation that processes more than 100 tons of feed per day (greater than 15 MW [megawatts] on a thermal energy input basis), or produces more than 20 tons per day of biochar. An appreciable number of plants have been proposed that would process more than 1,000 tons of feed per day (greater than 300,000 tons/year).

Large-scale biochar and energy production plants are not unlike any other large biomass processing facility. They require a substantial investment, on the order of US$2,000–$8,000 per kW [kilowatt] of electrical generating capacity. That translates to project costs ranging from US$4M to $200M.

At the time of this writing, there are no operating large-scale biochar production facilities. One of the major hurdles to stimulating large-scale biochar production, particularly when competing with biomass to energy conversion, is establishing a viable financial model for producing biochar. Removing biochar drains energy output (because it contains 30%–40% of the feedstock's carbon atoms) and a stable, sustainable market and pricing structure for biochar or its carbon sequestration has not yet materialized. Research continues about whether producing energy and producing biochar can deliver comparable profits for various feedstock and market parameters. (For more on this subject, see the chapter of this book titled "Large Scale Pyrolysis for Dry Land Agriculture.")

Table 13.2 summarizes the differences between large-scale biochar production and small- to medium- scale production—the latter of which is the emphasis of this book.

## KEY POINTS FROM THIS CHAPTER

- Regardless of production scale, biochar production requires careful management of safety hazards, including toxic gas emissions, explosion, spontaneous combustion, burns, and dust irritation.

- As production scale increases from smaller to larger, continuous processes have five advantages over batch systems: productivity, yield, monitoring and control, potential automation, and emission control.

- Continuous biochar production processes and industrial thermal processes have a common basis of technology.

- An important subset of the industrial processes is mobile and relocatable systems, which allow the facility to go to the biomass rather than bringing the biomass to a central location.

- Large- and mega-scale biochar and energy production plants are similar to other large biomass processing facilities, and require substantial investment. Currently, there are no operating large-scale biochar production facilities.

# Part IV
## Testing, Conditioning & Using Biochar

"...producing and applying bio-char to soil would not only dramatically improve soil and increase crop production, but also could provide a novel approach to establishing a significant, long-term sink for atmospheric carbon dioxide."

*—Dr. Johannes Lehmann,*
*Professor of Soil Sciences, Cornell University*

# Chapter 14

# Gauging the Impact of Biochar:
# Simple Tests for Farmers and Gardeners

Julie Major, PhD
Agricultural Extension Director
International Biochar Initiative

Kelpie Wilson
Communications Editor
International Biochar Initiative

*[This chapter draws extensively from "A Guide to Conducting Biochar Trials" (IBI Guide), authored by Julie Major and published by IBI in April 2009. The IBI Guide is available online at www.biochar-international.org/publications/IBI.]*

**IN THIS CHAPTER YOU WILL LEARN:**

- Sources for biochar.

- Tests you can conduct to evaluate the quality of biochar at home or in the field.

- Tests you can perform to assess the impact of biochar application on your crops.

- How you can contribute from your own home to the global biochar initiative.

# INTRODUCTION

When added to soil, biochar has been shown to be beneficial for crops. Biochar provides a unique opportunity for farmers and gardeners to improve soil fertility for the long term, using locally available materials. Used alone or in combinations, compost, manure, or synthetic fertilizers are added at certain rates every year to soils, in order to realize benefits. Application rates of these inputs can potentially be reduced when biochar is also used as a soil amendment. However, biochar materials vary widely in their characteristics and so do soils. For these reasons, we recommend that farmers and gardeners always test a new biochar material before using it in their soil.

This guide is intended for farmers and gardeners who want to conduct basic, simple tests with biochar to ensure that the material is safe to apply to their soil, and to test its effects on plant growth. By carrying out these tests, farmers and gardeners should be able to decide whether to incorporate biochar into larger areas of soil and into their own management practices. For more complex testing of biochar to generate data valid for analyzing the statistical significance of results, see the *IBI Guide*, available online at http://www.biochar-international.org/ publications/IBI.

## POTENTIAL SOURCES OF BIOCHAR

Many small farmers and gardeners would like to begin experiments with biochar but do not have a readily available source of charcoal to work with. Depending on the location, the following sources of charcoal material may be available. Tests such as those described in this chapter will help determine whether such charcoal is suitable for use as biochar. (Other biochar tests are offered in the chapter titled "Characterizing Biochars: Attributes, Indicators, and At-Home Tests.")

Here are some potential sources of biochar:

- Campfires, which often leave behind chunks of charcoal.

- Wood burning stoves, which may be operated in a way that produces a small amount of charcoal.

- "Lump wood charcoal," which can be purchased in most regions for grilling food, can sometimes make useful biochar. Do not use charcoal "briquettes" because they contain additives that could be harmful to soil.

- One biochar researcher uses spent charcoal from an aquarium filter in her house-plants. As a bonus, this charcoal is already impregnated with fish waste nutrients.

- Students and hobbyists have created small gasifying stoves from tin cans and other materials that can cleanly produce small amounts of charcoal. (For more on this topic, see the chapter titled "Making Biochar in Small Gasifier Cookstoves and Heaters.").

- Those with metal fabrication skills can search the internet for open-source plans for clean pyrolysis units made from metal drums and other materials.

In any case, those interested in making biochar should strive to improve the way they make it by employing the simple, clean technologies that are being developed, as presented in this book and updated on the book's website. Those more inclined to buy rather than make biochar should look for product that is cleanly made with the least impact on the environment. For example, having biochar shipped over long distances reduces its usefulness as a carbon-sequestering tool. With this in mind, biochar has the potential to be successfully used to improve the soil and help mitigate climate change.

## PRELIMINARY TESTS

Before adding biochar or any amendment to field soil, one should ensure it will not be harmful in that environment at the intended application rate. Biochar made under certain conditions may contain substances that are harmful to plants. The germination and worm avoidance tests described below are designed to assess the presence of such substances. These tests are also described in IBI's *Technical Bulletin 101*, which is available online at http://www.biochar-international.org/publications/IBI.

Both tests use a "control." Test are conducted on biochar mixed with soil in the proportions being considered and on the soil alone (the control), and the results are compared. It is best to use soil taken from the field location where the biochar will actually be used. If field soil is not available, use another similar soil. Commercially sold potting mixes can also be used, although using actual soil is desirable if the biochar will be applied to soil, because potting mixes and natural soils can differ markedly. Remember also that the same soil must be used in both of the containers referred to below.

### Germination Test

Methodologies for germination tests are widely available. Basically, the goal of germination tests is to determine whether adding biochar to soil has an effect on seed germination. A negative effect may indicate the presence of undesirable compounds in the biochar material. Lettuce (*Lactuca sativa L.*) is the most widely recommended species to use for germination tests, due to its sensitivity to the presence of toxins and contaminants in general. Other species that could be used include radish (*Raphanus L.*) and clover (*Trifolium L.*).

Here are the steps to follow for the test.

## What You'll Need

- Two containers shaped like dishes to create shallow soil beds. These can be plastic lids with a relatively high side, plastic or ceramic plates, etc.

- Approximately 1 liter of soil, preferably from the location where the field trial will take place. If soil from the trial area is not available, use a similar soil.

- Approximately 1 liter of biochar

- One package of lettuce, radish, or clover seed

- A glass or other container for measuring

- A watering can or container with holes to gently water the soil

## What to Do

1. Set half of the soil aside for a control.

2. Use the other half to make a mixture with biochar. The proportion of biochar to soil can be calculated to simulate the ratio you intend to apply in the field, or you can use a half-and-half mixture if you intend to apply biochar non-uniformly such as in planting holes. Thoroughly mix the soil and biochar by hand or using a tool.

3. Measure a portion of soil into one container and an equal portion of soil/biochar mix, into the other container.

4. Count the seeds. You must use at least 20 seeds per container to make sure you get a representative sample. Some seeds might not germinate under any circumstance, and enough need to germinate to have statistical significance (for example, more than 10 germinations in one container).

5. Spread the same number of seeds on the surface of the both the soil and soil/biochar mix (that is, in each container).

6. Gently water the soil in each container and make sure it does not dry out afterwards. Placing a clear plastic bag around the containers helps to prevent drying out.

7. Place the containers in a location with good conditions for seed germination: normal room temperature is most important. Make sure the soil or soil/biochar mixture does not dry out; test it with a finger to ensure it is moist as looks can be deceiving.

8. Check the containers daily for germination. Once significant germination is observed, count the number of seeds that germinated in each container. Don't wait too long to do this, as seedlings might become entangled and will be harder to count.

9. Compare the number of germinated seedlings in the containers with and without biochar, to see if there are differences.

You might want to redo the test to convince yourself of the result. Having several replicates of each treatment (with and without biochar) and arranging them randomly while waiting for germination would allow more confidence in the results.

Fig. 14.1  Results of Germination Tests

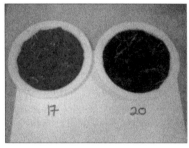 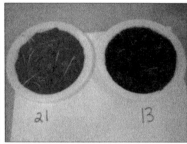

The outcome in the left photo shows many and even bigger sprouts in the biochar mixture (Sample 20) than in the control (Sample 17), indicating a biochar suitable for soil application. The result in right photo shows the opposite, indicating a biochar not suitable for soil application as-is (although it could be tested again after inoculation–see the chapter of this book titled "Conditioning Biochar for Application to Soils"). (Photo: Julie Major)

## Worm Avoidance Test

This is a more complex test than the seed germination test, since it requires live worms to complete. However, it may be more sensitive than a germination test.

A common type of worm used for this test is the white worm (*Enchytraeus albidus*). It is widely used as a live aquarium fish food and can be bought where aquarium supplies are sold, or on the internet. Alternatively, worm species *Eisenia fetida* and *Eisenia andrei*, commonly known as redworms, brandling worms, "tiger worms," and red wiggler can be used. Both species are used for vermi-composting and can be obtained from various suppliers.

Here are the steps to follow for the test.

### What You'll Need

- One bowl-shaped container, with a diameter of approximately 10 cm. For example, you can use a plastic bowl or a margarine container.

- Approximately 1 liter of soil, preferably from the location where the field trial will take place. If soil from the trial area is not available, use another similar soil.

- Approximately 1 liter of biochar

- Ten red or white worms

- One piece of cardboard or plastic sheeting

- Scissors

- A pen or marker

- A glass or other container to measure

- A watering can or container with holes to gently water the soil

### What to Do

1.  Cut the piece of cardboard or plastic sheeting, so that it will fit along the diameter of your container and to the bottom to split it in half. This will be used to physically separate the soil and soil/biochar mixture during test preparation and when looking for results.

2.  Place the separator in the container (see Figure 14.2). Using a pen or marker, mark the position of your separator on the edge of the container so you can insert it again at the same place later.

3.  Set half of the soil aside for the control. Use the other half to make a mixture with biochar as described in step 2 of the germination test.

Fig. 14.2  Worm Avoidance Test

Left: Container with separator and soil and soil/biochar portions.

Right: Container with separator removed and worms added.

(Photos: Julie Major)

4.  On one side of the separator, place soil and on the other side, place the same amount of soil/biochar mix. Make sure you use equal amounts of soil and soil/biochar mix.

5.  Before you remove the separator, gently water both sides until they are moist but not saturated. (If you water after removing the separator, the two sides could mix.)

6.  Remove the separator, and place 10 worms along the line where the separator was (see Figure 14.2).

7.  Place the container in an area where normal room temperature is maintained. To avoid drying, you may cover the container with a vented lid or plastic bag with holes in it.

8.  After 48 hours, insert the separator in the same position as before. Thoroughly observe the soil and count the number of worms on each side of the separator.

If worms have avoided the side of the container where biochar was applied, then the biochar should not be applied to soil without further investigation. Conversely, if worms did not avoid the biochar, it is safe for application to soil. Repeating the test more than once or using several replicates will give more conclusive results.

Note: A standardized methodology for this test is available from the International Organization for Standardization (ISO 17512-1:2008), and can be downloaded from the internet for a fee.

## TESTING BIOCHAR "IN THE FIELD"

Once you are satisfied with the results of the above test(s), you can test biochar "in the field"—in outdoor soil. Two concepts should be kept in mind when doing field trials: first, the biochar-amended soil needs to be compared to an appropriate, and separate, alternative treatment (a control). Second, if possible, the biochar-amended and control treatments should be repeated in more than one location ("replication").

### The Control Treatment

A control treatment is the basis for comparing and assessing the impact of the biochar. The control is often a "business as usual" treatment where you manage soil according to usual practices.

A simple experiment could be to compare the control treatment to one where biochar was applied, but which was otherwise treated identically. For example, if NPK fertilizer or bone meal is used in the control areas, they should also be used in the areas receiving biochar. The same goes for all other practices including tillage and pest and disease control. The only difference should be the presence or absence of biochar. If biochar is worked into the soil, the soil in the control plots should be worked in the same way, even if no amendments are being incorporated.

Thus, when you later compare results from the two treatments, any differences can be attributed to the presence or absence of biochar, and not to any other factors.

### Replication

Testing biochar in more than one location is desirable because there is a chance that the location which was chosen to apply the biochar is different from the location where the control is applied, and this can affect the results either positively or negatively, giving misleading results that can lead to incorrect conclusions. Such "confounding factors" might be variations in soil quality, drainage, weed pressure, shading, and so on. If their potential presence and effects are not anticipated and allowed for in the experiment design, you might interpret the outcome of the tests to mean biochar negatively or positively impacted yield when in fact other factors are responsible.

Consider an example of a small field that is separated into two halves for a biochar experiment. This is depicted in the following graphic (Figure 14.3), where the grayed portion indicates some non-uniform condition in the field.

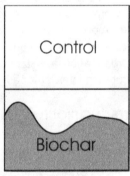

If, for example, the grayed portion of the biochar treated half is poorly drained, the biochar treatment will likely perform poorly. If you are not aware of this drainage problem, you might incorrectly conclude that biochar was detrimental to crop yields. On the other hand, if the grayed area contained fertilizer residues from previous land use, the results might lead you to incorrectly conclude that biochar improved crop yields.

While poor drainage can potentially be observed and consciously avoided, other types of results-altering differences may not—for example, agrochemical residues from previous management practices, weed seed banks, shading, or pest or disease pressure from an adjacent area. In the above example, if you were aware of the drainage issue you might think it could be ameliorated if the field was divided along the other

Fig. 14.3 Example of Small Field Separated for Biochar Experiment (with Non-Uniform Condition)

axis resulting in more equal apportioning of the non-uniformity to the control and biochar plots. However, that would assume the absence of other unknown confounding factors, such as fertilizer residues with entirely different distributions. Replication is the only way to reduce the impact of unknown confounding factors.

For this reason, it is best to apply each treatment in several plots or strips called replicates. Three "replicates" of each treatment is the minimum needed to conduct statistical analyses of the data, and draw conclusions that will be accepted by the scientific community. More replicates are better, but 3–4 replicates are often used to reduce the effects on the results of this kind of occurrence, while keeping down the cost and time needed.

In a garden setting where crops can be harvested by hand, the following three-replicate layout for plots can be used.

| Control | Biochar | Control |
|---------|---------|---------|
| Biochar | Control | Biochar |

In this layout, the treatments are spread out over the experimental area. Each plot can constitute a raised bed, or plots can be marked on field soil using strings and pegs. Make sure you can identify the location of each plot later on in the growing season.

A more rigorous experimental design would involve more plots in which treatments and controls are assigned at random, thus avoiding conscious or unconscious bias in the choices. Methods of making randomized designs are discussed in more detail in the IBI Guide.

The following pictures (Figures 14.4 and 14.5) show examples of a three-replicate layout and a randomized design.

Fig. 14.4   Example Three-Replicate Layout

A simple biochar field experiment in Honduras. Notice the location of the three biochar-amended plots. (Photo: Julie Major)

Fig. 14.5  Randomized Complete Block Design

This photograph shows an RCBD (Randomized Complete Block Design). Notice the three easily identified, randomly spaced, replicates of the highest biochar application rate.  (Photo: Julie Major)

Although plots are used in the above examples, the home gardener can set up replicates in much smaller confines, such as potted plants, a seedling tray, or a Petri dish.

In field crops where farm machinery is used, plots can be laid out in strips (as illustrated in the graphic and the photo below [Figure 14.6]), where each strip can be slightly wider than the width of harvesting equipment and of a length suitable for the equipment to generate yield data.

Fig. 14.6  Strip Layout
Biochar applied in a strip using field machinery in Hawaii.

(Photo: J. Hunt)

Strips have the disadvantage that they do not allow replicated treatment plots and controls to be interspersed in both directions over the experimental area. Although the strip layout could be used in long garden beds, dividing the beds to create more of a "patchwork" type design is desirable.

Spreading treatments out and using several replicates of each treatment helps ensure that the impact of unknown or invisible confounding factors (for example, poorly drained or highly fertile areas, as mentioned above) is reduced. This is because the treatment and control plots are scattered over the confounding landscape so that the effects are averaged out, leading to a more reliable result.

### Additional Considerations

In order to ensure accurate test results, here are some additional considerations:

1.  Plot size will vary with the type of plants you will be using. As much as possible, you should aim at having many plants in each plot, in order to work with a representative sample. Ideally, you should be able to measure yield or any other quality on several plants (at least 5–10), excluding plants which are located on the edges of the plot and which could be influenced by factors outside the plot (these are called "edge effects"). See the diagram below (Figure 14.7).

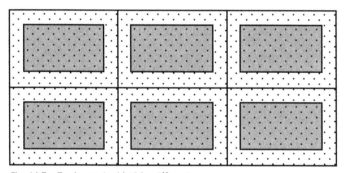

Fig. 14.7    Testing to Avoid "Edge Effects"

In this diagram, the dots represent plants, and areas where sampling occurs inside each treatment plot are shown in gray.

2.  As previously noted, all experimental plots should be managed identically, except for the treatment difference being investigated (such as the presence or absence of biochar). For example, tillage, weed, pest and disease control should be uniform on all units, unless these factors are being investigated.

3.  To avoid unconscious bias, trials can be set up (for example without labels) so that the field operators do not know which plots are receiving which treatment or no treatment.

4.  In order to obtain data that will allow easy comparisons of the treatments, you may wish to plant a crop that produces a yield that is straightforward to measure in plots, such as corn, beans, and carrots. Less desirable trial crops include squash and tomatoes. Squash plants may extend their runners outside plot boundaries, and tomatoes may prolong their yield over time, both of which make data collection more difficult.

5.  If biochar from different sources is being combined for the trial (rather than tested against each other), all materials should be well blended.

6.  Before applying biochar to the soil, keep a representative sample for later analysis. Among other things, keeping a sample will allow you to determine characteristics of biochar that produced a particularly good yield result, compare results for multiple biochars, or establish a baseline for determining changes in the biochar after time in the soil. To obtain a representative sample, select portions from many locations in a biochar pile, or from several barrels or bags of material. All of the "subsamples" can be pooled to make a single sample of the material you applied.

The assessment you make of how each treatment performed will depend on your interest: for example, you might be interested in the fresh weight of strawberries, disease incidence, sweetness of the fruit, or appearance. Data should be collected on all plots separately, and averaged by treatment when appropriate. You should also make sure you take written notes about all steps involved in setting up and carrying out the trials, as these may be useful later when results are available.

## HOW MUCH BIOCHAR SHOULD BE APPLIED?

In research and large-scale field operation settings, application rates for biochar are expressed in metric tons per hectare (t/ha). Rates of 5–50 t/ha have often been used successfully.

Use the equations in the box to convert these rates to different units. These conversion factors are approximate, based on the assumed densities for biochar and soil shown in the box. Biochar materials and soils vary widely. More accurate conversion factors can be calculated using the actual densities of your materials.

## CONVERTING BIOCHAR APPLICATION RATES

Rate in t/ha
$\div 10$ = rate in $kg/m^2$
$\div 4$ = rate in $l/m^2$*
$\div 1.8$ = rate in g/kg soil§
$\div 0.7$ = rate in ml/kg soil*§
$\div 0.6$ = rate in ml/l soil*
$\div 40$ = rate in cm* (i.e. thickness of the biochar layer covering the soil before incorporation)

* Assumes a bulk density for biochar of 0.4 $g/cm^3$. Among others factors, the greater the ash content and the finer the biochar material, the higher the bulk density.

§ Assumes a bulk density for soil of 1.2 $g/cm^3$ and an incorporation depth of 15 cm. Sandy soil and organic (muck) soil may have a lower density.

## APPLYING BIOCHAR TO SOIL

Biochar can be applied to soil alone or along with other amendments such as compost, manures, or crop residues. But unlike other soil amendments, biochar does not need to be applied each time a new crop is established. A single application may provide long-term benefits. On the other hand, if the goal is agricultural profitability or carbon sequestration, applying biochar must not increase costs or $CO_2$ emissions beyond acceptable levels.

Several techniques can be considered for applying biochar to soil. However, regardless of the technique, controlling erosion by wind and surface water runoff must be kept in mind. Erosion losses waste biochar, and the lost material will not be available in the intended soil for improving its fertility.

### Uniform Topsoil Mixing

To apply the biochar and incorporate it into soil, the most widely used technique is uniform topsoil mixing, which can be done after primary soil preparation and before planting the crop. In this technique, biochar is first broadcast over the entire application area using, for example, lime spreaders or other spreaders, or as a slurry, possibly mixed with liquid manure. After the biochar is applied, it is incorporated into the soil, by hand hoeing or with disking or chisel tillage. The most appropriate methods will depend on soil conditions and farm capabilities. Uniform application could be considered during the establishment of turf, golf greens, athletic fields, and general landscaping after construction.

### Application to Planting Holes

Applying biochar to individual planting holes minimizes erosion losses. This technique is useful when establishing orchards, or tree or palm plantations.

### Banding

Biochar can be banded at various depths, by hand or using machinery. Deep banding facilitates thoroughly covering the biochar with soil, thereby minimizing potential losses after application. This is an option where crops or trees are already established. Biochar can be applied in a circular band around trees, or in several holes around the base of the tree and covered with soil.

### Top-Dressing

Top-dressing, where biochar is applied to the soil surface, is an option for established crops. However, this method has the highest potential for erosion losses. These losses can be reduced by mixing biochar with other amendments, applying it to flat land with a thick vegetation cover, or mulching.

## HANDLING BIOCHAR

Biochar is a very light and brittle material of low density, and even if it is not fine-grained (as some biochars are), it usually contains a fraction of fine powder. This leads to three concerns:

1. As previously noted, controlling erosion by wind and surface water runoff. Incorporating biochar well into soil will minimize such losses.

2. Significant amounts of material can blow away while measuring, transporting, applying, and incorporating biochar. Dust problems can be controlled by adding water to the biochar, mixing it with clay slurry, pelleting, or agglomerating with a binder.

3. Care must be taken when transporting and storing biochar because of the risk of accidental ignition with some biochar materials. To combat this, commercial products might be moistened before shipping (thereby increasing the product's weight).

## YIELD MEASUREMENTS

Typically, yield is measured on several plants, from inside each experimental plot or unit. Several plants are analyzed to average out variability between individual plants. (This is not to be confused with replication, which is used to minimize the effect of variable environments among plots.) Data for all plants inside an experimental unit will be averaged into one value for the experimental unit. As you might guess, the more plants included in the analysis the better, but smaller sets of plants require less work. In making yield measurements, it is best to avoid plants near the edges of trial plots. As previously mentioned, the edges are more likely to have been affected by nearby treatments or conditions outside the zone being analyzed—these are the noted "edge effects."

Make sure you also record data required to scale up your yield data to accommodate the size of your field (for example, the number of plants in each linear meter, or number of plants per unit of area in the field).

Note: In the smaller-scale context of this chapter, this section on yield measurement assumes hand harvesting.

## SOIL SAMPLING

The tests discussed so far will give indicators as to whether a particular biochar will benefit a particular crop-soil combination. Some people may be interested in more specific information about the effects of that biochar in the soil over time, and for them, soil sampling can be done.

At its most basic, "before" and "after" soil samples can be taken. But to get a soil test truly representative of your changing soil, several factors should be considered.

### When to Sample

If the trial is intended to last for more than one growing season, annual soil sampling should be done, at about the same time each year. This is important because nutrient availability changes with cropping and other yearly cycles. As a practical matter, it is easiest to sample just before planting or just after harvesting. Soil that is very wet or very dry can be difficult to sample, so avoid times of the year when those conditions generally prevail.

### Where to Sample

Soil conditions can vary within short distances. Therefore, you should always dig samples from more than one location in each plot. For example, inside a 4 x 5 m (or yard) corn plot, soil can be taken from three to five locations. For the same reason as when measuring yield, plot edges should be avoided. Either a random or a regular pattern (for example, four corners, insides of edges, and the center) can be applied, with the same pattern used inside each experimental unit. Samples from each location can then be combined as described below.

In the case where there are defined crop rows, you should take this into consideration when sampling, especially if fertilizer is banded along these rows. For example, three of the sampling locations inside all plots could be on crop rows, and two at midpoints between rows.

### How to Sample

A variety of augers and corers are available specifically for taking soil samples, but a trowel or shovel can also be used. The important point is to be consistent in the way any tool is used. For example, if using a shovel, the same amount of soil from a uniform area and depth should be taken from each sampling location.

This is important because a steep gradient with depth may be present for the soil factors you intend to test.

For analysis, one composite sample per experimental unit is appropriate. To obtain a composite sample, place all subsamples taken from the various sampling locations inside each experimental unit into a bucket and mix well by hand, breaking large clumps. Then a composite sample, say about 300 g, can be placed into a labeled plastic bag, and the rest discarded. This ensures that you get a homogeneous sample that represents the entire experimental unit. It is also a good idea to label the bags to avoid confusion later on.

Since biochar can be expected to have a lower density than soil, if you are interested in analyzing changes in carbon stocks after biochar application you may consider sampling the soil's bulk density. Bulk density is usually measured by taking soil in undisturbed cores (aluminum cores are specifically made for this purpose), and then drying the soil completely at 105°C until there is no further reduction in weight. (For instructions on similarly drying biochar samples, see the chapter "Characterizing Biochars Prior to Addition to Soils.") After determining the mass of the dry soil (minus the core), this value is divided by the volume of soil to give bulk density.

### How to Handle the Samples

Some soil analyses (for example, inorganic nitrogen and soil biota) may require moist soil. However, most standard analyses use air-dried soil, and therefore soil should be set out to dry as soon as possible after sampling. This is important: keeping moist soil inside bags can favor the growth of molds and affect natural processes related to soil fertility, and therefore skew the sampling results. In a covered area (to avoid contamination, for example from dust) with ample table space, spread each sample out over pieces of plastic or paper, and leave it for several days until it looks and feels dry.

Make sure you don't lose track of sample labels while drying them. It's also a good idea to keep some soil samples in storage, to have the ability to re-run analyses or run different ones later.

### Analyzing the Samples

In keeping with the "at home" or small-scale theme of this chapter, do-it-yourself kits are available to analyze certain properties of soils (for example, pH).

However, for those seeking a more reliable analysis of soil fertility, a specialized laboratory is recommended. A regional soil-testing lab can conduct analyses specifically designed for the soils of your region. To find a soil-testing lab in your region, you can contact cooperative or government extension services, universities with agronomy departments, or gardening stores. Many labs have online order forms and offer analysis packages.

A word of caution should be interjected here. Specific methods for quantifying biochar in soil are being developed, and currently no routine commercial analyses are available. Until such tests become available to the public, the best current alternative is to analyze the soil for total carbon, and to compare how much total carbon is in biochar-amended soil versus the control soil (that is, the soil that did not receive biochar). The control soil will tell you how much non-biochar carbon is present in the soil. On the other hand, care must be taken with the type of analysis chosen: biochar does not easily degrade, and not all routine analyses for soil carbon or organic matter detect it. Therefore, to avoid wasting time and money, it is important to literally request a *total carbon analysis*, which is accomplished via dry combustion in a C/N analyzer. If in doubt, contact the lab and explain what you need.

## ANALYZING RESULTS

Once you have the data in hand, it is time to analyze the results of your biochar project.

Given the three or more replicates of each treatment, you can calculate, for each treatment, average values for such metrics as yield, available phosphorus, and pH. An effective and easy way to quickly understand the results is to arrange and present the data graphically. For example, the following graphs (Figure 14.8) were easily generated using Excel (other programs can be used to generate similar graphs):

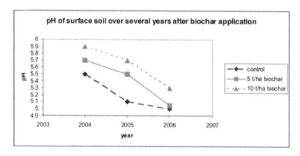

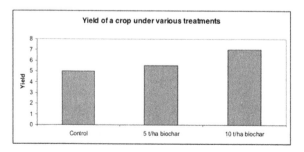

Fig. 14.8   Sample Graphs for Analyzing Biochar Project Results

These graphs depict differences between treatments that are sometimes small. However, with a well-designed experiment, it is possible to tell whether differences are real or whether they are attributable to other factors such as random variability in the field, or the way measurements were made. In the scientific world, statistical analysis is used to assess the significance of differences between treatments, and this requires lengthy calculations or the use of specialized software. If you are not familiar with these, you can seek help, or read the IBI Guide on how to use Microsoft Excel to calculate and display standard errors.

## DISSEMINATING RESULTS AND THE IBI BIOCHAR TRIAL REGISTRY

A high level of statistical sophistication is not necessary for you to obtain useful information and share it with others, including over the internet. The replication of your results by others can build confidence in the results, as the data accumulates.

These data can make valuable contributions to the body of knowledge about biochar, and its effects and benefits in a wide variety or biochar and soil types. After all, the biochar movement is global in scope, and critical knowledge can be obtained from many sources large and small.

By registering your results in the IBI Trial Registry, or on this book's website, your results can be disseminated to others. Over time, your results could be aggregated with others and subjected to scientific analyses to help advance the new and diverse field of biochar soil amendment.

## CONCLUSIONS

This chapter offers many ways for smaller-scale enthusiasts or farmers to reliably gauge how applying biochar will impact soil and to also track how well it works in the field. The principles, tests, and techniques offered could be readily used by those interested in only the rudiments for their own backyard gardens, and by those who have more expanded goals.

In any event all who participate—regardless of the extent of their participation— are making a genuine contribution to a much greater good.

## KEY POINTS FROM THIS CHAPTER

- When added to soil, biochar has been shown to be beneficial for crops. Farmers and gardeners can use biochar to improve soil fertility for the long term, using locally available materials.

- Biochar materials vary widely in their characteristics and so do soils. Therefore, before using any new biochar in the soil, it should be tested to make sure it will not harm plants and to gauge its effects on plant growth.

- Basic, simple, tests are available to famers and gardeners, including preliminary seed germination tests and worm avoidance tests.

- In testing in outdoor soil it is important to establish a "control" soil that is prepared, treated, and worked exactly the same as the biochar-applied soil and to replicate the test in several locations or containers.

- Biochar can be used alone or in combinations, and with compost, manure, crop residues, or synthetic fertilizers. But unlike other soil amendments, biochar does not need to be applied each time a new crop is established. A single application may provide long-term benefits.

- Biochar can be applied to soil using several techniques, including uniform topsoil mixing, application to planting holes, banding, and top-dressing. Take care to minimize loss through wind erosion and surface water runoff.

- "Before and after" soil sampling can be done to assess whether a particular biochar will benefit a particular crop-soil combination.

- Yield is measured on several plants, and from one or more replications. The more plants included in the analysis, the more reliable the resulting averages.

- There are many ways for smaller-scale enthusiasts or farmers to reliably gauge how applying biochar will impact soil and to track how well it works in the field. All who participate can share their results and make a genuine contribution to the expanding body of knowledge about biochar.

# Chapter 15

# Conditioning Biochars for Application to Soils

James Joyce BE Chem (Hons) MBA PhD
Principal Technologist
Black is Green Pty Ltd., Australia

**IN THIS CHAPTER YOU WILL LEARN:**

- The fundamentals of healthy soil, and the crucial role of microbes.

- How biochar contributes to healthy soil and provides a home for microbes.

- How the many benefits of biochar can be maximized by "conditioning" it before adding it to the soil.

- The benefits of composting with biochar.

- Specific ways to condition biochar—and some dramatic test results to show that it works.

"Composting can condition or 'load' biochar with beneficial microbes. A properly conditioned biochar can promote the formation of highly beneficial structures in weeks rather than months or years."

# INTRODUCTION

Biochars provide appreciable benefits to soils, which are best achieved with pre-conditioned biochars. Conditioning biochar includes a wide variety of post-pyrolysis techniques that generally involve two aspects: (1) charging the biochar with plant nutrients and (2) inoculating (seeding) the biochar with a combination of living organisms. After the biochar is conditioned, then the biochar is applied to the target soil.

Soil health is determined by very complicated interactions between soil organisms, plant roots, organic chemicals, and inorganic chemicals. It is therefore not surprising that very mixed results are reported for inoculation techniques in commercial and research applications. Fortunately, even a professional crop grower does not need to understand all of the complexities of biochar inoculation, because they all hinge on a handful of key principles. Get them right and nature will do the rest.

The overarching concept expressed in this chapter is that the best way to inoculate a biochar is to create the right conditions for natural organisms to proliferate, which are the same conditions as are required for effective composting. Hence we recommend treating biochar just like any other compost ingredient, with due regard to moisture, pH, temperature, and carbon to nitrogen ratio (C:N) of the overall blend.

## HEALTHY SOIL 101

Figure 15.1 summarizes the key interactions in a healthy soil. These interactions span from atomic scale (chemical reactions) right up to macro-organisms (for example, worms and insects) and physical structures (pores and granules). The resulting chemical and physical equilibrium makes a healthy soil quite resistant to temporary assault from disease, moisture stress, nutrient stress, leaching, and erosion.

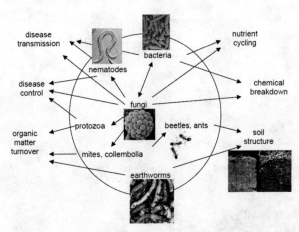

Fig. 15.1   A Summary of the Interactions in a Healthy Soil

Just as in the human body, there is a constant struggle between the good bugs and the bad bugs—and at the same time, each battles to survive conditions presented by the environment itself. In a healthy soil, if any component becomes imbalanced, the system will endeavor to compensate. However, there are limits and prices to be paid if these compensation mechanisms are pushed too far for too long.

**THE LIVING SOIL**

The cornerstone organisms in soil are microbes. Soil microbes are found primarily in two places: the top 2-3 cm of topsoil where they can "breathe," and close to root surfaces in the rhizosphere (Figure 15.2). The **rhizosphere** is the few centimeters of soil that immediately surrounds the plant roots and is affected by chemical secretions from them, including energy-providing sugars. Some of these secretions allow the plant to "communicate" with the microbes to encourage activities of mutual benefit. One of the key mutually beneficial activities is to maintain **pH** in the rhizosphere in a preferred range, which then assists the "mining" and transfer of nutrients from the soil to the plant.

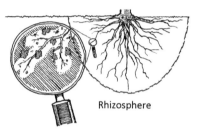

Rhizosphere

Fig. 15.2 Microbes and the Rhizosphere

The ability of microbes to "turn over" nutrients and to bind particles in soil is essential for plant growth and for the health of larger organisms living in the soil. The process of the macro-organisms feeding on the microbes further enhances soil structure—providing room for root growth, movement of water and nutrients, and gas exchange in the soil.

One of the useful roles of biochar arises purely from its structure. Because biochar is both porous and granular, each inter-granular space and intra-granular pore can, in time, become safe "housing" for microbes and fine root hairs (**hyphae**). (See Figure 15.3)

*Mycorrhizae (1 + 1 = 3)*

Within the **rhizome**—the horizontal underground stem of a plant that sends out roots and shoots—there is the potential for forming a mycorrhizal association, which is the colonization of fungus on or in the plant roots. The **mycorrhizae** blur the distinction between where the living soil ends and the plant starts.

The key benefits of mycorrhizal structures over the absence of mycorrhizae are:

- Mycorrhizal structures can accumulate as much as 100 times greater reserves of water and nutrients.

- Plants capture nutrients and water at increased rates.

- Nitrogen fixing takes place directly at the root, in response to plant requirements.

- Improved natural suppression of pathogens.

- Improved soil structure.

- Enhanced root growth.

Fig. 15.3 Biochar: Safe "Housing" for Microbes and Fine Root Hairs

Sounds too good to be true? There are limitations; the most prominent are that healthy mycorrhizae (a) can take years to fully develop (unless carefully inoculated and nurtured), and (b) can be damaged very quickly if the soil is grossly disturbed or sterilized by artificial chemicals.

Electron microscope image of beneficial fungi growing into the pores of biochar.

The well-established role of biochar in encouraging fungal growth indicates that inoculating a soil with a properly conditioned biochar can encourage the formation of highly beneficial mycorrhizal structures, in *weeks* rather than months or years.

## BREAKDOWN OF ORGANIC MATTER – THE ROLE OF C:N

Healthy soils require decomposed organic matter and nutrients. This is important in the context of inoculating biochars and soils to improve productivity, because it is not sufficient to put a "bunch of bugs" into a biochar or a soil that has no decomposed organic matter to feed them.

It is therefore beneficial to compost biochar. Composting establishes a large microbial population without necessarily having to resort to the application of a "high tech" inoculating mixture. The key point here is that if you co-compost biochar with other organic material you really don't need to seek out any special brews of proprietary microbes. What you need will already be present in healthy compost. In fact, given the tendency for soils to find their own balance, adding exotic organism is just as likely to be an expensive waste of time since the native microbes will progressively out-compete the exotics in a relatively short period of time. This is repeatedly borne out by scientific studies.

Biologically speaking, there are two pathways in the decomposition of organic matter—**putrefaction** and **fermentation**. Putrefaction provides food for plants, but also creates a **pathogenic** condition (a condition that can cause disease) within the soil, not to mention foul odors, nutrient loss, and a reduction of available nutrients to plants.

In contrast, the fermentative pathway tends to makes nutrients more available to plants. For this reason, fermentation is the target mechanism for composting. Fermentative cultures can be created by inoculating specific microorganisms. This is the basis of many commercial fermentation offerings such as the **bokashi system**, a commercial composting system that uses a mixture of microorganisms to inoculate compost. Echoing the introduction to this chapter, provide the right conditions and fermentation will commence naturally.

> **CONSUMER TIP 15.1**
> Because microbes need decomposed organic matter to feed on, it is beneficial to compost biochar.
> Composting biochar with other organic material automatically establishes a large population of microbes. "Special brews" of proprietary microbes aren't necessary—and are likely an expensive waste of time.

Soil science has determined that the fastest way to produce good soil ferment (compost) is to commence with an organic **carbon to nitrogen ratio (C:N)** ratio somewhere around 25 to 35 parts carbon to 1 part nitrogen. If the C:N ratio is too high, indicating excess carbon, decomposition is slow. If the C:N ratio is too low (indicating excess nitrogen), putrefaction or ammonia formation can occur, resulting in reduced microbial activity and a very low or very high pH, respectively.

Outlined in Table 15.1 are the average C:N ratios for some common organic materials. For the sake of simplicity, the materials containing high amounts of carbon are usually considered "browns," and materials containing high amounts of nitrogen are considered "greens." To achieve the correct C:N ratio for composting, the common rule of thumb is 1 volume of browns to 3 volumes of greens.

To this common terminology, the concept of "blacks" can be added to denote the use of biochars in the composting process. This process is sometimes described as "loading," "charging," or "inoculating" the biochar, although these terms are also used when chars are simply pre-soaked in a nutrient-rich liquid mixture immediately before addition to the soil.

Biochars have a high **recalcitrant** (fixed or inert) carbon content and a low organic carbon content. Typically, only 10–30% of the total C in the biochar is mobile and available to enter into the C:N balances. The C:N ratios for "blacks" in Table 15.1 are adjusted to better represent the mobile portion of the C available to enter into the organic cycle. It will be seen that in terms of C:N ratio, biochars can enter into the compost mix in volumes similar to straw, pine needles, or rice hulls. Hence, for composting purposes, the "rule of thumb" ratio becomes more like 1 volume of blacks to 5 volumes of greens, or alternatively 1 volume of browns plus 1 volume of blacks to 10 volumes of greens.

### How to Use the C:N Table

The C:N ratio of a combination of components is calculated as follows:

$$\frac{Volume\ of\ Ingredient\ A\ x\ C{:}N\ ratio + Volume\ of\ B\ x\ C{:}N\ ratio + ...etc.}{Total\ Volume\ of\ Ingredients\ Added}$$

For specified ingredients, the volumes are adjusted until the desired ratio of around 30 is achieved. To achieve the right ratio for conventional compost mix using lawn grass clippings and sawdust, the formula is:

*Volume of Lawn Grass x 15 + Volume of Sawdust x 450 / (Total volumes) = 30*

Here are a few examples of working with this target (arranged in a progression):

### Example 1.

Let's try to achieve the target C:N ratio of 30 by using 1 scoop (volume) of saw dust to 10 scoops (volumes) of grass. The result:

$$C{:}N = (10 \times 15 + 1 \times 450)\ /\ (10+1) = 55$$

This is too high, so it needs more N—specifically, grass. After a couple more tries we find 1 part sawdust to 30 parts grass puts us very close to our target.

$$C{:}N = (30 \times 15 + 1 \times 450)\ /\ (30+1) = 29$$

What happens if we want to add some biochar to improve the permeability of the compost (for improved aeration) and provide some "housing" for the microbes? If we add 1 scoop of biochar to the above mix we get:

$$C{:}N = (30 \times 15 + 1 \times 450 + 1 \times 100)\ /\ (30+1+1) = 31$$

Still well within our range.

### Example 2.

If we want to use more biochar, we could dispense with the sawdust and try 4 parts grass to 1 char:

$$C{:}N = (4 \times 15 + 1 \times 100)\ /\ (4+1) = 32$$

Along with the C:N ratio, it is still very important to get pH, moisture content, and temperatures in the right ranges. The recommended ranges are summarized later in this chapter.

| Table 15.1 Carbon:Nitrogen Ratios of Common Compost Ingredients | | | |
|---|---|---|---|
| Blacks = High Recalcitrant C | N | C*:N | Other notes |
| *Adjusted for the fact that in chars, the available carbon for composting is 10-30% of the total C. | | | |
| Slow pyrolysis wood biochar | 0.1 | 100:1 | Bark-free wood/sawdust. Mild liming |
| Slow pyrolysis green waste biochar | 0.1 | 100:1 | Moderate liming effect |
| Fast pyrolysis crop residue biochar | 0.8 | 80:1 | Mild to moderate liming effect |
| Slow pyrolysis rice husk & grasses | 0.1 | 75:1 | Moderate to strong liming effect |
| Fast pyrolysis green waste biochar | 1 | 50:1 | Mild to moderate liming effect |
| Wood ash | <0.1 | 25:1 | High in inorganics. Strong liming |
| **Browns = High Organic Carbon** | N | C:N | |
| Wood chips (bark free) | <0.1 | 600:1 | Low in other minerals |
| Cardboard, newspaper | 0.1 | 500:1 | Low in other minerals |
| Sawdust | 0.1 | 450:1 | Low in other minerals |
| Wood bark | 0.1 – 0.3 | 400:1 | Resistant to composting |
| Rice Hulls | 0.3 | 120:1 | High in silica |
| Pine needles | 1 | 80:1 | Resistant to composting |
| Straw | 0.7 | 75:1 | |
| Corn stalks | 0.7 | 70:1 | |
| Leaves | 0.8 -1 | 55:1 | |
| Sugarcane trash | 0.8 | 50:1 | |
| Woody weeds | 0.7 - 1 | 50:1 | |
| Fruit waste | 1 -1.4 | 40:1 | Moderate levels of P & others |
| Peanut shells | 1 | 35:1 | |
| **Greens = Low carbon / High N** | N | C:N | |
| Mixed garden greenwaste | 0.9 | 30:1 | |
| Hay | 0.7 | 25:1 | |
| Vegetable scraps | 1.5 | 25:1 | Moderate levels of P & others |
| Clover | 1 | 23:1 | |
| Mature compost | 1 | 20:1 | Ideally ~40% moisture |
| Rotted manure | 1 | 20:1 | |
| Seaweed | 2 | 20:1 | High in K and trace elements |
| Lawn grass clippings | 2.5 | 15:1 | |
| Herbivore manures | 1.5 - 3 | 15:1 | |
| Lucerne | 1.5 | 12:1 | |
| Chicken manure | 6 – 10 | 12:1 | Very high in P |
| Human and pig manure | 3 – 6 | 10:1 | High in P |
| Soil humus | 5 | 10:1 | Stable. Does not form ammonia |
| Bacteria and Fungi | | 7:1 | Included for reference |
| Sewage sludge | 5 – 6 | 5:1 | High in P |
| Blood | 14-Oct | 3:1 | High in P. Prone to putrefying. |
| Urine | 15 – 18 | 1:1 | High in P. |
| Meat scraps | 5 | <1:1 | High in P. Prone to putrefying |
| NOTE: The values indicated here for N and C:N ratio should be taken as a first approximation only. In practice there is more variability in these values than implied in the table, especially for biochars. | | | |

## Direct Composting of Biochar

The previous examples showed how biochar could be composted in combination with other **biomass**, but what about biochar as the main ingredient? A commonly recommended source of nitrogen for direct-composted biochar is urine (C:N ratio of 1:1). Using the same wood char and the above method, we can achieve our target of 30:1 using the following:

$$C:N = (1 \times 100 + 2 \times 1) / 3 = 34$$

That means adding 2 liters of urine for every liter of biochar, which is probably more than it can hold unless the urine is added progressively so that some water can evaporate. What we are describing here is, in effect, a biochar compost toilet, which is in fact used occasionally in India and elsewhere.

Another inoculant available in many locations is chicken manure. Let's try that at a one to one ratio with a **fast pyrolysis** greenwaste biochar:

$$C:N = (1 \times 50 + 1 \times 12) / 2 = 32$$

How about co-composting **greenwaste** and greenwaste biochar? If the greenwaste already has a C:N of 30, then any biochar we add will increase the C:N ratio. How much can we add? We find that we must keep the char to less than 1/3. That is, with 3 scoops of **greenwaste** and 1 of a fast pyrolysis biochar from the same greenwaste, the result is:

$$C:N = (3 \times 30 + 1 \times 50) / 4 = 35$$

This result is at the upper end of our 25–35 target range.

What about a more commercially attractive 50 volumes of greenwaste to 1 of biochar?

$$C:N = (50 \times 30 + 1 \times 50) / 51 = 30.4$$

Thus, greenwaste and fast pyrolysis biochars from greenwaste can be co-composted over a very wide range of blend ratios (presuming the pH of the blend is suitable).

What if you don't want to add anything to adjust the C:N ratio in your biochar, but you still want to compost it? In the case of **slow pyrolysis** chars, forget it: they are too inert. It is possible to compost fast pyrolysis biochars without doing anything more than bringing the pH below 8 by leaching with rainwater or, better still, with a **compost tea** (a liquid run-off from compost which can be collected or made) from a previous compost batch. Mixing some of the target soil into the biochar is a good idea to help inoculate it with local microbes. The other option is to blend freshly made biochar with water and then with an already well-composted biochar at no more than 1 part fresh biochar to 2 parts composted biochar. The composting process will be slower than a properly balanced blend, but it will happen.

---

**WHAT ABOUT P, K, S, CA, MG, AND MN?**

Phosphorous (P), potassium (K), sulfur (S), calcium (Ca), magnesium (Mg) and manganese (Mn) are essential nutrients that play key roles in plant nutrition, but a relatively minor role in composting. So, you want these in your mature compost, but these are not so much a prerequisite for composting.

The ideal N:P:K:S ratio varies considerably with different plants and environmental conditions, so general rules of thumb are not possible. For example, high amounts of P can be bad for plants adapted to poor soils (such as desert plants and many Australian natives), where other plants may benefit from additional P.

---

## RECOMMENDATIONS FOR INOCULATING BIOCHARS

The key principle for successfully conditioning biochars with beneficial organisms is that the best results come from working with nature—rather than trying to force it. In simple terms, this means ensuring that the condition of the mixture is compatible with microbial growth.

### Source of Starter Organisms

Most compost operations derive their starting material from either the naturally occurring microbes in the air and soil, or previous compost materials such as residual material left behind or compost teas. Many professional composters seed the compost with a proprietary starter mix. This will often accelerate the initial stages of composting, but scientific trials have reported mixed results in terms of the net financial value of this inoculation method, so it is best left to the professionals.

### Conditions for Microbial Growth

The essential specifications and target ranges for microbial growth are shown in Table 15.2.

Table 15.2 Biochar Conditions for Composting and Soil Amendment

| METRIC | SPECIFICATION/TARGET RANGE |
|---|---|
| pH | 5.5 – 8.5 (ideally 6.5 – 7) |
| Temperature | 20 – 40°C (ideally higher than 30°C) |
| Moisture | 30 – 40wt% (the point at which some can be just squeezed out by hand) |
| Nutrients (C:N) | 25:1 – 35:1 for composting<br>20:1 – 25:1 for direct soil inoculation, with due consideration of N:P:K:S ratios for the given crop |
| Char particle size | Mixed size range from fine dust to 5mm will provide sufficient scope for all physical and biochemical properties to be achieved |
| Source organisms | From the local soil (if healthy), previous compost, or compost tea |

The specifications and target ranges contained in Table 15.2, taken as a whole, represent the starting point for conditioning biochars. From this starting point, it will typically take 3–9 weeks in subtropical conditions for the material to mature enough to use it, with confidence, directly on plants. The composting process may not be fully complete for months; however, once a good level of microbial activity has been established, the product is suitable for addition to the soil.

## COMPOSTING METHODS

There are many methods for composting; these can be grouped as actively aerated (for example, turned windrows and drums) to passively aerated (piles and bins). In addition, there are anaerobic digestion and vermicomposting (using worms). Ultimately, the choice comes down to the upfront and operating costs for a given circumstance. As a first approximation, the process suited to the parent biomass material will be best.

The key benefits of biochars in composting are as follows:

a. Biochar (especially the larger particle fractions) aids the passage of gases, thus enhancing aeration processes.

b. Biochar reduces the loss of nitrogen to the atmosphere, especially in the early stages of the composting process.

c. Biochar aids in water retention.

d. Biochar provides "micro-climate controlled" housing for the microbes to proliferate in, possibly speeding the composting process.

### pH (Acidity/Alkalinity, or Liming Effect)

As a general rule, biochars have a liming effect—that is, they raise the soil pH. This effect is mild for chars from bark-free wood or sawdust. However, biochars from a source with a high inorganic content (for example, rice husks and grasses) will often have an unbuffered pH in the region of 8.5–10.5.

Similarly, fast pyrolysis biochars tend to have a lower unbuffered pH than slow pyrolysis biochars from the same feedstock. This is because fast pyrolysis biochars contain a higher residual organic carbon fraction, unless produced closer to the ash end of the biomass conversion scale.

> **ORGANIC FERMENT**
> An organic ferment solution is a mixture of a starch- or sugar-containing material (for example, molasses, ground grains, ground fruit, or vegetable scraps) that is mixed with 90% water and allowed to ferment for a few days or weeks. Technically, the result is called a beer. This will have a pH in the range of 4.5 to 5.5, due to the formation of organic acids.
> At the small scale, vinegar can be used to lower the pH of biochar

The unbuffered pH of a biochar can be moderated by blending it with an organic ferment solution, or by blending it into a starter compost mixture, as described previously. (See the textbox labeled "Organic Ferment.") The exact ratio depends on economics, compost availability, C:N considerations, and the liming strength of the biochar.

In Australia, Black is Green prepares conditioned fast pyrolysis biochars from sugar cane trash and from greenwaste. The process involves water saturation and pH adjustment of the chars using rainwater leaching or the addition of molasses ferment solutions, followed by natural decomposition in porous bulk bags or covered stockpiles. The resulting product is a rich, black, earthy-smelling, and soil-like material with an unbuffered pH of approximately 8, which can be used at rates up to 100% with most plants in conjunction with moderate addition of fertilizer.

**Dunder** or **vinasse** (see textbox) from the local ethanol distillery has also been considered for use as a pH-lowering agent, because each has a pH as low as 4, as well as additional nitrogen, phosphorous, potassium, and other minerals. For pot trials, Black is Green has also used vinegar as a pH-lowering agent.

> **Dunder,** also known as **vinasse,** is a by-product of the production of ethanol from sugar cane juice or molasses. It is the residue after fermentation. Sometimes dunder is fortified for use as "one shot" liquid fertilizer.

*Worms – Canaries in the Coal Mine and Mini-aerators*
Worms in soil are like the proverbial canaries in the coal mine. If something is wrong, they will move on—or in the worst case die. (For instructions on testing with worms, see the chapter titled "Gauging the Impact of Biochar: Simple Tests for Farmers and Gardeners.")

Ideally, worms should be added to compost blends after the initial period of maturation (that is, once the internal temperature is below 34°C). Worms will provide a clear indication as to the toxicity of the compost blend. If the worms cannot be found in the compost blend after a few days, then there is something wrong with it. Worms also help the composting process, by turning over and aerating the mixture.

## ADDING BIOCHAR TO SOILS

After the biochar conditioning process is complete, the biochar can be spread on, or worked into, the target soil for the best results. Typically, biochar is added to soil during the planting stage. However, for permanent plantings like lawns and gardens, biochar is added to the surface in smaller, more frequent increments.

As previously noted, the soil microbe populations are located in the rhizosphere—the first few inches or centimeters of the soil and around the plant roots. So it makes sense to place biochar where the microbes are, near the soil surface and near to the plant roots. Anywhere else is likely to be of less direct benefit.

## How Much Biochar to Add

Expressed in a number of approximately equivalent measures, the rates that conditioned biochar is added to soils varies within the following ranges:

- 2–20 tons/ha

- 0.2–2 kg/m²

- 0.2 to 2.0% by weight (incorporation to depth 10 cm in soil with density 1.0)

- 0.5 to 5% by volume (if biochar density is 0.4, 1 to 10% with density 0.2)

## Nutrient Suppression

Organic materials and biochars share a common characteristic. When first added to a soil, they suppress the nitrogen available to plants. For organic material, this is largely due to a surge in microbial activity in the presence of readily available organic carbon. For biochar, this effect is combined with—in fact, dominated by—chemical **adsorption** of nutrients into the char, which extends beyond just nitrogen to affect most nutrients (see the textbox labeled "Adsorption Properties of Biochars"). For this reason, it is very unwise to add an unconditioned biochar directly to soil without adding compensating nutrients at the same time.

## Can't I Just Dig It In?

Given all the above discussion about conditioning biochar before adding it to the soil, the natural question might be "Can't I just use biochar directly?" Yes, you can, but it is risky, because unconditioned biochar may upset the soil by causing a change in moisture, pH, or nutrient availability. In some applications (for example, large-scale soil remediation) this risk is economically justified, but for commercial crops it is the equivalent of Russian roulette until you have definitive proof that the biochar won't do more harm than good. The risk can be minimized by conditioning the biochar to conform to the recommended parameters before adding it to the soil.

### ADSORPTION PROPERTIES OF BIOCHARS

Adsorption is not strictly the same as absorption, but either way it means that something is grabbed and held onto. For biochars this can extend to grabbing, and thus reducing the effectiveness of, chemicals like pesticides, fungicides, and herbicides. This is an important consideration for farm operations that use these chemicals.

## BIOCHAR POT TRIALS

The photographs shown next were taken 27 days after planting corn seeds in a range of soil blends (Figure 15.4), and 29 days after planting tomato seeds (Figure 15.5). The soil was a good quality, previously uncultivated, basaltic soil from southeast Queensland (Australia).

The biochar used in the trials was prepared from mixed greenwaste using a fast pyrolysis process and conditioned by simple dampening and holding for approximately 3 weeks.

## Corn Trials

Fig. 15.4    Biochar Pot Trials – Corn at 27 Days

Here is how the pots were prepared for the corn trial, and the trial results:

- *Pot 1:* prepared with the soil only (control).

- *Pots 2 and 3 (not shown):* prepared with a blend of 2% and 5% char in the control soil with no fertilizer added. Pots 2 and 3 showed enhanced growth relative to the control plants, but the results were not as obvious as the plants pictured in Figure 15.4.

- *Pot 4:* prepared with soil and with 0.75% of liquid NPK fertilizer added. On average, these plants grew 11% higher than the control plants.

- *Pot 5:* prepared with soil mixed with 0.74% of NPK fertilizer plus **2 wt% char.** On average, these plants grew **38% higher** than the control plants

- *Pot 6:* prepared with soil mixed with 0.68% of NPK fertilizer plus **5 w% char.** On average, these plants grew **41% higher** than the control plants.

## Tomato Trials

For the tomato trials, equal doses of a soluble NPK fertilizer were added to all pots (including the control Pot 1) on Day 20. All except the three best plants in each pot were removed at day 24, to avoid overcrowding.

Fig. 15.5    Biochar Pot Trials – Tomatoes at 29 Days

Selected plants from the tomato trial

Here is how the pots were additionally prepared for the tomato trial, and the trial results:

- *Pot 1:* prepared with the soil only (control).

- *Pot 2:* prepared with soil mixed with **2.4% char**. The plants grew **50% higher** than the control plants.

- *Pot 3:* prepared with soil mixed with **4.8% char**. The plants grew **70% higher** than the control plants.

- *Pot 4:* prepared with soil mixed with 2.4% char and acidified with 2.4% white vinegar. The plants grew **37% higher** than the control plants.

- *Pot 5:* prepared with soil mixed with 4.6% char and acidified with 2.3% white vinegar. The plants grew **77% higher** than the control plants.

## OTHER STUDIES AND TRIALS

The following examples of inoculating biochar are obtained primarily from the archives of the International Biochar Initiative website (www.biochar-international.org).

### Composting with Rice Bran

Dr. Yoshizawa and his co-workers at Japan's Meisei University described co-composting bamboo charcoal with rice bran as a nutrient at a weight ratio of 1:1.15. The mixture was adjusted to 65% moisture and then seeded with an aerobic microorganism complex. The mixture was maintained in ambient air at 23°C and stirred daily to aerate. Examination with a scanning electron microscope revealed that microorganisms had proliferated on the surface and in the pores of the charcoal after as little as 70 hours.

The same team also described the successful routine composting of a mixture of 10% charcoal and garbage from 55 houses over a 2-month period in April and May of 2005 in the city of Suwa, Japan. Vigorous microbial growth was evident in and on the char when examined after 1–2 months.

### Inoculating Soil with Biochar and Compost

Gabi Soto of the Center for Tropical Agriculture Research and Teaching in Costa Rica is using the bokashi composting system with a sugar cane bagasse biochar to make a marketable fertilizer for organic farming. Bokashi, as previously noted, is a commercial composting system that uses a commercial inoculum of microorganisms. In Soto's system, the microorganisms used are a mixture of the bokashi commercial inoculum, augmented with local microbes sourced from forest leaf litter which has been fermented using a molasses substrate mixed with rice polishings. The compost blend is composted anaerobically for 10 to 15 days, then spread out and sprayed with the inoculant, then composted aerobically again for a period of approximately 20 days. [See next chapter for more details and photos.]

The typical composition of the product is N 1.6%, P 1.4%, K 2.7%, organic material 32.3% (C:N of approximately 18:1). Soil application rates for the resulting product are 1.5 to 3 tons/hectare.

### Experiments on Co-composting Poultry Litter with Biochar

Christoph Steiner and his co-workers at The University of Georgia have conducted experiments on the composting of poultry litter with 20% pine chip char biochar. The composting period was 42 days. The results indicated that the biochar increased the rate of composting, and reduced total N losses by up to 52%. Their conclusion was that biochar may be an ideal bulking agent for composting N-rich materials.

Bruno O. Dias and his co-workers in Brazil and Spain evaluated the use of eucalyptus wood biochar as a bulking agent for the composting of poultry manure, against coffee husks and sawdust. They found that despite the inert nature of the biochar, the composting mixture prepared with biochar underwent a comparatively rapid organic matter degradation of 70% of the initial content. The biochar also reduced the losses of nitrogen.

## CONCLUSION

The chapter has discussed composting as a way to condition or "load" biochars with the microbes that provide many of the benefits attributed to the biochar phenomenon. Adaptation of composting parameters, such as C:N ratio, to the co-composting of biochars with other biomass was also discussed.

Recommendations were made to achieve successful microbial growth, with or without special inoculant mixtures. Attention to pH, nutrient balance, and moisture in the composting process were advised as ways to help ensure a positive plant response when the conditioned biochar-compost blend is added to the soil.

## KEY POINTS FROM THIS CHAPTER

- Biochar provides benefits to soils, which are best achieved by "conditioning" it before adding it to the soil. This means: (1) charging it with plant nutrients and (2) inoculating (seeding) it with living organisms.

- Soil health is determined by complex interactions between microorganisms, plant roots, and organic and inorganic chemicals.

- The best way to inoculate a biochar is to create conditions for natural microbes to proliferate—as required for effective composting. It is therefore beneficial to compost biochar, and treat it like a compost ingredient.

- Microbes play a pivotal role in healthy soil and plant growth. Microbes "mine" and transfer essential nutrients from the soil to plants. Because biochar is both porous and granular, it provides a safe "housing" for microbes and fine root hairs.

- Composting biochar with other organic material automatically establishes a large population of microbes. Therefore, proprietary microbes are not needed.

- Composting with biochar also offers other benefits. Biochar (a) aids the passage of gases, enhancing aeration; (b) reduces the loss of nitrogen to the atmosphere; and (c) aids water retention.

- Although unconditioned biochar can be added to the soil, this is risky and unwise. Unconditioned biochar may cause unwanted changes in moisture, pH, or nutrient availability.

- Positive results from conditioned biochar can be seen in weeks rather than months or years. Pot trials show dramatic improvements in plants grown in soil treated with conditioned char combined with fertilizers.

- Other studies and trials of inoculated or composted biochar showed rapid proliferation of microbes, increased rates of composting, and reduced nitrogen loss.

# Chapter 16

# Making and Using Biochar Mixed with Organic Matter, Minerals, and Wood Vinegar

Stephen Joseph, PhD
Vice Chairman
International Biochar Initiative

Julie Major PhD
Agricultural Extension Director
International Biochar Initiative

&

Paul Taylor, PhD
Biochar Consultant
BiocharBooks.org

## IN THIS CHAPTER YOU WILL LEARN:

- About the long-standing traditions of producing and using various mixtures of biochar, minerals, and organic material, to prepare or improve soil.

- How smoke-derived compounds can make important contributions to the growth of microorganisms and the germination of seeds and growth of seedlings, and thus a beneficial effect on plant health and growth.

- What currently is known about, and the ongoing research into, these practices and their effects.

- Initiatives to produce lower-cost biochar and biochar-mineral complexes (BMC) that increase crop yields while maintaining and building soil carbon.

"Growing evidence indicates that adding biochar-mineral complexes to soil improves microbial growth and crop yields."

## INTRODUCTION

Farmers in Asia and South America have long used biochar in complex mixtures and **wood vinegar (smoke water)** from **pyrolysis**. However, much of the technical information on the subject is recent, and comes from researchers and practitioners in Asia, Central and South America, Australia and New Zealand. Their publications and presentations have shed more light on the manufacture and use of biochar, biochar/biomass mineral complexes, and the smoke chemicals produced at low temperatures during pyrolysis.

Growing evidence suggests greater microbial growth and crop yields result from application of biochar-mineral complexes to soil than from application of biochar alone (Steiner 2006; Chia, *et al.* (in press); Joseph, *et al.* 2010). Biochar-mineral complexes (BMC) are manufactured by baking, at low temperature (<250°C), a mixture of biochar (including high-mineral ash biochar such as that made from some animal manures), biomass, clay, and minerals.

Research from Japan, South Africa, and Australia indicates that smoke- derived compounds make important contributions to the growth of microorganisms and the germination of seeds and growth of seedlings of many plants (Hiyashi 1990 and Ishigaki 1990, Ishii *et al.* 1990, Light, *et al.* 2009, Dixon 1998).

This chapter summarizes what is known about biochar in complex mixtures and smoke water. The chapter has four sections:

Section 1.    Recent research aimed at re-creating *terra preta* soil using BMC
Section 2.    An overview of the science behind BMC
Section 3.    Traditional methods of manufacturing complex biochar mixtures
Section 4.    The production and use of smoke water, a by-product of producing biochar through pyrolysis

### SECTION 1.   RECENT RESEARCH ON BIOCHAR-MINERAL COMPLEXES

Recent research aims to create *terra preta*-like soils by amending them with bio-char-mineral complexes. One research project, started in 2008, is led by Professor Stephen Joseph at the University of New South Wales, Australia in collaboration with Professor Paul Munroe, Dr. Lukas van Zwieten (NSW Department of Industries and Investment), and Dr. Paul Blackwell (Western Australian Department of Agriculture and Food). They are testing the hypothesis that **torrefaction** of **biomass** (with or without biochar) will produce a carbon structure that reacts with clay and other minerals to produce a material that has properties similar to the Amazonian *terra preta* soils in terms of stability and soil fertility––for example, it would have similar **cation exchange capacity (CEC)**, electrical conductivity (salt content), pH, and **adsorption** of dissolved organic matter. The project leaders also hope that reacting biomass and minerals at below-pyrolysis temperatures will shed more light on the mechanisms responsible for forming the organo-mineral particles found in *terra preta*.

Phase 1 of this research involved forming a BMC by reacting biomass, biochar, clay, and minerals in a laboratory oven at temperatures below 250°C. Raw materials used included a mixture of raw clay, crushed brick, lime, bones, calcium phosphate, chicken manure, and sawdust. These materials were chosen based on a detailed examination of the internal carbon and mineral structure of *terra preta* soil particles (Brodowski *et al.* 2005) and from examining archeological evidence.

The BMC was analyzed using a range of microscopic and spectroscopic techniques. Structures similar to those observed in *terra preta* soils were found (Chia *et al.* 2010).

Field trials using this BMC were conducted in a poor, sandy soil, where wheat plants were grown in tubes inserted into field soil. PVC tubes, 10 cm in diameter, were driven into the soil vertically, with the base of the tube open to the natural subsoil. In-ground tubes were used, since the amounts of biochar and BMC available were insufficient for extensive field plots. It was believed that this technique would yield results that were more representative of large-scale field trials than pot trials in a greenhouse.

The BMC materials used in these field trials were heated for 3 hours at 220°C and 240°C. The experiment also included a treatment of wood[1] biochar produced at 600°C in a retort used for making metallurgical-grade charcoal. All materials were incorporated at a rate of 10 t/ha (air dry weight) with or without adding appropriate synthetic fertilizers, with 4 replications. At planting, a base phosphorus (P) fertilizer (single superphosphate) was applied at 100 kg/ha to all tubes. Fertilizer treatments consisted of ammonium nitrate (equivalent to 28 kg/ha nitrogen - N) and potassium (K) (26 kg/ha).

The results of these field trials show that the BMC applied alone gave yields similar to those obtained by applying biochar and synthetic fertilizer, and the greatest yields were obtained when the BMC was applied along with synthetic fertilizer (Figure 16.1). These results may be partly explained by the fact that the BMC contained more and different plant nutrients than the biochar alone.

In Phase 2 of the research project, funded by Anthroterra Pty Ltd, a new BMC material was made and tested in larger, 40-cm diameter bins. It was hypothesized that adding this new biochar mixture to soil would result in greater plant yields at lower application rates (less than 1 ton/ha of biochar, or 3 t/ha of BMC).

Biochar used for trials in Geraldton, Western Australia (WA) was made from *Acacia saligna* at approximately 400°C (held for approximately 30 minutes) in a small batch reactor. The biochar was cooled and then activated with a solution of 10% phosphoric acid.

---

[1] *Eucalyptus marginata Donn ex Sm.* (commonly known as jarrah).

Fig. 16.1    Results of BMC Field Trials: Wheat Yields in Western Australia

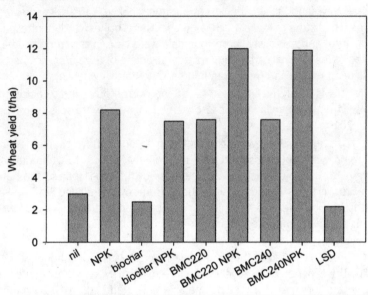

Figure Notes:

• Overall high yields are an artifact of the methodology, where plants grew inside tubes.

• Nil = no organic amendment.

• NPK = synthetic fertilizer.

• BMC220 = BMC heated at 220°C temperature.

• LSD = least significant difference. Differences between treatment bars that are smaller than this bar are not statistically different, and therefore no difference can be inferred between the two treatments.

After standing for 1 hour, the treated wet biochar was mixed with chicken litter, kaolinitic clay, sand high in calcium carbonate, rock phosphate, and small amounts of other trace elements (e.g. manganese and rutile, which contains titanium[2]). The composition of the resulting mixture was approximately 30% clay, 30% biochar, 30% manure, and 10% minerals.

---

[2] Titanium (Ti) seems to be an important mineral both in *terra preta* and in BMC. Kuzel et al (2003) have shown that Ti is an important micronutrient that has a hormetic effect. Hormesis is the name given to the stimulatory effects caused by low levels of potentially toxic agent. It is possible that Ti plays a role in making nutrients more available to plants through its involvement in redox reactions (Thompson *et al.*, 2006).

The mixture was then heated in a small reactor to 220°C for 3 hours. Once this material was cooled, smoke-related butenolide[3] was added to the BMC to assist in germination and growth of microorganisms.

The agronomic properties of this Phase 2 BMC were measured by the Department of Industries and Investment of New South Wales. Those properties are shown in Table 16.1.

Table 16.1 Agronomic Properties of BMC

| Laboratory No | | | 3284 |
|---|---|---|---|
| Sample ID | Unit | Limit of reporting | Anthroterra BMC5/09 |
| EC | Ds/m | 0.01 | 3.6 |
| pH (CaCl2) | pH units | 0.04 | 5.7 |
| Bray #1 Phosphorus | mg/kg | 0.06 | 1500 |
| Colwell Phosphorus | mg/kg | 2 | 2700 |
| Total Nitrogen | % | 0.02 | 1.2 |
| Total Carbon | % | 0.20 | 24 |
| KCl extractable Ammonium | mg/kg | 0.3 | 100 |
| KCl extractable Nitrate | mg/kg | 0.2 | <0.2 |
| Organic Carbon | % | 0.05 | 18 |
| ANC | % CaCO3 equivalent | 0.5 | 7.4 |
| **Exchangeable Cations** | | | |
| Aluminium | cmol(+)/kg | 0.034 | 1.1 |
| Calcium | cmol(+)/kg | 0.013 | 29 |
| Potassium | cmol(+)/kg | 0.085 | 5.3 |
| Magnesium | cmol(+)/kg | 0.003 | 7.7 |
| Manganese | cmol(+)/kg | 0.001 | 6.7 |
| Sodium | cmol(+)/kg | 0.037 | 4.2 |
| *Pre-digest* | | | |
| Aluminium | cmol(+)/kg | 0.034 | 7.2 |
| Calcium | cmol(+)/kg | 0.013 | 73 |
| Potassium | cmol(+)/kg | 0.085 | 12 |
| Magnesium | cmol(+)/kg | 0.003 | 22 |
| Manganese | cmol(+)/kg | 0.001 | 21 |
| Sodium | cmol(+)/kg | 0.037 | 8.4 |

Table Notes:

- Bray #1 and Colwell are two different ways of extracting phosphorus from soil in amounts similar to those extracted by plant root activity.

- EC = electrical conductivity.

- ANC = acid neutralizing capacity.

- Pre-digestion is used to remove labile compounds that may cover the exchange sites.

- Limit of reporting: values lower than the limits given cannot be detected.

[3] The butenolide 3-methyl-2H-furo[2,3-c]pyran-2-one has been identified as the main germination cue from smoke. It was produced by heating sugar with arginine for 30 minutes at 180°C (Light et al., 2005).

These analyses indicate that this BMC has a sum of exchangeable cations of 53.2 cmol(+)/kg and a relatively high level of available phosphorus. Wood biochar has a sum of exchangeable cations of approximately 5–10 cmol(+)/kg and available phosphorus of 15 mg/kg. It should be noted that the CEC of biochar and BMC, i.e. its ability to retain cations, depends on how long the biochar or the BMC has been exposed to the environment.

Trials in containers with *Sorghum* sp. (a C4 plant) and sunflowers (*Helianthus sp.*, a C3 plant) were conducted during the summer in Geraldton WA, with BMC application rates of 50 kg/ha, 100 kg/ha, 200 kg/ha, and 300 kg/ha. In this trial, 30 and 60 kg/ha of a NPK (2:4.9:13.4) synthetic fertilizer were also used to determine the relative merits compared with BMC. In addition, Dr. Z. Solaiman of the University of Western Australia measured crop root colonization by **mycorrhizal** fungi (AMF).

The Geraldton container trials, conducted by Dr. Blackwell, reported a significant increase in yield of approximately 25% (compared with the unamended control) in the growth of sorghum at a BMC application rate of 300 kg BMC/ha. With a 60kg/ha synthetic fertilizer application, yield increase was approximately 35%. No significant increase in yield was measured when 30kg/ha of synthetic fertilizer or 200kg/ha of BMC was applied. Root colonization by mycorrhizal fungi was much greater for the plants growing in soil that had been amended with BMC (Figure 16.2). Similar improvements in grain yields with BMC were not detected for sunflowers.

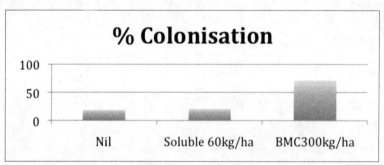

Fig. 16.2    Soluble Synthetic Fertilizer vs. BMC in Wheat: Mycorrhizal Fungi Root Colonization
Source: Dr. Z. Solaiman, UWA

It is apparent from this research that the BMC provides a suitable habitat for microorganisms and the indications are that small additions of BMC can result in higher growth rates of a C4 plant such as sorghum, compared with unamended controls.

Preliminary trials on forage crops (mixture of **forage rape** (*Brassica* sp.) and millet (*Poaceae*)) in a loamy soil were also undertaken in Victoria, Australia by a fertilizer company. The yields of forage crops with application of 300 kg BMC/ha were considerably greater than the yields where only 100kg/ha of conventional diammonium phosphate fertilizer was applied.

Results from these Australian trials indicate that relatively low applications of BMC complexes (<1 ton/ha), when compared with larger amounts of biochar alone typically applied, have the potential to improve crop yields beyond levels attainable using only synthetic fertilizers. Microscopic examination of the BMC particles and plant roots extracted from the soil post-harvest indicates an increase in the microbial populations of fungi, bacteria, and faunal grazers. Plant root hairs surround the BMC particles and extract the BMC's macro- and micronutrients with the assistance of microorganisms or plant exudates.

Preliminary field trials using BMC were also carried out in Costa Rica by Dr. Tamara Benjamin (of Purdue University) and Gabriela Soto, M.Sc. of the Tropical Agriculture Research and Teaching Centre (CATIE). The biochar used was made from Melina tree (*Gmelina arborea* Roxb.) sawmill waste, in a Foidl kiln. The BMC was made by reacting phosphoric acid-activated biochar with organic waste and other materials under heat, blending continuously for 1 hour at 80°C and then raising the temperature to 220°C for several hours while continuing to blend the mixture. The BMC was produced at the facilities of Biocombustibles de Costa Rica in Puerto Jiménez from the following ingredients:

- 3 parts biochar—treated with phosphoric acid to activate biochar surfaces.

- 3 parts manure/organic waste—chicken litter and oil-palm rachis (the residue left after fruits are removed from the stem structure that holds them) were selected for the initial run.

- 3 parts clay—both blue and red clays, obtained locally, were used in the initial run.

- 1-part plant nutrient minerals—mainly rock phosphate and calcium carbonate.

- Boiling water in sufficient quantities to permit mixing/blending.

Trials were conducted in 2009 by planting corn between oil palm plants in an agroforestry system, on a farm in the village of San Juan, in the Osa peninsula in southwestern Costa Rica (Figure 16.3). The soil has a low pH of 5.1, has a low CEC and available P, and has nearly equal amounts of clay and sand (approximately 40%), but has a relatively high concentration of carbon (3.5%). BMC, fertilizer, and/or biochar were added prior to seeding. Six separate treatments were tested with three replicates as detailed in Table 16.2, along with the resulting yields.

Fig. 16.3    BMC Field Trial in Costa Rica – Growth of Corn Plants after 90 Days

Left: Corn growth with BMC + urea. Right: Corn growth with biochar + urea

| | | Corn Seeded at 27,000 plants/ha | Yield (g dry weight) |
|---|---|---|---|
| **Treatment** | | **Application Rate** | **Mean** |
| 1 | Control | Unamended | 45.8 |
| 2 | Urea | 50 kg/ha = 23 kg N/ha | 50.3 |
| 3 | Biochar + Urea | 12 t/ha (dry basis) + urea as above | 49.1 |
| 4 | Biochar + P + Urea | 7.7t/ha (dry basis) + urea as above | 87.4 |
| 5 | BMC + Urea | 13.5t/ha (dry basis)+urea as above | 109.1 |
| 6 | 10-30-10 (NPK) | 230 kg / ha = 23 kg N/ha | 131.3 |

Table 16.2  Field Trials in San Juan, Costa Rica:
Treatments and Dry Weight Yields for Corn from 19 m² Plots

The yield achieved using BMC + Urea treatment was significantly higher than that obtained with Biochar + Urea, but was not statistically different from that obtained with NPK or Biochar + P + Urea. In other words, treatment 5 produced higher yield than treatment 3, but due to variability in the data, no real differences can be inferred between treatments 4, 5 and 6 and these must be assumed to have performed equally. Further trials with lower application rates are planned.

## SECTION 2.    THE SCIENCE BEHIND COMPLEX BIOCHAR MIXTURES

### Interaction of Clay and Biomass During Heating

Clays are composed mainly of aluminum (Al) and silica (Si), and have layered structures. Elements within the building blocks of this structure can be substituted; for example, aluminum or iron (Fe) can replace silica. These substitutions lead to the development of negative surface charge on clays, and this charge is responsible for the CEC of clay minerals. The CEC of a soil is an important measure of its ability to retain nutrients occurring as positively charged ions such as $Ca^{2+}$, $Mg^{2+}$, $NH_4^+$ (cations), and make them available to plants. Organic matter and biochar also contribute to the CEC of bulk soil, because they also develop negative surface charge in soil.

When many different types of clay are heated to 80–100°C, their CEC, porosity, and surface area can increase (Heller-Kallai 2006). Mixing and heating clay, wood waste, and high mineral ash animal manure at 80°C will result in the dissolution of water soluble organic compounds, positively charged ions, and negatively charged ions (anions), from the biomass into the water present in the mixture. These dissolved compounds are transferred to the clay surface. As this happens, chemical bonds are formed between minerals and organic matter within the mixture. It is probable that some of these rearranged compounds and ions will be intercalated (inserted or introduced) within the clay structure (Lagaly 1984). Fine clay and silica particles can move into the pores of the biomass. These particles come into intimate contact with the biomass surface.

As the mixture of the clay and the biomass is heated above 100°C, water is lost as it begins to "boil off." When this water is lost, cations and anions can begin to precipitate on both the clay and the biomass. Once the temperature rises above 110°C, other water, which was held more tightly inside the biomass and clay, is released as vapor. As this water leaves the mixture, chemical reactions occur, creating more negative charges on both clays and organic matter.

As the biomass reaches 180°C, light volatile organic molecules are released from the mixture. As the temperature continues to rise, heavier volatile molecules will be released and will react with the clay. New polymers can be formed, and reactions between mixture components can form organo-mineral complexes (Laszlo 1987).

Examination of the surface of biochar organo-mineral complexes in a number of different BMC formulations has been carried out using x-ray photoelectron spectroscopy (XPS), nuclear magnetic resonance (NMR), sweep voltametry, scanning electron microscopy (SEM), transmission electron microscopy (TEM), pyrolysis gas chromatography/mass spectrometry (Py-GC/MS), and Fourier transform infrared spectroscopy (FTIR). The data indicate that the surfaces are very reactive, have a high concentration of nutrients that are plant available and have a high volume of pores that would facilitate the growth of microorganisms. Slices made through these particles reveal similar structures to those found in *terra preta* particles.

## SECTION 3.    TRADITIONAL METHODS OF PRODUCING COMPLEX BIOCHAR MIXTURES

The manufacture and use of complex biochar mixtures may seem like a new idea, and perhaps even premature, given current efforts to better understand the value and functioning of "simple" biochar application to soil. However, in many places around the world, people have been making and using complex biochar mixtures for a very long time. These techniques are sparsely documented. Here we provide several examples of how complex biochar mixtures are produced for use as soil amendments.

### 3.1    Making Biochar-Mineral Complexes without Kilns

A recent BBC program, "Around the World in 80 Gardens," provides an example of how present-day Amazonian indigenous peoples manufacture a biochar mineral complex. A woman is shown mixing charcoal and ash from a fire with soil and partly composted biomass. She then bakes this mixture in an open fire. This mixture is used to amend soil where medicinal plants are grown.

Christoph Steiner's Ph.D. thesis discussed these open burn techniques in greater detail. After working with small-scale farmers near the city of Manaus in the Brazilian Amazon, he made the following observations:

> The first level of soil fertility enhancement is the burned soil (*Terra Queimada*, TQ). To produce TQ they pile up woody biomass and let it dry for about a week. Burning the biomass on the soil they pay attention that the fire is strong and hot. Three days after the burn the soil is called *Terra Cheirosa* (TC–smelling soil). The soil has a very strong scent of the condensates from smoke (pyroligneous acid). The TC is left unplanted for three weeks, otherwise…nothing will grow or the plants die. This soil remains fertile for 3 years. Only undemanding crops like manioc, pineapple, and trees (although the main food crops) are planted directly on TQ. For special plantings like vegetables and medicinal plants further soil management is necessary. These are abundant between their houses and mainly done in elevated or isolated gardens. For further soil fertility improvements all abundant types of OM [organic matter] at the settlement are used (bones, wood, leafs, chicken manure), as are materials collected in the forest (*Pau*). *Pau* are rotten tree trunks and they are selected with certain preferences. Unexpectedly, the OM is burned too before it gets mixed with the TQ.

This recent information on soil fertility management is intriguing, especially coming from a region where the *terra preta* soils are found (see text box)

*Ankara*, the practice of burning vegetable material that has been buried in soil beds or mounds is common among the food growers of the Western and North-Western Highlands of Cameroon (Lyonga, 1980). Urs Guyer[4] described the *Ankara* technique:

> In the NW-Province of Cameroon, when the elephant grass is completely dry, the people start to clear the plots to prepare the farms for the planting season. The farm plots are arranged in ridges, so the dry grass is placed in between the old ridges. Then the grass is covered with a rather thin layer of soil taken from the old neighboring ridges. At certain distances a hole is left open to aerate the grass layer below the soil. Then the grass is lit from the two ends of the ridge. Under the soil the grass is transformed to char. Depending on the quantity of grass the fire can burn for several days. When the soil is cold it is mixed with the char. Planting starts when the rains begin to fall. This can be weeks or even months after the *Ankara* was made.

---

[4] Personal communication, Urs Guyer, Switzerland.

## A NOTE ON *TERRA PRETA*

As previously mentioned in this book, Amazonian "Dark Earths," locally known as *terra preta de Indio*, or "dark earth of the Indians," have inspired recent interest in using biochar for improving soil fertility and sequestering carbon in soil. These biochar-rich, highly fertile soils are found where indigenous, pre-Columbian villages existed, and were created as a result of human activity. However, the extent to which these soils were intentionally made is still not known, since the *terra preta* soils were not used predominantly for growing crops but rather occurred in living areas. Except for these patches of fertility, the unflooded soils of the Amazon basin are characteristically acidic and poor. Dark Earth soils remain fertile today, after hundreds to thousands of years.

Although numerous Dark Earth sites likely remain covered by forest vegetation and unmapped, several can be found near present-day towns and cities, and are successfully used in local farming. For example, Major *et al.* (2005) reported on productivity differences between the Dark Earth soils and the surrounding degraded soils near Manaus. She conducted on-farm field trials at four-paired locations without any added fertilizer, and found that:

> Soil fertility among the Dark Earth varied considerably with differences largely attributable to [recent] past-use history. Consequently, maize yield and weed pressure varied among field locations, reflecting these differences in soil fertility in addition to differences in weed reservoirs such as seed banks. Maize yield in weeded plots was as much as 63 times greater on Dark Earth (550 kg/ha) than on corresponding adjacent soil (9 kg/ha), and single location averages varied from 0 to 3.15 t/ha for Dark Earth.

For more detail on the history and creation of *terra preta*, see Chapter 1, Ancient Origins, Modern Solution."

Fig. 16.4 *Ankara* System: Charring Biomass in Clay

(Photo: Urs Guyer)

After a study of the *Ankara* system, Osinamea and Meppeb (1999) reported the following:

> *Ankara* (a local practice of slow burning partially buried dry plant residues) was compared with surface burning and burying plant residues under the ridges without burning. The comparison was made under no fertilizer and with fertilizer application.
>
> Intensive heat generation under the *Ankara* resulted in aggregation of soil colloids into larger particles. The clay-sized fraction fell by 48% while the silt-sized fraction rose by 30%. The *Ankara* released large amounts of phosphorus (P) and potassium (K), and trapped adequate nitrogen (N) to sustain a maize yield six times that where residues were buried under the ridges without burning and no fertilizer application, and three times that of surface burning plant residues. The residual effects of the *Ankara* on a second maize crop were not significant unless fertilizer NPK was applied. Poor residual effects of the *Ankara* may be due to enhancement of leaching losses of N, K, and magnesium (Mg) from the root zone as a result of changes in the textural characteristics of the soil. Surface burning plant residues did not produce any adverse effects on soil particle size distribution.

The earlier study by Lyonga (1977) was continued for 5 years and showed that if plots were burned every year, maize yields were maintained at about 4 times that of plots with no burning (and no manures). If burning was discontinued the yield dropped, but was brought back to the same level if P and N fertilizers were added.

Some tribal communities in India use the *Raab* system of charring biomass. This system consists of making beds of various layers of Dry, half-dry, and fresh woody and leafy biomass, dung, and clay. This layered bed is fully sealed with clay and char fired (burning in low oxygen conditions). The resulting material is used as an amendment to establish rice nurseries. The tribe members affirm that rice growth is optimal when this amendment is used.

### 3.2    Making Biochar-Mineral Complexes in Simple Brick Kilns

In Asia, biochar has been produced during the manufacture of bricks and clay pots. Fresh biomass and minerals are often added to clay before firing in order to improve the plasticity of the material and hence facilitate shaping it into bricks and pots, and also to improve heat distribution during cooking (in the case of pots).

The shaped mixtures are placed in a simple kiln. Rice husks or sadust are packed around the bricks or pots and then a fire is started. Much of the inside of the pot or brick is only partly fired (Figure 16.5) and can contain small amounts of biochar from the pyrolysis of the incorporated biomass.

This method of pyrolysis is very inefficient (producing abundant smoke) and a lot of char remains along with ash and fired pieces of broken bricks or pots ranging in size from sub-millimeter to centimeters in diameter. This leftover ash, biochar, and biochar-containing fired clay is either used as a soil amendment by the kiln's owners or occasionally sold to surrounding farmers.

Fig. 16.5   Biochar Inside a Brick Fired at 500°C

The dark color inside the brick shows charred organic matter. The lighter outside is the oxidized clay, which contains very little biochar. (Photo: S. Joseph)

On using these leftover materials, Dr. Sai Bhaskar Reddy Nakka, CEO of the Geoecology Energy Organisation in India, reports the following on his website (http://e-terrapreta.blogspot.com/):

> The left over material from the traditional potters kiln after baking pottery items is a good additive for the soils. These kilns yield charcoal, ash, broken pieces of pots and burnt soil used to cover the kiln. All the above components form a good additive for the acidic soils as is. The potter rarely shares this material with others, he uses it as the most precious material for his own fields.

Unfortunately, current scientific literature offers little information on how adding this material affects yields and soil health.

### 3.3   Fermenting Mixtures of Biochar, Biomass, and Minerals: Bokashi

Bokashi is the end-product of the fermentation reaction of many ingredients. Biochar is often, but not always, included as an ingredient. The reaction is started by inoculating biomass and minerals with microbes (known as efficient microorganisms or EM), with the goal of producing an amendment for improving soil health.

Despite long-term empirical knowledge indicating that bokashi is a valuable soil amendment, very little scientific research has been conducted to test the effects of bokashi on soil fertility and plant growth. Some researchers have found better yields of peanuts (*Arachis hypogaea* L.) and greater numbers and fresh biomass of N-fixing nodules on peanut roots when bokashi was used as opposed to synthetic fertilizer (Yan and Xu, 2002). Lwin and Ranamukhaarachchi (2006) found that bokashi was effective as a bio-control agent against a bacterial wilt pathogen, both in the greenhouse and in the field.

Two studies indicated that improved banana (*Musa* sp.) plant growth over 5 weeks (Formowitz *et al.* 2007) or improved crop yields in arable land in Switzerland over 4 years (Mayer *et al.* 2008) could not be attributed to EM in bokashi. Thus it seems that while bokashi materials can provide crop growth improvements, this is true whether or not EM is added during the preparation process. Formowitz and colleagues further concluded that:

> Under the conditions of this study (EM application rates, frequency of compost pile turning), effects of EM-Bokashi on the decomposition process and growth of young and adult banana plants were only minor. However, our results are in contrast to data mainly published in non-reviewed literature reporting stronger effects of EM-Bokashi especially on N-mineralization. Further research under varying composting conditions, with higher treatment rates and optimized banana growing conditions may be needed to verify our results.

The bokashi used in the Formowitz study did not contain biochar, and it is not known whether biochar was contained in the bokashi used by Yan and Xu or Mayer, *et al.* The role that biochar plays in this soil amendment has not been studied, but adding biochar to bokashi can provide habitat and support for microbes. [This phenomenon is discussed in further detail in the chapter of this book titled "How Biochar Helps the Soil."] The combination can produce a fertilizer for organic farming, as reported by Gabriela Soto and Stephen Joseph ("20 Years of Biochar in Costa Rica." International Biochar Initiative. http://www.biochar-international.org/bocashi).

### Case Study: Bokashi Production in Costa Rica

Shogo Sazaki, a Japanese volunteer working with farmers, introduced the manufacturing process for bokashi in Costa Rica about 20 years ago. Today, Henry Guerrero of Coopebrisas[5] is integrally involved in building on bokashi-biochar technology, using the biochar-making techniques originally introduced by the Japanese.

Henry has established a factory in Costa Rica, where he is conducting research and development to produce lower-cost biochar and BMC that increase productivity of crops while maintaining and building soil carbon. He is the president of the Organic Farmers Association (APODAR), an active 26-member alliance of farmers who supply the main supermarket chains with organic vegetables and have used bokashi in their farming for the last 15 years.

---

[5]Coopebrisas, is a large cooperative located north of the capital city of San Jose, and is involved in agriculture and food processing.

Henry told the authors that the yields obtained using these organic methods are comparable to the yields of conventional farms, and that bokashi-biochar technology is spreading to other Central American countries.

While many "recipes" exist for making bokashi with varying ingredients, Henry's process for making bokashi consists of the following steps:

1.  *Fermenting microbes*, using litter taken from a nearby forested mountain and treating it with a molasses substrate mixed with rice polishing. These microorganisms are known as MM (for mountain microorganisms).

2.  *Fermenting other microbes*, purchased at the EARTH (Escuela Agrícola Regional del Trópico Húmedo), with Japanese EM (see Figure 16.6A). Henry notes that the EM works faster than the MM, but the MM has a greater effect on plant and soil health—so both are mixed in a 1:1 ratio.

3.  *Collecting biochar derived from bagasse*. This biochar is manufactured in a sugar mill via inefficient combustion in a simple furnace (see Figure 16.6B). The sugar mill burns **bagasse** in this furnace to produce heat for forming crystallized sugar. [More on bagasse biochar is contained in the chapter titled "Producing Biochar on Sugar Cane Farms."]

4.  *Mixing the following ingredients* on the factory floor, with 60% moisture content:
    -   Fine biochar from bagasse furnace
    -   Chicken manure [previously treated with MM]
    -   Cow manure [previously treated with MM]
    -   Rice husks
    -   Calcium carbonate (added at the end of the fermentation process)
    -   Rock phosphate
    -   Molasses

5.  *Placing this mixture in a concrete-lined pit*. Once filled, the entire pit is covered with plastic sheeting anchored in place with concrete blocks (see Figure 16.6C). A person walks over the top of the pit every day for 10 to 15 days to ensure that anaerobic conditions are maintained inside the pit.

6.  *Removing the material*. The material is then taken out of the anaerobic pit (see Figure 16.6D) and spread on a large floor. A mixture of the EM and the MM (1:1 as noted above) is sprayed on the material and the pile is aerated with a small rotary tiller. The batch is then composted aerobically for approximately 20 days (see Figure 16.6E).

7.  *Bagging the material*. The material is bagged in either 1kg or 17kg bags (see Figure 16.6F).

Fig. 16.6  Bokashi Production in Costa Rica

The composition of the materials, as listed on the bags, is N 1.6%, P 1.4%, K 2.7%, Mg 1.4%, Ca 8.81%, Zn 394 ppm, Co 8 ppm, Fe 8 ppm, Mn 620 ppm, and organic material 32.3%. Application rates are given for various crops and range from 1.5 to 3 t/ha.

Henry manages 3 hectares of fields where he grows a range of vegetables for 6 families (see Figure 16.7). The earth is mounded and bokashi applied at the recommended rate for the crop grown. He digs small holes from the top of the mounds, approximately 25 mm in diameter and 50 mm deep. The holes are filled with bokashi and seedlings placed in them. He has separate greenhouses where he prepares different types of bokashi for different types of plants (see Figure 16.8).

Fig. 16.7 Field with Mixed Vegetable      Fig. 16.8 Greenhouse Seedling Production

## SECTION 4.     MAKING AND USING WOOD VINEGAR

China and Japan have a long tradition of condensing the volatiles (often referred to as **pyroligneous acids, wood vinegar,** or **smoke water**) contained in gases emitted from kilns. They have developed a method of separating out and aging the compounds that can be used as a bio-pesticide and are beneficial to plant germination. These refined products are now sold in Australia and throughout Asia. The Japanese have developed standards for their production and utilization, and they appear to be safe for horticultural application (Kato 2005).

Various techniques are used to make smoke water. A simple device (Figure 16.9) is described by Gavin Flematti from the University of Western Australia and Dr. Dixon from the WA botanical gardens. They suggest generating smoke by slow, controlled pyrolysis, in a 200-liter drum, of a mixture of fresh and dry leaf and twig material from a range of plants. Prunings of native species are usually used in order to emulate the natural smokes likely to occur after a wildfire in bush-land habitats; for example, *Melaleuca sp.* readily produces smoke.

As shown in Figure 16.9, the drum is fitted with an inlet, through which air is pumped at the rate of 60–100 liters per minute. An outlet is connected to a 1.5 meter-long pipe that then passes through 10–40 liters of de-ionized water for one hour by suction from either a vacuum cleaner or a fan. The resulting dark brown solution can then be used for promoting seed germination.

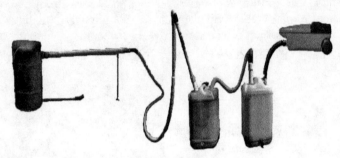

Fig. 16.9   Simple Device for Making Smoke Water

Guan Mingjie (2004), in his publication *Manual for Bamboo Charcoal Production and Utilization*, describes a technique for collecting crude bamboo vinegar from brick kilns. More detailed information is presented by a number of authors in "The Research Report on the New Uses of Wood Charcoal and Wood Vinegar" [cited at the end of this chapter].

The volatile compounds that are released early during the pyrolysis process (when temperatures are between 180–300°C) can contain active ingredients that promote plant seed germination or **sesquiterpenes** that promote mycorrhizal fungi growth (Akiyama and Hayashi 2005). The compounds that are released at these low temperatures are classified as primary tars (Reed and Evans 1998). They consist of a wide range of esters, ketones, aldehydes, furfurals, alcohols, and some phenols and terpenes.

The individual constituents of wood vinegar vary, depending on the feedstock material and carbonization methods (including the temperature). Because the charcoal industry in Japan is dispersed regionally on a small scale, there is considerable variation in both the constituents and quality of the wood vinegar produced. These wood vinegar variations translate into different effects when they are used, similar to biochar materials.

Therefore, in 2003, related organizations in Japan formed a committee to qualify wood and bamboo vinegar, and in 2005 set a quality standard for wood and bamboo vinegar on the market. Seventy products made by over 50 companies have met this standard and have been authorized by the committee.

Numerous studies and reviews that have examined the agronomic benefits of using wood or bamboo vinegar, for example Bortolomeazzi et al. (2007), Lu *et al.* (2007), and Light *et al.* (2009). In most cases, these compounds had a beneficial effect on plant health and growth. Further work is required to test the long-term toxicity to human health.

## CONCLUSION/KEY POINTS FROM THIS CHAPTER

This chapter shows evidence, often preliminary or anecdotal, of the usefulness of using biochar-mineral complexes and wood vinegar in agriculture. The detailed research work in Japan has shown that high quality biochar and wood vinegar can be produced in modern kilns meeting standards set down by the relevant government regulators. These technologies should be thoroughly investigated in the face of global climate change and declining fossil fuel reserves (most agrochemicals and many fertilizers used today are made from or require large amounts of fossil fuels in their manufacture). The challenge is to further verify the benefits of these techniques, to measure their impacts on human and environmental health, and to develop modern, clean and safe methods for generating these products on needed scales.

## REFERENCES

Akiyama, K., K. Matsuzaki, and H. Hayashi. 2005. "Plant sesquiterpenes induce hyphal branching in arbuscular mycorrhizal fungi." *Nature* 435: 824–827.

Bergman, P.C. 2005. "Combined torrefaction and pelletisation–the TOP process." Netherlands ECN [Energy Research Center] Report ECN-C—05-073.

Bourgois, J., and R. Guyonnet. 1988. "Characterization and analysis of torrefied wood." *Wood Science and Technology* 22:143–155.

Bourgois. J., M.C. Bartholin, and R. Guyonnet. 1989. "Thermal treatment of wood: analysis of the obtained product." *Wood Science and Technology* 23:303–31.

Bortolomeazzi, R.; N. Sebastianutto, R. Toniolo, and A. Pizzariello. 2007. "Comparative evaluation of the antioxidant capacity of smoke flavoring phenols by crocin bleaching inhibition, DPPH radical scavenging and oxidation potential." *Food Chemistry* 100 (4):1481–1489.

Brodowski, S., W. Amelung, L. Haumaier, C. Abetz, and W. Zech. 2005. "Morphological and chemical properties of black carbon in physical soil fractions as revealed by scanning electron microscopy and energy-dispersive X-ray spectroscopy." *Geoderma* 128:116–129.

Chia C.H., P. Munroe. S. Joseph, and Y. Lin. 2010. "Microscopic characterisation of synthetic *terra preta*" (in press). *Australian Journal of Soil Research.*

Dixon, K. 1998. *Smoke Germination of Australian Plants.* Canberra, Australia: Australian Government Rural Industries Research and Development Corporation [RIRDC]. RIRDC Report 98/108, KPW-1A.

Formowitz, B., F. Elango, S. Okumoto, T. Muller, and A. Buerkert. 2007. "The role of 'effective microorganisms' in the composting of banana (Musa ssp.) residues." *Journal of Plant Nutrition and Soil Science-Zeitschrift Fur Pflanzenernahrung Und Bodenkunde* 170:649–656.

Heller-Kallai, L. "Thermally modified clay minerals." In *Handbook of Clay Science.* Bergaya, F., Theng, B.K.G., Lagaly, G. (Eds.). Elsevier: 2006.

Hayashi, R. 1990. "Effects of purified wood vinegar as soil amendment and leaf surface spray." In *The Research Report on the New Uses of Wood Charcoal and Wood Vinegar*, ed. Technical Research Association for Multiuse of Carbonized Materials (TRA), Tokyo, 331–341.

Ishigaki, K., H. Fujie, and K. Suzuki. 1990."The effect of the soil amendment materials with charcoal and wood vinegar on the growth of citrus, tea plant and vegetables." In *The Research Report on the New Uses of Wood Charcoal and Wood Vinegar*, ed. Technical Research Association for Multiuse of Carbonized Materials (TRA), Tokyo pp. 107–120 (in Japanese).

Ishii H., S. Matsubayashi, and A. Nagai. 1990. "Effects of purified wood vinegar on the growth of crop plants." In *The Research Report on the New Uses of Wood Charcoal and Wood Vinegar*, ed. Technical Research Association for Multiuse of Carbonized Materials (TRA), Tokyo, 343– 362 (in Japanese).

Joseph, S. D., M. Camps-Arbestain, Y. Lin, P. Munroe, C.H. Chia, J. Hook, L. van Zwieten, S. Kimber, A. Cowie, B.P. Singh, J. Lehmann, N. Foidl, R. J. Smernik, and J. E. Amonette. 2010. "An investigation into the reactions of biochar in soil" (in press). *Australian Journal of Soil Research.*

Kato, H. 2005. Panel discussion, Charcoal Symposium at EXPO 2005 Aichi, Japan.

Kuzel S., M. Hruby, P. Cígler, P. Tlustos, and P.N. 2003. "Mechanism of physiological effects of titanium leaf sprays on plants grown on soil." *Biological Trace Element Research* 91(2): 179–90.

Lagaly, G. 1984. "Clay-organic interactions." *Philosophical Transactions of the Royal Society* 311:315.

Light M.E., M.I. Daws, and J. Van Staden. 2009. "Smoke-derived butenolide: Towards understanding its biological effects." *South African Journal of Botany* 75:1–7.

Light, M.E., Burger, B.V., Van Staden, J., 2005. "Formation of a seed germination promoter from carbohydrates and amino acids." *Journal of Agricultural and Food Chemistry* 53: 5936–5942.

Lu, K. C.; C.V. Kuo, and C.T. Liu. 2007. "Inhibition efficiency of a mixed solution of bamboo vinegar and chitosan against Ralstonia solanacearum." *Taiwan Journal of Forest Science* 22(3): 329–338.

Lwin, M. and S.L. Ranamukhaarachchi. 2006. "Development of biological control of *Ralstonia solanacearum* through antagonistic microbial populations." *International Journal of Agriculture and Biology* 8(5): 657–660.

Lyonga S.N. 1980. "Some common farming systems in Cameroon, their influence on the use of organic matter and the effects of soil burning on maize yields and on soil properties." In: *Organic Recycling in Africa*. FAO Soils Bull. 43: 79 –86. FAO, Rome.

Major J., A. DiTommaso, J. Lehmann, and N.P.S. Falca. 2005 "Weed dynamics on Amazonian Dark Earth and adjacent soils of Brazil." *Agriculture, Ecosystems and Environment* 111:1–12.

Mayer J., S. Scheid, and H. Oberholzer. 2008. "How effective are 'effective microorganisms'? Results from an organic farming field experiment." 16th IFOAM Organic World Congress, Modena, Italy, June 16–20, 2008.

Mingjie, G. *Manual for Bamboo Charcoal Production and Utilization.* Nanjing, China: Bamboo Engineering Research Center, Nanjing Forestry University 2004.

Ogawa, M. and Y. Okimori. 2010. "Pioneering works in biochar research, Japan" (in press). *Australian Journal of Soil Research.*

Osinamea, O. A. and F. Meppeb. 1999. "Effects of different methods of plant residue management on soil properties and maize yield." *Communications in Soil Science and Plant Analysis* 30(1&2):53–63.

Reed T., and R.J. Evans. 1998. *Biomass Gasifier "Tars": Their Nature, Formation, and Conversion.* Colorado USA: National Renewable Energy Laboratory [NREL]. NREL Report TP-570-25357.

Steiner, C. 2006. *Slash and Char as an Alternative to Slash and Burn.* Unpublished PhD thesis, Bayreuth University.

Thompson A., O. Chadwick, and J. Chorover. 2006. "Colloid Mobilisation During Soil Iron Redox Oscillations." *Environmental Science & Technology* 40: 5743–5749

Yariv, S. 2004. "The role of charcoal on DTA curves of organo-clay complexes: an overview." *Applied Clay Science* 24:225–236.

Yariv, S., and K.H. Michaelian. 2001. "Structure and surface acidity of clay minerals." In Yariv, S., and H. Cross (Eds.), *Organo-Clay Complexes and Interactions.* New York: Marcel Dekker, 39–111

# Part V
## Changing the World

"Carbon sequestration in soil also has significant potential. Biochar, produced in pyrolysis of residues from crops, forestry, and animal wastes, can be used to restore soil fertility while storing carbon for centuries to millennia. Biochar helps soil retain nutrients and fertilizers, reducing emissions of GHGs such as $N_2O$..."

—*Dr. James Hansen, Director*
*NASA Goddard Institute for Space Studies*

Chapter 17

# The Greener Revolution

Christoph Steiner, PhD  &  Paul Taylor, PhD

**IN THIS CHAPTER YOU WILL LEARN ABOUT:**

- The "Green Revolution," a dramatic increase in agricultural production over the past 50 years.

- The impending explosion in the world's population and with it, the need to *double* agricultural production over the next 50 years.

- The environmental costs of the Green Revolution—and why its methods, by themselves, are inadequate for the coming expansion.

- How historic methods of building and managing organic carbon in soil may have significant implications for the future.

- How biochar could be integral to a new, "greener" revolution.

"Mixing some black into green makes green greener."

# THE GREEN REVOLUTION

Modern agriculture feeds 7 billion people worldwide. In contrast, the early hunter-gatherer lifestyle supported only about 4 million.

Over the last several decades, a surge in global population has been accommodated by a dramatic increase in agricultural productivity known as the "Green Revolution." The Green Revolution has introduced new technologies, including new crop strains and greater use of fertilizer, water, and pesticides. Cereal production has doubled globally since 1960, mainly because of those technologies.

India exemplifies this productivity revolution. Before 1967, efforts to increase food production simply by expanding farming areas failed. The population grew much faster than production and many starved to death. India turned to Green Revolution methods to increase productivity of existing farmland, and eventually became a food exporter, with a record grain output of 131 million tons in 1978-79.

## ENVIRONMENTAL COSTS, CHALLENGES, AND LIMITATIONS

Notwithstanding the accomplishments, the Green Revolution came with an environmental cost, globally imposed. Increased production over the past 50 years has depleted soil and irrigation water at a rate much faster than they can naturally regenerate—the United States is losing arable soil ten times faster. Humans now appropriate more than a third of the production of terrestrial (land-based) ecosystems and about half of usable freshwaters.[1]

The Green Revolution's productivity gains were largely attributable to, and food production now depends on, the heavy use of fertilizers made from non-renewable resources such as rock phosphate and fossil energy. Nitrogen fertilizer generated from ammonia demands hydrogen ($H_2$), the main source of which is natural gas (methane, $CH_4$). Therefore, in essence, the Green Revolution's advances have been based on the use of fossil fuels. Globally, modern agriculture uses the energy equivalent of about one barrel of oil per **hectare** (ha) to produce annual yields of about 2–3 tons/ha.[2]

Between 1960 and 1995, global use of nitrogen fertilizers increased 7-fold and phosphorus use increased 3.5-fold. But nitrogen and phosphorous fertilizers have diminishing returns, becoming less efficient at higher levels of application and in soils depleted of organic carbon. Today, crops take up only 30–50% of applied nitrogen fertilizer and 45% of phosphorus fertilizer.[3] As a result, the annual nitrogen and phosphorus input to terrestrial ecosystems has doubled; these excess nutrients are detrimental to many aquatic (water-based) ecosystems.

The Green Revolution approach to replacing depleted nutrients in soil—using more and more mineral fertilizers—ignored another serious problem: accelerated loss of soil organic carbon (SOC). Most soils have lost 30% to 75% of their original carbon pool, or 30 to 40 tons of carbon per hectare. This loss is associated with decreased yields, reduced cycling of nutrients, and reduced effectiveness of fertilizer.

Overall, the unsustainable demands and environmental costs of the Green Revolution signal a problematic prognosis. It is projected that by 2050, the global population will increase 50% and global food demand will double. But already—despite the Green Revolution—increased grain production is not keeping pace with world population growth and wealthier populations' demand for more meat in their diets. Sixty-six percent of U.S. grain production is already fed to livestock.[4] In addition, agriculture will be pushed to provide more fiber and **biofuels**, even while land is continuously lost to erosion and to urbanization.

To meet the impending upsurge in demand, the past 50 years' expansion in agricultural production must be replicated during the next 50. This means that a projected 10 billion additional hectares of natural ecosystems—*an area larger than the United States*—would have to be converted to agriculture.

However, even if all that land could be converted, accomplishing the contemplated expansion using Green Revolution methods would intensify the adverse environmental impact of the past 50 years. For example, the new expansion would be accompanied by projected 2.4 to 2.7-fold increases in nitrogen- and phosphorus-driven **eutrophication** (depletion of oxygen in water). The previous wave of expansion has already initiated a major extinction event—species loss at 100 to 1,000 times faster than the background evolutionary rate.[5] Additional eutrophication and habitat destruction would cause unprecedented ecosystem simplification, loss of ecosystem services, and species extinctions[1].

Moreover, considering the environmental damage already done and declining resources, it is uncertain whether the previous expansion in agricultural productivity can be replicated through Green Revolution methods. For example:

- **Peak oil**. Many agree that the world reached peak oil and natural gas in 2007.[6] This has important consequences for agriculture that depends on fossil fuel. Recent increases in fossil fuel prices were accompanied by higher nitrogen fertilizer prices.

- **Peak phosphorus**. Modern agriculture depends on phosphorus derived from phosphate rock, a non-renewable resource. The global peak in phosphorus production is predicted to occur around 2030. The current global reserves may be depleted in the next 50 to 100 years, even as the global demand increases.[7]

- **Soil degradation**. A significant proportion of cultivated soils are already degraded, some so severely that they can no longer be used for agriculture.

- **Global warming**. Even slight climate changes are likely to reduce our ability to produce food. In a warming climate, floods, droughts, crop diseases, and pests are likely to increase. Subsequent rises in sea level will permanently submerge important agricultural areas.

If the Green Revolution's technologies fall short (as it seems they will), the required doubling of food production can be achieved only by converting *more* than the projected 10 billion hectares of land—a nearly unfathomable prospect—or by finding new ways to improve agricultural productivity and optimize efficiency in using and cycling nutrients.

## BIOCHAR: THE "GREENER" REVOLUTION?

Against this troubling background, the challenge to double food global production by 2050—and to do so without causing more environmental harm—is extremely daunting. Meeting that challenge will require timely, effective action on several fronts, including:

- Judicious use of natural resources (renewable and non-renewable)

- Using fertilizer and water more efficiently

- Reversing soil degradation

- Mitigating global warming

- Adapting to a warming climate

According to Tilman and colleagues[1], nothing less than an environmentally sustainable, *"greener"* revolution is needed. A growing global community believes that one component of this greener revolution will be production and application of biochar to soil. **Biochar** is a renewable resource, proven to be agriculturally and environmentally beneficial and stable in the soil for hundreds, even thousands of years. Biochar may not substitute for Green Revolution methods, but shows promise to increase their efficiency, reduce global warming and help adaptation to a warming climate.

## HISTORIC MANAGEMENT OF SOIL FERTILITY

Before mineral fertilizers were invented, managing soil organic carbon (SOC) was the only way to restore or maintain soil fertility. The relationship between soil fertility and SOC has been well known since the first half of the 19th century, after the German agronomist Albrecht Thaer published his "Humus Theory." Thaer's approach was used successfully for half a century. In 1849, Sprengel and Liebig published their work on the mineral nutrition of plants.[8] From then on, their "minimal nutrition theory" progressively displaced and ultimately abandoned the traditional practice of recycling nutrients from settlements to agricultural fields[9]— and laid the foundation for the Green Revolution's synthetic fertilizers.

Historically, before Sprengel and Liebig's work gained primacy, sedentary farmers had two basic choices: deplete their SOC stocks—rendering their fields infertile—or find ways to maintain SOC. They maintained SOC by rotating crops, leaving fields fallow, and fertilizing with manures.

Maintaining SOC is particularly difficult in the tropics, where most soils are naturally infertile and SOC quickly decomposes. That infertility is often compounded by an inability to buy or trade for fertilizers; as a result, many poor farmers have been forced to leave land fallow for a long time (up to 30 years). In regions where soil is depleted of SOC, an estimated 300 to 500 million people cope by migrating. This agricultural system is called "shifting cultivation"—moving from one spot to another as soil fertility declines.

All too often, intensive agricultural land use throughout the world has caused physical and chemical degradation of soil, erosion, and higher losses than input rates of nutrients and organic matter. However, in some locations, nutrient-rich materials have been deposited into soil—intentionally and unintentionally—within human habitation sites and fields, maintaining and actually improving fertility over centuries.[10]

One prominent example of **anthropogenically**-enriched soil (that is, soil enriched by human activity) is ***Terra preta de Índio*** (Figures 17.1 and 17.2). This dark, fertile soil is found throughout the Amazon Basin lowlands, an otherwise infertile region. It contains high concentrations of very **recalcitrant** (stable) charcoal and significantly more plant-available nutrients than the surrounding soils.[11,12] (For more discussion on *terra preta* and other soils, see Chapter 1, "Ancient Origins, Modern Solution.")

Fig. 17.1 *Terra preta* Soil

Fig. 17.2 *Terra preta* in the Field

Dark *terra preta* horizon above light-colored parent material.

Man-made *terra preta* soils with cash crop production.

Similar to *terra preta*, **plaggen** are **Anthrosols**––soils that have been formed or heavily modified by long-term human activity. Plaggen were created in the Middle Ages in northern Europe (Denmark, Netherlands, northwestern Germany, and Belgium), as a result of intentional cultivation. Peat was used as bedding for cattle, and along with manure, was applied to agricultural fields, creating rich, **humose** topsoils over sandy soils. Over time, from the late Bronze Age to the last century, the humose soil horizon in plaggen accumulated to over 1 meter (m) in depth. In the Netherlands, more than 221,000 ha of land have a humose cover thicker than 50 cm, and more than 196,000 ha have a cover from 30- to 50-cm thick. Because of their fertility, plaggen stand out among the sandy soil areas of Western Europe.

**Chernozem ("black earth")** soils are not man-made, but are also characterized by black surface horizons, rich in organic matter. They are typically found in grass steppes, where grassland fires have contributed a high content of **pyrogenic** carbon (**carbonized** organic matter, or char that is resistant to breakdown). (Chernozems fall into the U.S. soil classification **mollisols**, which occur extensively in prairie regions such as the Great Plains.) This resistant carbon fraction becomes an increasing portion of the total carbon pool as the SOC pool declines due to cultivation. In U.S. agricultural soils, for example, charcoal now constitutes up to 35% of the total SOC.[13]

These fertile soils, both man-made and naturally occurring, all have high organic carbon content, which is of prime importance for insuring vital soil functions such as retaining soil nutrients.[14] Such soil transformations cannot be achieved solely by Green Revolution methods, which replenish mineral nutrients only.

## RESISTANT CARBON: THE KEY TO LASTING FERTILITY

In natural and agro-ecosystems, carbonized and recalcitrant organic matter is produced by incomplete burning (**pyrolysis**) of **biomass** (such as wood, crop residues, and grasses). Using recalcitrant carbon (such as biochar) is the most effective way to increase SOC, particularly in moist and hot tropical environments. In colder climates, such as in northern Europe (where plaggen are found), the cold slows decomposition; therefore, these environments have a higher carbon sequestration capacity. However, in the humid tropics, organic matter decomposes rapidly, making it difficult to sequester carbon in soil. Therefore, only a very recalcitrant form of carbon—biochar—can create *terra preta*.

Even today, carbonized organic matter is frequently used in the Brazilian Amazon as a soil amendment (Figure 17.3).

Fig. 17.3 Carbonized Organic Matter as Soil Amendment

The residues of charcoal production (pieces too fine to be otherwise marketable) are frequently used as a soil amendment.

In many other places and circumstances, humans have found ways to overcome environmental limitations through the agricultural use of intentionally carbonized materials. For example, in northwest Cameroon, another tropical environment, grasses are intentionally carbonized, and reportedly, tribal communities in India use a similar carbonization technique, known as the Raab system. (More detail on these practices is offered in Chapters 1 and 16.)

Historical agriculture use of charcoal (biochar) has also occurred outside the tropics. It was used in Japan as far back as the 17th century,[15] as well as elsewhere in Asia, since rice cultivation began.[16] During the 19th century in United States, charcoal was used for many agricultural purposes, but mainly for nutrient (nitrogen) conservation.[17] In both Asia and the United States, human excrement was mixed with charcoal powder and used to replenish nutrients in the field.[17,18] (For more detail on historical practices, see Chapter 1.)

## PAST LESSONS, PRACTICAL LIMITS

Historic land use systems and techniques have potentially significant implications for the future.

- First, they illustrate that humans can use and adapt natural processes as beneficial technologies to promote healthier soil and agricultural production.

- Second, the very existence of *terra preta* proves that poor soil—one of the world's poorest—can be transformed into enduringly fertile soil. More pointedly, it proves that long-lasting SOC enrichment is possible, even in the tropics, if done with a highly recalcitrant source of carbon such as biochar.

Given the difficult challenges at hand, these points are intriguing, even encouraging.

However, despite the allure and potential modern adaptability of various historical practices, none are inherently sufficient to meet the current challenges. Modern agriculture must—on a vast, unprecedented scale—sustain and increase current productivity, feed a burgeoning population, and supply biofuels. Shifting cultivation, with its long fallow periods, leaves too much unproductive land, and in any event a growing sedentary population has already altered most fallow-based land use systems.

Moreover, traditional carbonization techniques, focused solely on soil fertility issues, would have negative environmental consequences if practiced on a large scale. The products of incomplete combustion (PICs) have detrimental impact if released to the atmosphere, because they have higher global warming potentials than carbon dioxide ($CO_2$). Therefore, despite the noted agricultural benefits of biochar, simply producing it without also avoiding the related PIC emissions can produce a net *increase* in global warming commitment. Modern technology—specifically, modern pyrolysis methods—can fully avoid these emissions, and use the PICs, such as $H_2$, carbon monoxide (CO), and methane ($CH_4$), to produce renewable energy.

On the other hand, modern approaches miss an important historical point. Abundant nutrient-rich materials (urban wastes, wastes from concentrated livestock, and human wastes) are all around us, but are generally considered useless and toxic. Valuable nutrients are dumped or leached into rivers, where they do harm, or are relegated to landfills. The above historic examples can teach us a great deal about recycling nutrients.

In order for us to meet the current challenges, the overarching lesson is this: sustainable agricultural expansion needs to close nutrient cycles, and incorporate both nutrients *and* carbon, into modern land-use and material management systems. At the same time, for our increasingly crowded planet, the methods employed must be environmentally beneficial—or at least benign—over their entire life cycle. This enlightened approach may well lead to the formation of *terra preta*-like soils.

## THE BIOCHAR OPPORTUNITY

In light of the above analysis, modern biochar systems offer unique options and opportunities for addressing the current complexities, for many reasons:

- Biochar is a by-product from pyrolysis of biomass—an abundant resource. In addition to crop residues (frequently burned for no reason other than to dispose of them), biomass from invasive species, yard waste, or dead trees, and biomass generated from forest fuel reduction treatments, could be carbonized.

- Pyrolysis gases can be readily kept out of the atmosphere by containing and combusting them, thereby generating renewable energy and reducing dependency on fossil energy.

- Biochar can be used in agriculture to increase inherent soil fertility *and* the effectiveness of fertilizers, thereby reducing the use of synthetic fertilizers (see also Chapter 7).

- Biochar systems can mitigate climate change by (1) reducing consumption of fossil fuel and (2) capturing $CO_2$ and sequestering carbon in the soil (see Chapter 1).

- Biochar may increase water efficiency and reduce vulnerability to changing climate.

- Biochar systems can be accomplished on a small scale (improved kilns, stoves, **gasifiers**) or on a large scale (for example, bio-refinery). The small-scale options further expand the quantity of available biomass to include the otherwise "uneconomic" biomass (such as yard wastes) mentioned above and "thinly dispersed" feedstocks (as discussed in the next chapter).

Thus, biochar can help improve agricultural productivity, provide renewable energy, mitigate climate change, reduce vulnerability to global warming, and meet other environmental imperatives. By extension, use of biochar can positively influence food security, soil fertility, and biodiversity, helping to balance the competing choices around cultivating crops for different purposes—such as for energy or for carbon sequestration or for food. Better yet, we already have the knowledge and technology to integrate biochar synergistically into most agricultural systems.

For all of these reasons, biochar may represent a key component for the needed "greener revolution."

## CARBON SEQUESTRATION VIA BIOCHAR

The principles behind capturing and sequestering carbon dioxide via biochar systems are discussed in Chapter 1.

Although this idea is now gaining more attention, it is not entirely new. Storing carbon by depositing charcoal into landfills was proposed in 1993.[19] The proposal languished, until recent research on *terra preta* revealed the importance of charcoal to maintain soil fertility, particularly in the humid tropics. [20, 21]

Notably, *terra preta* soils still contain large amounts of biochar-derived SOC in a climate pre-disposed to rapid decomposition, hundreds and thousands of years after they were produced. This opens up a vast opportunity for low carbon content soils in the tropics to be used for carbon sequestration while increasing their fertility for food production.

The question arises whether biochar production and sequestration results in larger **greenhouse gas** (GHG) reductions than direct combustion of the entire **feedstock** (including charcoal, if produced). This depends on the particulars of the feedstock, transportation, the production process, and the greenhouse gas intensity of the fossil fuel being replaced. Research must consider many factors over the entire life cycle of each process.

However, as previous noted, a modern biochar system has these important benefits: it provides soil enhancement and increased food productivity while actually *removing* $CO_2$ from the atmosphere. In contrast, avoided fossil fuel consumption only reduces the rate of increase in atmospheric GHG concentrations, which alone is insufficient to resolve the climate problem. Moreover, fossil fuel emissions avoided today are not avoided forever, particularly when only part of the world adopts a carbon policy. In a free market, fossil fuel avoided in one place makes it available for consumption by others elsewhere, leading to continued or future high emissions.

Others have proposed increasing carbon sequestration by burying biomass or biochar in sediments or the deep ocean. However, this proposition disregards the importance of SOC—as the Green Revolution has done—and the known capacity of biochar for maintaining or improving soil fertility, and also forgoes the potential for producing renewable energy.

Furthermore, as also noted in Chapter 1, biochar is different from traded reductions in current emissions. Because biochar is an effective and permanent carbon sink, it has the potential to recapture historic emissions, thus providing an important path for industrialized nations to reduce their historic carbon debt. Therefore, on top of all its other attractions, biochar may present a pathway for negotiating reductions in GHG emissions with fast-growing economies such as China and India.

## A DOSE OF PERSPECTIVE

Any sensible program to sequester carbon for mitigating climate change must involve careful and sustainable management of feedstock sources and resources.

- When a unit of biomass is converted to biochar, about half the carbon can be sequestered in the soil, but the other half winds up in the atmosphere (ideally with generation of energy and the avoidance of fossil fuel usage—but the latter is not guaranteed). Therefore, to establish the sequestration, vegetation must be replenished. Moreover, research has shown that even mature forest ecosystems are still accumulating carbon. Therefore the carbon stocks in biomass, and the ability of the natural system to sequester carbon, must be maintained over the long term, in order to gain net new sequestration with biochar.

- If biochar competes with food production, or with other needs for the land or biomass, that may induce land use changes elsewhere to satisfy the need, such as deforestation, which again could offset the gains from biochar.

Therefore, biomass sources and management are closely linked to carbon sequestration potential, reiterating the importance of utilizing waste biomass that would otherwise decompose or be burned. Properly implemented, biochar presents an opportunity to avoid these conflicts because it has the potential to increase biomass and food production, at the same time as it creates the carbon sink and provides energy.

Notwithstanding the sound premise and appreciable promise of the biochar approach, policy makers should not be misled. The biochar revolution does not envision a loophole for business as usual; using biochar to sequester carbon and offset emissions does not equate to a license to continue wasteful consumption of fossil fuel or deforestation, and thinking otherwise implies poor biomass management. Unless those problems are arrested, our global problems will outpace our solutions—with or without biochar.

A global solution mandates a broad, multi-faceted strategy that includes the following:

1. Energy efficiency and conservation to avoid and reduce harmful emissions, including those caused by induced land use change.

2. Securing the carbon stocks in vegetation and soils by avoiding deforestation, and through reduced tillage and other agricultural practices.

3. Sequestering carbon by increasing SOC and carbon in vegetation, for which biochar is a particularly suitable vehicle.

In sum, biochar production and utilization can be an effective tool if used in context with these priorities and combined with other renewable and sustainable approaches.

## CONCLUSION

Since biochar is essentially recalcitrant carbon, and is a renewable resource, it offers a potential pathway for addressing the current soil productivity/environment conundrum. Amid the worrisome landscape, the historic *terra preta* and plaggen examples echo from the past, proving that humans have found, and can adapt, relatively simple, low-tech ways to sustainably overcome environmental limitations.

This theme is central to the Biochar Revolution—a promising part of the called-for "greener" revolution. Another theme, repeated throughout this book, is that this transformation can be pursued on a small or large scale, individually and industrially. Each person, each community, and each enterprise can contribute, and the aggregated contributions of millions will generate genuine, enduring change.

## REFERENCES

1. Tilman D., *et al. Science*, 2001: 292,281.

2. Hall, C. A. S., and M. H. P. Hall. *Agriculture, Ecosystems and Environment*, 1993:46,1.

3. Tilman, D., K. G. Cassman, P. A. Matson, R. Naylor, and S. Polasky. *Nature*, 2002:418,671.

4. World Resources Institute. *World Resources 2000–2001: People and Ecosystems: The Fraying Web of Life.* Washington, DC: World Resources Institute, 2000.02:418,671.

5. Lawton, J.H. and R.M. May, Eds. *Extinction Rates.* Oxford, UK: Oxford University Press, 1995.

6. Pimentel, D., *et al. Human Ecology*, 2009: 37, 1.

7. Cordell, D., J.O. Drangert, and S. White. *Global Environmental Change*, 2009:19,292.

8. Feller, C. L., L. J. M. Thuriés, R. J. Manlay, P. Robin, and E. Frossard. Journal of Plant Nutrition and Soil Science, 2003:166, 687.

9. Manlay, R. J., C. Feller, and M. J. Swift. Agriculture Ecosystems & Environment, 2007:119:217.

10. Woods, W. I. in *Amazonian Dark Earth: Origin, Properties, Management*, J. Lehmann, D. Kern, B. Glaser, W. Woods, Eds. Dordrecht, The Netherlands: Kluwer Academic Publishers 2003, 3-14.

11. Glaser, B., G. Guggenberger, L. Haumaier, and W. Zech, in *Sustainable Management of Soil Organic Matter*, R. M. Rees, B. C. Ball, C. D. Campbell, C. A. Watson, Eds. Wallingford: CABI Publishing 2001, 190-194.

12. Lima, H. N., C. E. R. Schaefer, J. W. V. Mello, R. J. Gilkes, and J. C. Ker. "Pedogenesis and Pre-Columbian Land Use of '*Terra preta* Anthrosols' ('Indian Black Earth') of Western Amazonia." *Geoderma* 2002:110,1.

13. Skjemstad, J. O., D. C. Reicosky, A. R. Wilts, and J. A. McGowan. *Soil Science Society of America Journal,* Jul–Aug 2002: 66,1249.

14. Zech, W., L. Haumaier, and R. Hempfling, in *Humic Substances in Soil and Crop Sciences; Selected Readings*. P. McCarthy, C. E. Clapp, R. L. Malcolm, and P. R. Bloom, Eds. Madison: American Society of Agronomy and Soil Science Society of America, 1990, 187–202.

15. Miyazaki, Y. *Nihon Nousho Zenshu.* Nougyouzennsho (Encyclopedia of Agriculture) Tokyo: Nousangyoson Bunka Kyokai, 1697:12, 91–104.

16. Ogawa, M. *Unpublished manuscript,* 2008:15.

17. Allen, R.L. *Brief Compend of American Agriculture.* New York: C. M. Saxton, 1847

18. Ogawa, M. *Farming Japan*, 1994:28:5, 21.

19. Seifritz, W. *International Journal of Hydrogen Energy*, 1993:405.

20. Glaser, B., L. Haumaier, G. Guggenberger, and W. Zech. *Naturwissenschaften* 2001: 88,37.

21. C. Steiner, Dissertation, University of Bayreuth, Germany (2007).

Demonstration in support of climate action in front of the Mongolian Parliament, December 2009. Note "Biochar: Black is the New Green". Photo: K. Frogner

Biochar Feedstock (field dried manure), Altai Mountains, Mongolia. Photo: K. Frogner

Chapter 18

# Climate Change Mitigation Using Thinly Distributed Feedstock

Karl J. Frogner, PhD, OZP          Paul Taylor, PhD

*[This chapter is based on the UBI program, which is dedicated to the concept that low-tech biocharring of thinly distributed feedstock can significantly mitigate global warming in the context of sustainable rural development. For further information on UBI, see http://www.biochar-international.org/regional/ubi.]*

**IN THIS CHAPTER YOU WILL LEARN:**

- About a simple plan for sustainable rural development that will produce timely climate change mitigation *and* increase local food production.

- How the same simple plan can reduce air pollution, stimulate economies, and empower communities.

- Easy steps anyone can take to reduce their carbon footprint and participate in the movement to mitigate climate change.

"Human activities have so severely impacted the environment that it is approaching dangerous tipping points. To help pull the environment back from the brink, prompt, urgent action is needed to offset carbon dioxide pollution."

# INTRODUCTION

Human activities have so severely impacted the environment that it is approaching dangerous tipping points. One of the requirements to pull the environment back from the brink is prompt, urgent action to offset carbon dioxide ($CO_2$) pollution. Time is growing short. Despite the urgency, global leaders have yet to commit to a comprehensive plan.

This chapter describes a simple program for mitigating climate change by mobilizing the $CO_2$ sequestration potential in biochar. This idea is not new. But what is new about this program is that it focuses on low-tech, small-scale, local efforts, particularly in developing countries, that can be initiated from the bottom up. In this program, low-tech ovens and stoves would use "thinly distributed" **feedstock** to produce biochar in a sustainable and ecologically beneficial way.

Notably, this program would be driven from the bottom up as well as the top down. It contemplates a chain reaction that would start with local pilot projects, and then proliferate regionally—even globally—through community-mentoring-community programs.

The program has yet another positive attribute. Attacking climate change through local, small-scale biochar production would directly aid those who have done little if anything to cause climate change, but are most at risk from it.

This chapter addresses the particulars of small-scale biochar production, local benefits of the program (enhanced crop production and carbon credits), useful rural development methods, how the principles of the program might also apply to urban and suburban settings, and areas for further research.

## PROGRAM OVERVIEW: BIOCHAR BENEFITS AND PRODUCTION

### RECOGNIZED BENEFITS OF BIOCHAR

Adding biochar to soil can help soil retain moisture, help maintain soil fertility, and increase crop production. In addition to agricultural benefits, adding biochar to soil sequesters carbon, keeping it from returning to the atmosphere as $CO_2$ for hundreds, even thousands of years. Using biochar to sequester carbon is the only practical way now available, except for planting trees, to safely remove $CO_2$ from the air.

Perhaps more surprisingly, adding biochar to soil could also help prevent acidification of the ocean. $CO_2$ is removed from the air mainly via absorption by the world's oceans. However, as the oceans absorb $CO_2$ they acidify, which endangers marine life. Since ocean absorption of $CO_2$ is a direct function of its concentration in the air, reducing $CO_2$ in the atmosphere will mitigate ocean acidification.

### "THINLY DISTRIBUTED" BIOMASS FEEDSTOCK: TRASH OR TREASURE?

A particular merit of the program described here is that biochar would be produced from "thinly distributed" biomass feedstock, such as crop residue, manure, deadwood and trimmings, and logging slash.

The term "thinly distributed" means that the volume of a particular feedstock is not sufficiently concentrated in any single place for economical charring through high-tech pyrolysis. In other words, it hasn't been gathered up and hauled to a central depot (such as usually occurs with sugar production; see the chapter of this book titled "Producing Biochar on Sugar Cane Farms"), and doing so is not economically viable.

However, if small-scale, low-tech approaches are implemented, thinly distributed feedstock can be used to produce biochar economically, sustainably, and in an environmentally benign—even beneficial—way.

### PYROLYSIS OVENS AND STOVES

On the small scale, biochar can be produced by pyrolysis in low-tech biochar ovens and small gasifier cooking stoves.

### Biochar Ovens

In this program, biochar would be produced primarily by low-tech biochar ovens. Many, if not most, rural smallholders (that is, managers of small plots of land) engaged in agriculture, herding, or forestry will have access to significantly more than the 2–5 tons of feedstock per year needed for family cooking and other requirements. For smallholders who have a feedstock surplus ranging from 5 to 100 tons per year, a low-tech biochar oven is the best option for family-scale production.

Biochar ovens are typically built from modified oil drums, though other designs are also used. Usually, the ovens are constructed simply, without complex moving parts. A single 100–200 liter oven will make 10-20kg of biochar per batch in 2–3 hours.

Readers interested in learning more about low-tech biochar ovens, including how to make a simple working model and viewing designs for fully operational ovens or other topics covered in this chapter, are invited to visit the UBI website, http://www.biochar-international.org/regional/ubi, or this book's website, www.TheBiocharRevloution.com.

Biochar oven designs are also discussed in the chapter of this book titled "Biochar Production Basics: From Colliers to Retorts."

Fig. 18.1 and 18.2  Hollow Core Fired Biochar Oven.  Photo: K. Frogner

This biochar oven is made from a 200-liter oil drum, fired through a hollow core. The side pipes bring pyrolysis gases from the outer oven into the core to burn cleanly while heating the oven. In the right photo the oven has an experimental load of sawdust and manure to be fired when closed and inverted.

## Biochar Stoves

Biochar-producing cookstoves originated as an adaptation of clean-burning gasifier stoves, which are designed to burn agriculture residue and minimize the smoke-related health hazards from cooking with open fires in kitchens and dwellings.

Pyrolysis stoves are being introduced in developing regions primarily for heating and cooking, but because of their design, some can produce biochar in the process. Although a stove's volume is much smaller than that of a typical biochar oven, millions of people could use them to produce 0.5 to 2 kg of char a day.

Moreover, smallholders may well produce approximately 0.5 t/yr of biochar from cooking alone.  Added income from carbon credits could be significant to the rural poor.

For these reasons, as well as the biochar benefits in smallholders' gardens, biochar-producing stoves should be one of the key elements for attracting the buy-in of prospective program participants. (To learn more about biochar-producing cookstoves, see the chapter of this book titled "Making Biochar in Small Gasifier Cookstoves and Heaters.")

By processing bulk feedstock in biochar ovens and using pyrolysis stoves instead of ordinary fires, the aggregated, global efforts of millions of small-scale farmers, herders, and forestry workers in undeveloped regions could significantly alter carbon emissions from human activities.

## Putting It Together

The above elements can now be assembled into a program.

The program starts small, and from the bottom up. Successful local initiatives, tailored to local conditions, would attract buy-in at the community level. Successful communities would then mentor other communities, and the mentored communities would mentor yet others via proliferating communities-mentoring-communities (CMC) initiatives.

The example of this geometric growth would present a credible model that both non-governmental organizations (**NGOs**) and government agencies could support. Top-down sponsorship—by governments or large NGOs—will be necessary for the program to realize its full potential

## THE PROGRAM IN GREATER DETAIL

### Economic Benefits for Smallholders
Thinly distributed feedstock is widely available to Third World smallholders in the context of sustainable, ecologically friendly rural development.

As a practical matter, the program's main motivator for smallholders' participation will be increased returns on their labor—that is, profit. The program features two profit drivers:

- **Biochar's Soil Benefits.** The first profit driver is the well-known soil enhancement qualities of biochar, which results in increased crop yield. This generally maximizes at 10 to 20 tons of biochar per hectare. These soil enhancement qualities mean that less fertilizer and irrigation are needed, resulting in reduced production costs. Because this approach to $CO_2$ abatement increases crop production, the program would also help alleviate world food shortages.

- **Carbon Credits**. The second profit driver comes from cash return on carbon credits. Sequestering biochar on crop and pasture land can create carbon credits. Up to 90 t/ha of biochar can be added to soil without damaging crop yields. Carbon credits earned by individual farmers would be marketed through local community marketing organizations.

Carbon credits could also be an inducement to produce and sequester biochar on other land where increased plant productivity is not the primary economic concern.

Profit motives aside, the proposed program would also help rural smallholders to continue their cherished traditional lifestyles by enabling them to adequately support themselves and their families.

## $CO_2$ Sequestration Potential from Thinly Distributed Feedstock

### Maximum Potential for the Program

Lehmann and Joseph[1] have estimated that daily food preparation for a tropical African family using a biochar-producing cookstove would yield about 1.5 kg of biochar per day, or about 20% of the biomass used in cooking. Yevich and Logan[2] estimated that in 1985, 2,057 megatons (MT) of biomass were burned as fuel in the Third World.

The potential environmental impact of the proposed program can be gauged by following this line of reasoning:

- If the heat value of that 2,057 MT of biomass were to be delivered by biochar-producing stoves, approximately 2,940 MT of biomass would be used. This is because the biochar produced represents lost heat, and we assume 30% of the heat value of the biomass would be retained in the biochar and therefore excluded from cooking or heating.

- This amount of biomass would produce approximately 590 MT of biochar, assuming 20% biomass to biochar yield.

- These 590 MT of biochar would equate to about 1.35 gigatons $CO_2e$, assuming every ton of biochar soil amendment results in 2.3 tons of $CO_2$ sequestered.[3] (Since one ton of pure carbon is equivalent to 3.67 tons of $CO_2$, this implies that 62.7% of the biochar weight is carbon that remains long-term in the soil, with the balance of the biochar being other constituents such as oxygen, hydrogen, and ash, as well as labile carbon that returns to the atmosphere in the short term).

Of course, this result is overstated, since small-scale family cooking and heating are not the only uses of biomass fuel in the Third World. Also, where fuel is expensive or requires considerable labor to obtain, people would opt to use gasifier or charcoal stoves, which convert biomass to heat energy more efficiently than biochar stoves, unless biochar production could be shown to offer an offsetting advantage.

Nevertheless, the overall point is clear: using biochar-producing stoves alone in the proposed program has enormous climate mitigation potential.

### Agricultural Wastes

Yevich and Logan also estimated that in 1985, 408 MT of agricultural waste were burned in fields in the Third World, and estimate this amount increased to 496 MT by 1995. Based on the 1995 estimate, if instead of simply burned off, the

[1] Lehmann, J. and S.Joseph. 2009. "Biochar Systems." In *Biochar for Environmental Management: Science and Technology.* Lehmann, J., Joseph, S., Eds.; Earthscan: London, UK, 147-168.
[2] Yevich, R. and J.A. Logan. 2003. "An assessment of biofuel use and burning of agricultural waste in the developing world." Global Biogeochemical Cycles 17(4): 6-1–6-40.
[3] As stated in Chapter 20 of this book. Quirk, R.G., et al. "The Role of Biochar in Management of Sugarcane." Proceedings of 17th Congress, International Society of Sugar Cane Technologists (ISSCT). Vera Cruz, Mexico, 2010.

agricultural waste had been converted to biochar in low-tech biochar ovens at approximately 25% efficiency, this would have yielded 124 MT of biochar, or approximately 285 MT $CO_2$e.

It also appears that much more agricultural feedstock is available for producing biochar in low-tech ovens. In addition to burned-off agricultural waste, the following sources are available:

- Significant volumes of residue, which are now plowed back under or left to decompose in the field as mulch.[4] (Given biochar's beneficial effects on plant growth when added to soil alone or in combination with mulch, a substantial portion of that residue could also be turned into biochar sequestered in the field, and still improve crop production.)

- Farm manure and manure from herding operations.[5]

- Deadfall and trimmings from agroforestry operations and simple harvesting of rough vegetation from fallow or neglected areas.

### Forest Deadfall, Trimmings, and Slash

Trimmings and deadfall from reforestation, and from land unsuitable for crop production or not needed for undisturbed reserves, are sources of feedstock for small-scale biochar production.

In forested areas where major mechanized logging operations are in place, high-tech biochar production would probably be more economically productive. However, in smaller-scale operations, high grading, or in rough terrain, where slash is traditionally left in place and is not economically amenable to the use of high-tech pyrolysis apparatus, portable biochar ovens—carried by humans or pack animals—could be used to convert the slash into biochar on the spot.

Considerable biochar could also be produced from reforestation schemes that are well managed to assure sustainability, species diversity, protection of endangered species, maintenance of standing crop biomass, and other important ecological considerations. (One such program is outlined on the UBI website, http://www.biochar-international.org/regional/ubi.)

### Massively Replicated Small Production to Leverage Large Impact

As already noted, the program proposed here emphasizes family-level smallholders and low-tech production. Regardless of the production source, total production is the key, which can be achieved through fewer high-production units or massive numbers of low-production units.

---

[4] Yevich and Logan's estimates for 1985 indicate that of 2,004 MT of agriculture residue available, 597 MT was burned as fuel and 408 MT was burned in the fields, indicating that 999 MT or 50% might have been left in the fields.

[5] The reference in the previous footnote also states that 136 MT of dung was included in the 2,057 MT of fuel burned in the third world in 1985.

Thus recognizing that both high-tech and low-tech contributions are essential for mitigating climate change, the program focuses on small production sources that can be massively reproduced.

## Village-level Production

In certain situations, it may make sense to produce biochar initially at the village or community level, as opposed to the family level. This might be the case, for example, if a crop is brought into the village to be processed. The contemplated village-level production is analogous to that described in Peter Hirst's chapter, "From Blacksmith to Biochar: The Essence of Community."

In fact, as also suggested by Hirst, the "village" or community referred to throughout this chapter may be a *virtual* village—a group of people closely aligned by a common interest. In the program discussed here, the "village" will be defined by the local marketing organization and may not literally involve village-level biochar production.

Of course, village-level production brings with it other complexity. Flexibility and sensitivity relating to local biological and cultural environments is imperative. Central production may be susceptible to threats from corrupt government officials or predatory profiteers. To ameliorate these threats, local biochar marketing organizations must work closely and transparently with a not-for-profit (NFP) NGO bundler or marketing agent (broker).

## RURAL DEVELOPMENT ASPECTS AND CHALLENGES

Clearly, this initiative represents a pronounced shift in thinking, away from "business as usual" rural development. Although other pilot projects have adopted a rural development theme, we recognize that in addition to emphasizing sustainable rural development and crafting a viable program to induce geometric growth in overall production, this program must also include stakeholder participation in order to promote local community buy-in.

As an example, we advocate a program along the lines of the Save the Children NGO's Nakhon Sawan (Thailand) program (Suutari and Mittelman).[6] In that program, field workers first had discussions with area smallholders about local problems as the smallholders *themselves* perceived them, the causes and dynamics of those problems, and what the smallholders saw as components of a desirable outcome. To those discussions, the field workers added technical elements and innovations that might contribute to the expressed desired outcomes and joined with the stakeholders in further discussions that led to implementation.

Adding biochar production to such a discussion could be a good way to initiate a pilot project. In this regard, it would be advantageous to work with an established rural development program, so that local smallholders can perceive biochar as a beneficial addition to the mix.

---

[6] Suutari, A. and A. Mittelman. "Ecosystem restoration with agroforestry and community forests in Nakhon Sawan, Thailand." http://www.ecotippingpoints.org/indepth/thailandforest.html.

The carbon credit marketing community could be used to further encourage production and adherence to best practices by using a small percentage of carbon credit income as a "brokerage fund"—a fund to be returned for community projects, such as improving community pastures and communications, to reward good compliance.

The precise form of local buy-in will vary depending on local biological and cultural environments. Thus, a "one size fits all" program will likely not be as successful as the customized, localized, from-the-ground-up pilot projects and the community-mentoring-community system of geometric expansion envisioned in this chapter.

## CARBON TRADING TO BOOST CLIMATE CHANGE MITIGATION

As previously suggested, two elements transform the proposed program from "business as usual rural development" into an opportunity to effect significant climate change mitigation: geometric growth in biochar production, and carbon offset trading. Both elements are important in meeting sequestration potential in the time frame imposed by climate change.

Three aspects of carbon trading merit particular focus:

- The local marketing organization.

- The not-for-profit (NFP) brokering mechanism.

- The structure of the carbon trading market itself.

The local marketing organization (community) bundles the carbon credits of individual organization members for passing on to the broker. The local marketing organization monitors and enforces sustainability and the quantity and quality of the biochar produced and its proper sequestering. Enforcement can be done through peer pressure, spot checks, and denial of service privileges.

The proposed structure for the NFP brokering mechanism is a network of transparent NGOs working with the local marketing organizations, acting as intermediary bundlers or brokers, and aggregating credits from local marketing organizations until they have accumulated a sufficient volume to participate in the greater carbon trading market. A transparent, NFP structure in participating broker NGOs would, among other things, avoid heavy administration cost, thereby allowing most of the profit to be passed down to primary production labor—to the people actually taking $CO_2$ out of the atmosphere. The NFP broker would also monitor community marketing organizations to assure they comply with their own monitoring responsibilities. The broker would function as the next level of control by denying service at the community level and/or withholding the community bonus from the "brokerage fund."

In the beginning, carbon credit trading would be pursued in the voluntary market, the kind of market that can be found on the internet.

This market works through brokers serving entities desiring to offset their carbon footprint or to "green" their business. Such entities send money to a firm (in this case the NFP broker) to retire the desired number of carbon credits (from the pool of bundled smallholder credits).

However, it is likely that this market will not have sufficient volume to accommodate the proposed program very long in its geometric growth phase. For the program to reach its maximum potential, biochar will need to be accepted into the mandatory UNFCCC[7] carbon trading markets. But this may not be enough. All markets are structured and their structure determines winners and losers. The mandatory markets are not primarily designed for post-sequestration trading, but rather for speculating on future offsetting and incentives to reduce pollution from greenhouse gases. They are designed to minimize the cost to advanced economies of transitioning to a reduced carbon economy, not to pay a fair labor price for taking $CO_2$ out of the atmosphere. And often, it is the brokers and speculators that stand to reap most of the profits.

Clearly, a market could be structured to promote maximum utilization of the thinly distributed feedstock resource documented here. And there seems no compelling argument against creating such a market; the major obstacle is the political will to do so. Although a number of carbon markets already exist, none serve the smallholder's interests or, arguably, maximize production over profit. In order for the market to meet the goals outlined above, it appears that the brokering and support organizations must be transparent, not-for-profit NGOs. It is no less important that the smallholder biochar producer's interests be represented "at the table" for discussions determining market structure.

## ADAPTATION TO URBAN AND SUBURBAN SETTINGS

The principles that apply in using thinly distributed feedstock to produce biochar in low-tech ovens and stoves in the developing world also apply in rural, suburban and urban settings in the developed world with ready access to that feedstock. The biochar produced could be used in gardens and lawns, cutting down on the use of fossil fuel-derived fertilizer.

Yard trimmings are an obvious source of biomass. Other sources of thinly distributed feedstock that might be tapped by individuals or groups include tree-trimmings, waste from invasive species eradication programs, garden residue, and park and road verge cuttings.

Groups could run processing centers to collect and process biomass from those who have feedstock but do not want to produce biochar themselves. This would seem to be natural for community garden projects, where a "biochar for biomass" exchange program could be set up using low-tech production.

---

[7] The United Nations Framework Convention on Climate Change, an international environmental treaty adopted in 1992 and intended to stabilize greenhouse gas concentrations in the atmosphere to an extent that would prevent harmful *anthropogenic* impact on the world's climate.

Those who want to produce biochar themselves can use a small backyard oven. Or, they could use an enlarged version of a biochar-producing stove as a backyard barbeque. Their carbon credits could also be handled through a marketing organization. Since the individual carbon credit value might be insignificant in terms of a typical western income, the proceeds might be used in aggregate to further the organization's goals or contributed to a charity. There is a growing movement towards "Green Theology"—people concerned about good stewardship of the planet. Some of the above suggestions might well serve as a hands-on expression of such concerns.

In sum, for people in developed areas who wish to contribute to climate change mitigation, there are myriad ways to adapt the above concepts. Interested readers are invited to visit the UBI website, http://www.biochar-international.org/regional/ubi.

## CAUTIONARY NOTES

### The Dangers of Uninformed Opposition

This chapter has thus far addressed the positive attributes of the described program. The pros and cons of rural development in general are beyond the scope of this chapter.

Unfortunately, some people have begun to oppose biochar production vociferously. They seem to fear that if biochar is seen as useful in—and made profitable for—climate change mitigation, forests will be cut down and turned into vast biomass farms. The program discussed here does not advocate or anticipate such a result, or anything like it. Rather, this program is repeatedly emphasized as sustainable and ecologically friendly and incorporates monitoring and control safeguards to those ends.

Recognizing that greed and ill will can usurp good intentions, the program is designed to minimize this threat by advocating responsible not-for-profit governance from the local to the international level, the functions of which would include quality verification and compliance with sound sustainability and ecologically friendly practices.

### Unintended Consequences

A more serious consideration is that of unintended consequences.

The fact that biochar agriculture has been practiced for thousands of years overall, and sometimes for hundreds of years on the same plot of ground, gives some confidence that it is a useful and benign intervention, perhaps one of the most benign interventions in all of agriculture. But we are proposing to apply it in various environments as well as those in which it was traditionally practiced, and on a much more massive scale. Therefore, contemplation of possible serious unintended consequences, and research on them, is warranted.

Instead of delaying all action until the research is in, and then starting a massive global program, the pilot project and geometric growth advocated here allows rapid, small-scale implementation, and close monitoring to identify and solve problems. The close association of the program leaders with the local community also increases the chance that problems can be identified as they develop and local adaptations made to solve them or to suspend the local program.

## NEEDED RESEARCH

### Biochar in Temperate and Subtropical Agriculture

Much more research is needed on biochar production and its effects in soil. A broad program such as the one outlined in this chapter will bring biochar technology into biological and cultural environments where it has not been used before. Research is needed to see if the expected positive benefits actually occur, particularly effects on crop yields, without unintended harmful outcomes.

Reliable data are also needed to determine the labor and expenses required for obtaining feedstock and processing it into biochar, as well as sequestering biochar in non-crop enhancing situations.

### Biochar's Effect in Reforestation Systems

Adding biochar to soil changes the soil's physical and biotic properties. This is bound to have some effect on species diversity. Removing biomass from a system is also likely to have effects. Thus research is needed on the effect of producing biochar from thinnings, trimmings, dead fall, and other biomass harvesting, and the effects of biochar sequestration on plant and animal life in affected non-agriculture areas, such as managed forests.

Moreover, reforestation initiatives will stress carbon sequestration, but as this analysis suggests, maximizing sequestration should involve more than simply planting trees. The proposed research should also determine best practices for thinning and trimming biomass for use as biochar feedstock.

In reforestation projects, especially those designed primarily to increase standing crop biomass to sequester carbon, there should be more leeway for the described biochar-related activity. Such projects may be the best place to carry out research on systems to increase $CO_2$ sequestration and increase species diversity through the co-production of biochar by integrated smallholders using low-tech biochar production methods. (This topic will be further explored on this book's website, www.TheBiocharRevolution.com.)

### Uses of Co-Produced Heat in Low-tech Biochar Ovens

Further research is needed to quantify and improve the methods of low-tech biochar production and the possible uses for co-produced heat. For example, in biochar ovens used outdoors, co-produced heat could be used for drying feedstock.

The heat might also be economically used to cogenerate electricity to supplement the use of **photovoltaic** (solar) cells, which are being increasingly used in off-grid rural areas.

Biochar ovens may also put out enough heat to be used in small, low-heat-to-mechanical energy systems, if those systems can be economically scaled down. However, their mechanical complexity may pose a problem in remote rural areas. Heat that is co-produced with biochar in cookstoves may also be used for purposes other than household cooking, particularly where such stoves are the primary source for heating dwellings in cold regions.

## HELP WANTED!

Here, we post a "help wanted" sign. Even at the initiation of pilot projects, many researchers, field workers, volunteers and support groups will be needed in various parts of the world, in both the biochar and rural development/sociology areas—and this need will intensify as the system proves itself.

We encourage all interested people to think about the application of the system, and communicate your critiques, specific local refinements, or general system improvements; and to become involved. The system proposed here would benefit from an amalgamation of individual action and networked interaction. We welcome local initiation of pilot projects and those interested are invited to join in with the UB International program at http://www.biochar-international.org/regional/ubi.

But it needs to be done soon.

## SUMMARY OF THE PROGRAM/KEY POINTS

We conclude by summarizing the four fundamental components of the program proposed in this chapter.

### Component 1.   Pilot Projects

These are needed to test and adapt aspects of the program to cultural and biotic environments of particular areas, and generate buy-in by the larger community.

### Component 2.   Communities Mentoring Communities

CMC programs are vital to generate the geometric growth in sequestration necessary for this program to make a significant and timely contribution to mitigating climate change.

### Component 3.   Community Marketing Organizations; Not-for-Profit Brokerage; Well-structured Carbon Market

All three ingredients are vital for establishing the degree of control and verification necessary for:

- Biochar's acceptance into the carbon market.

- Assurance that fair compensation is given for labor done.

- Driving the full extent and speed of the climate change mitigation potential of thinly distributed feedstock.

### Component 4.   Safeguards Assuring Sustainability and Ecologically Friendly Implementation

These safeguards—implemented through the marketing community and NFP brokerage oversight described above—are necessary to assure that the program stays within ethical boundaries of sustainability and ecological propriety.

# Chapter 19

# Producing Biochar on Sugar Cane Farms: Industry Benefits, Local and Global Implications

Robert Quirk                                    Paul Taylor, PhD

*[Robert Quirk's story about how he become a pioneer and respected authority in the field of biochar is offered in his earlier chapter titled "The Accidental Scientist: Lessons in Large-Scale Farming, Biochar, and Collaboration." That chapter serves as an insightful prologue to this one, and amplifies the history set out below.]*

**IN THIS CHAPTER YOU WILL LEARN:**

- About the international revival and adaptation of ancient "black earth" technology from the Amazon—producing biochar—that may greatly benefit the sugar cane industry, especially the millions of small-scale farmers in India and throughout Southeast Asia.

- Why cane farming is particularly amenable to using pyrolysis technology and producing biochar.

- The valuable properties of biochar in abating greenhouse gases on a local and global scale.

"The vast potential for using sugar cane biomass to produce biochar and energy is especially relevant in Australia."

# INTRODUCTION

An ancient agricultural practice of Amazonian indigenous peoples, best known by the name of the soil they built—***terra preta de Indio*** ("Indian black earth")—is having an international revival that may greatly benefit the sugar cane industry. In its modern incarnation, this ancient practice is being researched and implemented through the **pyrolysis** technology that produces biochar.

The potential benefits of this technology apply to both large- and small-scale cane farmers, but smaller farms could be particularly helped. Major beneficiaries could include the 6 million farmers in India who work small (0.4 hectare), medium (0.8 hectare), and larger (1.2 hectare) farms, as well as approximately 4 million small-scale farmers throughout Southeast Asia.

Cane farming is especially amenable to using pyrolysis technology. Global production of sugar cane was 1,700 million tons in 2008 (which yielded nearly 170 million tons of sugar). Assuming 35% average residue, this leaves about 600 million tons of available residue. Some residue is burned at harvest, some is used as fuel for generating power, and the remainder is available for pyrolysis.

This chapter examines the many benefits of pyrolysis in the sugar cane industry and the unique compatibility of sugarcane and pyrolysis, which in combination present significant environmental and economic opportunity. These benefits and opportunities are illustrated in trials and studies conducted in the Tweed and Burdekin shires of Australia. The valuable properties of biochar in abating greenhouse gases, on both a local and global scale, are also discussed.

## HISTORY

Quirk's farm is located on a flood plain adjacent to the Tweed River in the Tweed Valley, in coastal northeast New South Wales, Australia. This family farm has operated for over 100 years, producing sugar for the past 70.

The farm's sugar operation has come full circle, having done green cane harvesting (GCH) up until 1949 and then returning to GCH in the early 1990s. Prior to 1949, GCH was the only method used globally; all cane was harvested without burning. Prompted by labor shortages, pre-harvest burning was introduced: one man could double his cane-cutting rate by first burning off the voluminous leaves on the stalks. Eventually, it was recognized that burning increases carbon emissions and deprives the soil of organic matter, leading to poorer soil health.

In 1987, a catastrophic fish kill occurred in the Tweed River. At the time, it was generally believed in the wider community that pesticides had caused the fish kill. The local cane farmers disagreed, claiming the fish kill was a natural event. The farmers teamed up with researchers to discover the exact cause. (See the chapter of this book titled "The Accidental Scientist: Lessons in Large-Scale Farming, Biochar, and Collaboration.")

## ACID SULFATE SOILS: RESEARCH AND SOLUTIONS

### Research

The local farm landscape in the Tweed was extensively monitored over the next fifteen years. This monitoring showed that on farms adjacent to rivers, iron and aluminum naturally present in the soil, along with sulfuric acid, were released after rain events into the farms' drainage systems, and then into the river. These soils are now referred to as acid sulfate soils.

Acid sulfate soils are among the nastiest in the world. When drained or exposed to prolonged drought, sulfides contained in soil sediments oxidize, ultimately to sulfuric acid. This acid leaches iron, aluminum, and other metals from the soil, and these materials then migrate into waterways, making a toxic brew for plants and fish.

Acid sulfate soils are not confined to the Tweed estuary; Australia has 4 million hectares (ha) of them. Around the world there are between 100 million and 1 billion hectares of sulfidic lowlands, with particularly large deposits in Asia, the Far East, Africa, and Latin America. Therefore, addressing the local acid soil problem in the Tweed could have global implications.

The Tweed monitoring program also made other important local findings. Numerous program-related studies and later solutions—resulting in nine PhD theses—showed that:

- The subject soils have very low porosity. Therefore, the water from rains did not move through the soil laterally but only vertically through the old root zone from previous crops.

- The soil contained *50 tons* of sulfuric acid per hectare.

The last finding was particularly telling. Prior research from others had established that if only 0.5 tons/ha of sulfuric acid (that is, only 1% of the amount contained in the Tweed's soil) were released from soil into a river, a major fish kill would occur. Natural soil conditions had caused the 1987 fish kill.

### Solutions

Based on the findings from the Tweed monitoring program, an innovative system was designed to retain the acidity in the landscape and keep it from reaching the rivers. This system included the measures detailed in Table 19.1.

## Outcomes

As a result of these acid control measures, and as the "before and after" photos in Figure 19.1 suggest, the fields at Quirk's farm showed marked improvements in health and productivity. The myriad benefits included the following:

- Fertilizer application was reduced by 25%

- Herbicide application was reduced by 30%

- Fuel usage was cut by 47%

- Tractor hours were reduced by 40%

- Labor component was cut by 66%

- Reduced use of phosphorous fertilizers

- Organic matter had a reduced discharge of heavy metals

- Macrofauna proliferated and has been sustained

- Soil biota population has positively evolved and increased

## THE NITROGEN PROBLEM AND THE INTRODUCTION OF BIOCHAR

### $N_2O$ Emissions and Global Warming

The system just described solved the release of acid from the soil. However, another problem emerged. Research that compared a Tweed trial site with acid sulfate soils to a trial site at Mackay, Queensland with alluvial soils established that the Tweed site discharged ten times more **nitrous oxide** ($N_2O$) than the Mackay site.

This was an alarming discovery. $N_2O$ is a **greenhouse gas** (GHG) that absorbs the sun's heat in the atmosphere—trapping almost *300 times more* heat per molecule than carbon dioxide ($CO_2$). $N_2O$ is a major culprit in global warming (see the text box labeled "Agriculture, $N_2O$, Climate Change, and Biochar").

Similar to the acidic soil problem, the concern about $N_2O$ emissions reaches beyond Australia and is global in scale. Globally, an estimated 2 million hectares (ha) of similar landscapes produce sugar cane, all contributing to $N_2O$ emissions. Even modest farm-by-farm reductions in emissions, taken cumulatively, could provide significant overall benefits for climate mitigation.

### Using Biochar to Reduce $N_2O$ Emissions

Biochar offers a way—farm-by-farm—to counteract this global problem. Research has shown that biochar reduces $N_2O$ emissions by capturing $N_2O$ before it escapes into the atmosphere. Moreover, biochar may retain the captured $N_2O$ for a very long time, since biochar is known to be stable in the soil for hundreds, if not thousands, of years.

Table 19.1    System to Control Acidity in Cane Farm Soils

| MEASURE | PURPOSE/REFERENCE |
|---|---|
| Laser grading for uniform gentle slope | Improve surface runoff and reduce frequency of acidic water table reaching the soil surface (White *et al.*, 1993) |
| Filling selected field drains | Reduce conduit for acid flows and increase production area (6 km of drains were filled in at the study site) |
| Developing shallower drains | Avoid intruding into the acid layer and make for easier drain maintenance (White *et al.*, 1996) |
| Liming drains | Increase pH of discharge water (Melville and White, 1996) |
| Liming cane fields | Maintain soil pH above that required by the crop |
| Opening floodgates in dry periods | Stop drain sludge from drying and acidifying, and allow tidal exchange and fish passage (Quirk *et al.*, 2002) |
| Use of mounds | Improve surface drainage and create a healthy microenvironment for growing crops |
| Using GCH and retaining residue | Iron and aluminum bind to the organic matter and are not discharged |

Source of information in table, with references: Australian Government, Sugar Research and Development Corporation. Final Report, 2007, pp 29, 31. Available at: http://www.srdc.gov.au/ProjectReports/NSC007_Final_Report.pdf.

Fig. 19.1   Quirk Farm Before and After Acid Control Measures

1997: Note the barren land in the central upper region of this image, indicating chronic acid sulfate soil problems. Production: 6,800 tons/yr.

2005: Acid sulfate soil rejuvenation completed. Production: 11,000 tons/yr.

Laboratory trials have shown that:

- $N_2O$ is emitted from soil even in the absence of nitrogen fertilizer.

- Adding nitrogen fertilizer could result in a very large release of $N_2O$ (up to 0.9 kg/ha/day) (Denmead, 2007).

- Merely applying fertilizer did not stimulate emissions. Emissions did not occur until soil was wetted to 90% water-holding capacity.

- Where acid sulfate soils underlie sugar cane, up to 25% of the urea added to the sugar cane is converted into $N_2O$. This was equivalent to an emission exceeding 20 tons/ha of carbon dioxide.

- Biochar could reduce the emissions of $N_2O$ from acid sulfate soils by up to 70% (Quirk et al., 2010).

The GHG-reduction potential of biochar was demonstrated by using experimental microcosms containing soils from the Burdekin cane region in Queensland, Australia. Soils were amended with biochars derived from trash and bagasse, to a rate equivalent to 10 t/ha, and compared with unamended control soil. Nitrogen fertilizer was applied at either 0 or 165 kg/ha to all treatments, and the atmosphere in the microcosms was analyzed over a 49-day trial period. The microcosms were flooded on day 21 (as previously suggested, emissions occur only after the soil is flooded). Results for nitrous oxide emissions from the bagasse biochar are depicted in Figure 19.2. Notably, those results show that $N_2O$ emissions are reduced if the soil contains bagasse biochar.

Fig. 19.2 Nitrous Oxide Produced from Control and Bagasse Biochar-Amended Soils (With and Without Nitrogen Amendment)

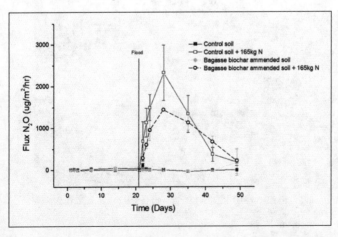

## AGRICULTURE, N$_2$O, CLIMATE CHANGE, AND BIOCHAR
Excerpted from Quirk 2010

Climate change caused by increase in atmospheric concentrations of greenhouse gases (GHGs) is predicted to cause catastrophic impacts (IPCC, 2006). Human-influenced sources of nitrous oxide (N$_2$O) contributed 3 GT [gigatons] CO$_2$e (carbon dioxide equivalents), around 8% of global emissions, in 2004. It was estimated that agriculture was responsible for 42% of this total.* Sources for N$_2$O emissions from soils include application of N [nitrogen] fertilisers, biological N fixation and excreta of grazing animals. A range of factors influence the emission of N$_2$O including N application rate, crop type, fertiliser type, soil organic C [carbon] content, soil pH and texture.*

Soil is both a significant source and sink for the greenhouse gases (GHG) nitrous oxide (N$_2$O) and methane (CH$_4$). Emissions from sugarcane soils in Australia have shown very significant production of nitrous oxide (21% of applied N converted to N$_2$O).* A total of 45.9 kg N/ha was emitted from a northern NSW sugarcane farm in the season following application of 160 kg N fertiliser. As the global warming potential of N$_2$O is 298 times greater than the equivalent mass of CO$_2$ in the atmosphere,* this equated to emissions of 43 t CO$_2$e/ha. Hence, small reductions in emissions could potentially provide significant benefits for climate mitigation.

Recent work by Van Zwieten et al.* has demonstrated the potential for biochar to reduce emissions of N$_2$O from soil. Current work using soils from the Burdekin region in Queensland, Australia, and bagasse and trash biochars are demonstrating very significant potential for reducing emissions of this potent GHG from soil.

*Exact references are provided in Quirk 2010

## DEFINITIONS FOR NON-SCIENTISTS

### Cane Trash
The green and dead leaves attached to the sugar cane stalks that are removed during harvest and left in the field.

### Bagasse
The fibrous pulp that remains after sugar cane is crushed to extract its juice. If industrially processed, this pulp is dry, dusty, and fine because it is ground to maximize juice extraction. When processed by cottage industry methods—essentially vertically mounted rollers (like on old washing machines) that squeeze the cane stalks—the resulting bagasse is long and stringy.

## Field Assessment of Biochar in Sugar Cane

One of the first sugar cane field experiments to use biochar for reducing $N_2O$ emissions and ascertaining agronomic yield benefits was established on Quirk's farm in 2008. This research, which continues today, is aimed at exploring how applying biochar affects $N_2O$ emissions, not just at the Quirk farm and not just in the Tweed Valley—but to obtain insights that would apply globally to similar landscapes.

In the experiment to suppress $N_2O$ emissions, the approach is to use heavy farm equipment with GPS guidance to compact the interspaces, mound the cane plots, and amend the mounds with biochar. Through this approach, the only place $N_2O$ can exit the soil is through the biochar-amended mounds, where it is captured and held.

In the field trial, fifteen 30 m-long plots were set up, each containing three rows of cane. The outside rows of the cane, as well as 2 m on each end of the middle row, were used as buffers between plots. Only the interior of the middle row was used for soil analyses, GHG emissions testing, and yield data (to avoid contamination by edge effects). Treatments were allocated to experimental units in a randomized manner. Treatments included control; paper mill biochar at 5 t/ha; council green waste biochar at 5 t/ha; council green waste biochar at 10 t/ha; and lime (1.5 t/ha). (Note: The chemical properties of these biochars are different from the properties of the sugar cane-derived biochars described elsewhere in this chapter.)

Cane was harvested using standard commercial harvesting equipment, and bin weights were recorded at the completion of each 30 m harvest length. Yield from the first season (2008) following planting is shown in Table 19.2.

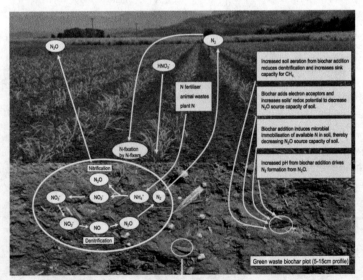

Fig. 19.3 Biochar Field Site in Tweed Valley

This figure illustrates the nitrogen cycle and the possible mechanism for biochar's influence on it.

| TREATMENT | YIELD (KG) | STD DEV | N IN LEAF TISSUE (% dry matter) | STD DEV |
|---|---|---|---|---|
| Paper mill biochar 5 t/ha | 433 | 28 | 2.13 | 0.05 |
| Greenwaste biochar 5 t/ha | 450 | 100 | 2.13 | 0.05 |
| Greenwaste biochar 10 t/ha | 416 | 76 | 2.10 | 0.10 |
| Control | 433 | 76 | 2.00 | 0.05 |
| Lime 1.5 t/ha | 416 | 76 | 2.00 | 0.10 |

Table 19.2   Yield (kg Fresh Weight) from Tweed Valley Field Plots in 2008

During the first two years of the trial, normal fertilizer was added to the plots including the control plots. As reflected in Table 19.2 for the first year's harvest, leaf analysis tests in each year so far have shown no difference in the uptake of nutrients between the plots. Now, in the third year, the amount of nitrogenous fertilizer applied has been drastically reduced.

We think the minimal agronomic benefit reported to date of applying char is probably attributable to the high levels of organic matter already native in the plots. (Without an agronomist on the trial team, we had not set the trial so that nutrients were the limiting factor.) As noted elsewhere in this book, the benefits of biochar application on crop yield may not be expected immediately, but develop over time as soil **cation exchange capacity** (CEC) increases.

Given the notable reductions in $N_2O$ emissions in laboratory trials, this season, field monitors have been set to measure the fluxes of GHGs after adding nitrogen fertilizer. So far, measurements have shown no significant amounts of GHG leaving the fields. Since the farm has the same acid sulfate soils as the local site, this result is very promising, although it could be related to prior improvements on the farm instead of, or in addition to, the biochar amendment. The trial was set up using GPS guidance on the tractor, and the plots were also GPS referenced, so the trial can continue after the cane is plowed out and replanted.

## BIOCHAR'S POTENTIAL IN THE SUGAR CANE INDUSTRY

The experiments described above have already yielded significant insights about biochar's unique capacity to sequester nitrous oxide and how bagasse biochar, in particular, notably reduces emissions. Many additional factors indicate the vast potential of using sugar cane for biochar production. Those factors are now articulated in greater detail.

### Abundant Biomass

In 2008, 24.4 million ha of sugar cane were harvested worldwide, with a biomass residue greater than most other crops (averaging 30 tons dry residue/ha).

As one of the most efficient photosynthesizers in the plant kingdom, sugar cane is grown in 110 countries with an estimated production of 1,743 million tons in 2008. Brazil produces more than one-third of all global cane, with an average yield of 75 tons/ha, much of which is used to produce ethanol fuel.

Globally, more than half the cane is hand-harvested. Typically in this technique, the field is set on fire, which burns the leaves without harming the water-rich stalks and roots. The cane delivered to the processing plant is called "burned and cropped" (b&c), and in Brazil averages around 77% of the mass of the raw cane. A textbook on renewable energy (Da Rosa 2005) provides information on the yields of various components from 1,000 kg of this b&c. These components and yields are summarized in Table 19.3, and are used to compute estimates for global figures.

Table 19.3 Component Yields from "Burned and Cropped" Sugar Cane in Brazil, with Global Extrapolations

| COMPONENT | YIELD related to 1,000 Kg of B&C | % | GLOBAL (Millions of tons) |
|---|---|---|---|
| Cane | 1,299 | 100.0% | 1,743 |
| b&c | 1,000 | 77.0% | 1,342 |
| Juice | 740 | 57.0% | 993 |
| Sucrose | 135 | 10.4% | 181 |
| Water | 605 | 46.6% | 812 |
| Moist bagasse | 260 | 20.0% | 349 |
| Dry bagasse | 130 | 10.0% | 174 |
| **Total dry residue** | **429** | **33.0%** | **575** |

Source of yield components and data: Da Rosa 2005, pages 501-502.

Although globally the dry residue varies with yield and other factors, the figure of 33% dry residue represents a reasonable and credible world average.

Of this biomass residue, some is burned during harvest, some is used in cogenerating power for the mill, and the rest is available for use in pyrolysis—making biochar. Moreover, modern cogeneration plants have become more efficient, leaving more cane residue available for pyrolysis. Furthermore, there are growing political, governmental, and industry pressures to reduce burning and carbon footprint. Because of climate change concerns, those pressures will no doubt increase, resulting in a potential biomass residue of up to 500 million tons.

## Minimal Carbon Footprint, No Extra Transport Cost

Sugar cane is uniquely suited to large-scale biochar operations. To extract sugar, the entire biomass is taken to a nearby central point (the mill) for processing, and the press residue (mill mud) is returned to the fields. Thus the cost and carbon (C) footprint to assemble the feedstock for biochar production, and to return the biochar for deployment to the fields, is minimal. Most other crops/biomass require special transport to assemble field residues at a central pyrolysis plant and then return the biochar to the field, which would impair the profitability and net C sequestration of a biochar soil amendment and C sequestration scheme.

## C Negative Energy

Pyrolysis of abundant crushed sugar cane feedstock (minus the juice) can produce both soil-amending biochar and energy. This provides two important climate mitigation paths: mitigation can be achieved by displacing fossil fuels and by converting the **labile** organic carbon into very stable organic carbon (biochar) that is used as a long-term soil amendment. Thus the biochar system can simultaneously produce energy and a net reduction of $CO_2$ in the atmosphere.

Recent work has demonstrated that pyrolysis of sugar cane residues can generate electricity by combusting the syngas (methane, hydrogen and carbon monoxide) in a gas engine. Pyrolysis produces energy in quantities comparable to cogeneration, while producing biochar at the same time. Table 19.4 shows biochar and energy yields from slow pyrolysis of sugar cane residue.

Table 19.4   Converting Sugar Cane Residue into Biochar and Energy

| FEEDSTOCK | BIOCHAR YIELD % (Dry basis) | SYNGAS ENERGY PRODUCED MWh/Ton dry feed) | ELECTRICITY PRODUCTION (MWh/Ton dry feed) |
|---|---|---|---|
| Sugar cane trash | 33.6 | 1.33 | 0.5 |
| Bagasse | 31.3 | 1.35 | 0.5 |
| **Notes** Feedstock was pyrolyzed at a highest heating temperature of 550°C with mean residence time at this temperate of 40 minutes and a heating rate of 5°C/min. The electricity output is based on the use of a gas engine at 37% conversion efficiency. It should be noted that larger-scale applications might use gas or steam cycle turbines with higher conversion efficiencies. Source of Table: Quirk 2010 | | | |

## BIOCHAR RETAINS AND RECYCLES NUTRIENTS

### Chemical Constituents of Biochar from Cane Feedstocks

Table 19.5 compares the chemical constituents of bagasse and trash feedstocks, and the biochar made from them.

Pyrolysis transforms the feedstock into gases, which are extracted for energy, and a residual char. The gases carry off much of the hydrogen (H), as well as the more volatile fractions of the carbon (C). That is why carbon increases from approximately 40% of the mass of feedstock to 65% or more of the mass of biochar. Similarly, the H/C ratio drops from around 1.5 for the feedstock to less than 0.5 for the cane residue biochars. The remaining solid char is rich in carbon that has been converted to the form of conjugated **aromatic** structures. These stable structures give the char the longevity and soil-benefitting properties that characterize biochar.

H/C ratios of 0.5 are characteristic of chars formed at temperatures above 400°C, which have been shown to have a turnover rate of around 2,000 years (for references, see Quirk 2010). Therefore, it can be expected that when these chars are applied in soil, they will remain there for many hundreds of years, highlighting their carbon sequestration and climate mitigation potential.

| PROPERTY | MATERIAL | | | | |
|---|---|---|---|---|---|
| | Trash Feedstock | Bagasse Feedstock | Trash Biochar | Bagasse Biochar | Paper Mill Biochar |
| Total Carbon | 41% | 38% | 68% | 65% | 37% |
| Molar H/C Ratio | 1.50 | 1.45 | 0.45 | 0.43 | 0.5 |
| CEC | N/A | N/A | 40 mol+/kg | 3.5 cmol+/kg | 16 cmol+/kg |
| Bray Phosphorus | N/A | N/A | 250mg/kg | 67mg/kg | 20mg/kg |
| Total Potassium | 0.64% | 0.14% | 2% | 0.25% | 0.05% |
| Total Nitrogen | 0.61% | 0.64% | 1.2% | 1.1% | 0.44% |
| Acid Neutralizing | N/A | N/A | 4.6% lime | 1.1% lime | 7.5% lime |

Table 19.5 Comparative Summary: Chemical Properties of Biochar

Table source: Quirk 2010

## Cation Exchange Capacity

**Cation exchange capacity** (CEC) is a measure of biochar's capacity to retain and exchange nutrients with its environment, including microorganisms and plant roots. As shown in Table 19.5, trash biochar has an especially high CEC; this highlights biochar's potential to be applied in conjunction with fertilizers to enhance fertilizer efficiency.

## Nutrient Recycling

Trash biochar has a high level of available phosphorus (P) and a high level of potassium (K), both important plant nutrients. Since the biochar yield from trash is 33.6% (Table 19.4), the results in Table 19.5 indicate 100% retention of potassium in trash biochar, which is thus available for recycling back into soil with almost 100% efficiency.

The high levels of potassium in trash are a problem in traditional cogeneration facilities, where it can lead to fouling of combustion equipment. These fouling problems are overcome by using slow pyrolysis. Instead of infiltrating the equipment, nearly 100% of the potassium is retained in the biochar.

## Liming Quality

Table 19.5 also shows that trash biochar has a high acid neutralizing capacity (4.6% of agricultural lime).

As summarized in Quirk 2010:

> Many of the biochar trials undertaken have application rates of 10 t/ha. This equates roughly to 1% by weight assuming incorporation into the top 10 cm soil profile. Applications of this rate would be equivalent to increasing soil carbon from, say, 2.0% to close to 2.5% carbon, assuming a bulk density of 1.5 g/cm³. The application would be equivalent to a 200 kg application of potassium, which would satisfy the potassium requirement of the crop, as well as a minor addition of phosphorus. The pH of soil would be expected to increase, equivalent to an addition of 460 kg agricultural lime.

## POTENTIAL OF UNUSED AUSTRALIAN SUGAR CANE BIOMASS

The vast potential for using sugar cane biomass to produce biochar and energy is especially relevant in Australia. It has been estimated that over 2.5 million tons of unutilized biomass are generated in the Australian sugar cane industry every year.[1] Based on the biochar and energy yields from slow pyrolysis of sugar cane residue provided in Table 19.4, this waste biomass could generate around 1,250 gigawatt-hours of electricity and produce close to 850,000 tons of biochar annually.

[1] Bernard Milford, personal communication.

To put this in perspective, the electricity generation potential is over 2.5% of annual electricity consumption in Queensland (approximately 50,000 GWh consumption in year 2007-08).[2] It would reduce emissions of $CO_2$ by 1.2 million tons through avoided consumption of coal (average greenhouse gas intensity of close to 1 ton of $CO_2$e per MWh),[3] and sequester around 2 million tons of $CO_2$ equivalents in soil. Since an average motor vehicle travelling about 20,000 km per year emits an equivalent of 5.2 tons $CO_2$ (US EPA, 2000), this would equate to offsetting emissions from approximately 600,000 motor vehicles.

### Case Study: Burdekin (Queensland, Australia)

The Burdekin produces over 1.2 million tons of sugar cane residue each year, most of which is currently burned pre-harvest. The Queensland Government has requested that the Burdekin sugar industry develop a plan to phase out pre- and post-harvest burning of sugar cane to reduce the emission of greenhouse gases— in effect, requiring canegrowers to adopt a green cane harvest (GCH) system (as used at Quirk's farm). This is indicative of the increasing political, governmental, and industry pressures to reduce burning and carbon footprint, as noted above.

This presents huge logistical issues, but as previously suggested, biochar could be part of a grand solution that more than offsets the logistics. First, using Burdekin cane residue to produce biochar could result in a reduction of one million tons of $CO_2$ equivalents/year.

Second, this environmental benefit is combined with the potential financial outcomes of the Burdekin case study shown in Table 19.6.

Table 19.6   Biochar in the Burdekin – Potential Financial Benefits

| COMPONENT | OUTPUT | ECONOMIC IMPACT/YEAR (AUD$) |
|---|---|---|
| Power | 600,000 MWh potential renewable energy generated from residue | $72 million (assumed sale price of power at 12c/kWh) |
| Biochar | 400,000 tons biochar produced at 68% C content | $40 million (assumes $100/t) |
| Carbon sequestration | 1,000,000 tons $CO_2$ sequestered each year* | $40 million (assumes C price of $40 t $CO_2$) |
| **TOTAL POTENTIAL ECONOMIC VALUE – EXISTING RESIDUE** | | **$152 million** |

*One ton of bagasse-derived biochar would sequester about 2.3 tons of $CO_2$ equivalents (Quirk 2010).

[2] ABARE 2009. "Energy in Australia."
[3] Greenhouse Indicator Annual Report 2009. ww.theclimategroup.org

## POTENTIAL BENEFITS FOR SMALL FARMS

What about the millions of small-scale farmers, including the 10 million in India and Southeast Asia? The above local, national, and global analyses are translatable, demonstrating that pyrolysis offers many benefits to small farms, including subsistence farms in emerging nations. Those benefits include:

- Smoke-free energy for cooking. (See the chapter of this book titled "Making Biochar in Small Gasifier Cookstoves and Heaters.")

- Retention of nutrients in biomass to be returned to the fields.

- Reduction in use of chemical fertilizers.

- Ability to sell biochar for additional income.

- Ability to claim carbon credits for the long-term sequestration of carbon. Individual farmers might not realize much profit, but the aggregate profits to cooperative ventures could be substantial.

- Generating village heat and electricity. In cane farming specifically, and as shown in Table 19.4 above, every ton of waste biomass can produce 0.3 ton of biochar, over 1000 kWh of syngas energy, and up to 500 kWh of electricity (based using the syngas in a gas engine operating at 37% efficiency).

- An additional sanitary benefit useful in less-developed areas. Not only cane residue, but also dried livestock and human waste, can be pyrolyzed for energy, and safely and beneficially returned to the fields.

Even without all of the facilities of a large-scale cane farm, small-scale canegrowers can realize much of the self-sufficiency highlighted in this chapter. For example, mobile pyrolyzers can be utilized for on-the-spot biochar production and deployment (see Figure 19.4).

Of course, the disadvantage of mobile in-field units is that the energy produced is not easily utilized, and connecting to the electricity grid is almost impossible.

Fig. 19.4   In-Field Pyrolysis Machine
Operates on residue; processes half a ton of feedstock per hour.

## CONCLUSIONS/KEY POINTS FROM THIS CHAPTER

The sugar cane industry is uniquely suited to produce biochar, and numerous biochar-related benefits can be realized for the Australian and international sugar cane industry. The above discussion makes the following important points:

- Cane residue is an abundant and ideal feedstock for slow pyrolysis.

- Pyrolysis of cane residue can provide the energy to generate 1 MWh for every 2 tons of dry material (about same energy as cogeneration at about the same cost).

- Slow-pyrolysis biochar that is produced from cane trash and bagasse has long-term stability in soils.

- One ton of bagasse-derived biochar applied to soils can sequester about 2.3 tons of $CO_2$ equivalents.

- The majority of the nutrients in the cane feedstocks is retained in the biochar—and can be returned to the field along with the carbon.

- Cane trash contains a high percentage of potassium. In conventional cogeneration, potassium causes fouling of equipment. Pyrolysis, on the other hand, releases the energy but retains the potassium in the biochar where it is recycled to the fields as a valuable nutrient.

- Biochar offers the potential for significant reduction in the emissions of nitrous oxide ($N_2O$) from soils.

- The long-term soil benefits of biochar allow reduced use of chemical fertilizers.

These myriad benefits can be realized in both large-scale and small-scale cane farming operations. In large-scale operations, the approaches suggested in this chapter will increase productivity and sustainability of the canegrowers, and will also promote the long-term viability of sugar mills. Pyrolysis can generate about the same electricity as cogeneration and may become an alternative to cogeneration, with the added benefits of long-term carbon capture. The industry would also be able to claim carbon credits for sale.

Granted, for the individual small-scale farmer, the benefit of carbon sequestration is limited. However, a collective effort by even a fraction of the 10 million small-scale sugar cane farmers worldwide could make a massive contribution to carbon capture. When small-scale pyrolysis plants (including mobile units) become available at a reasonable cost, long-term financial and agronomic sustainability will be greatly enhanced for small farmers.

In light of the significant economic, environmental, and climate outcomes that may be achieved—both locally and globally—field-scale assessment of this technology is warranted

## ACKNOWLEDGEMENTS

NSW Government Industry & Investment [New South Wales, Australia] – Lukas Van Zwieten, Stephen Kimber, Steve Morris, Josh Rust, Scott Petty

Burdekin Bowen Integrated Floodplain Management Advisory Committee (BBIFMAC) [Australia] – Adam Connell

Pacific Pyrolysis Pty Limited [NSW Australia] – Adriana Downie

## REFERENCES

Da Rosa, Aldo Vieira. *Fundamentals of Renewable Energy Processes.* Elsevier Academic Press, ISBN 978-0-12-088510-7, 2005, 501-502.

Denmead, O.T., MacDonald, B.C.T., Byrant, G., Wang, W., White, I. and Moody, P. (2007). "Greenhouse Gas Emissions from Sugarcane Soils and Nitrogen Fertiliser Management: II." Proceedings of the Australian Society of Sugar Cane Technology, 30: 97-105.

Quirk, R.G., Van Zwieten, L., Kimber, S., Downie, A., Morris, S., Connell, A., Rust, J. and Petty, S. "The Role of Biochar in Management of Sugarcane." Proceedings of 17th Congress, International Society of Sugar Cane Technologists (ISSCT). Vera Cruz Mexico 2010.

United States Environmental Protection Agency (EPA), Office of Transportation and Air Quality, Traverwood Drive, Ann Arbor, MI 48105. The National Vehicle and Fuel Emissions Laboratory (NVFEL) Library, 2000.

Chapter 20

# Large-Scale Pyrolysis for Dry Land Agriculture

Ben Rose, BSc (Env) Dip. Ed

**IN THIS CHAPTER YOU WILL LEARN:**

*   How mallee eucalyptus trees can protect the soil of the Australian wheat and wool regions and help achieve carbon reduction targets.

*   About the opportunity to create a new, viable biomass industry in rural Australia by growing mallee eucalypts as feedstock for pyrolysis plants, which would produce renewable energy, biochar, and sequestered carbon.

*   Potential applications and basic economics of biochar production in regional Australia.

*   How a proposed biomass industry utilizing 10% of wheat and wool growing lands could produce 4% of Australia's total electricity and significantly reduce $CO_2e$ emissions from agriculture.

*   How conservative scenarios could be scaled up and combined with solar and cogeneration technologies to increase benefits many fold.

"There is a great opportunity for Australian farmers, industry, and government to work together to establish a new industry that produces renewable energy and biochar."

## INTRODUCTION

In today's carbon-constrained world, renewable energy and carbon sequestration from biomass are urgently needed for Australia to meet its carbon reduction targets. Australia's utilization of biomass for electricity lags behind most developed countries at less than 2% of total generation compared with 5% to 15% for Scandinavian countries, which have a carbon-trading scheme. The Australian government has enacted a Renewable Energy Technology (RET) scheme, which mandates that sustainable power increase to 20% of all electricity used by 2020.[1] In addition, a carbon trading scheme is being planned.

These schemes together will make new biomass industries viable in Australia for three reasons:

First, eastern and southwestern coastal areas, with their higher rainfall, have significant biomass resources that are virtually unutilized. For example, waste from pine timber and blue gum woodchip plantations is still being burned or left to rot in the field.

Second, the vast potential for integrating dedicated woody biomass plantings with dry land agriculture is not yet widely recognized or understood.

Third, large-scale biomass pyrolysis is a proven technology. It can generate electricity using very little water, and also generates biochar as a by-product with many uses, including the potential to improve agricultural conditions and sequester carbon. Feasibility studies have also identified several potential higher-value oil by-products, but there is no need to wait for such niche products to be developed. Large-scale biomass pyrolysis, as a business enterprise, will be viable based on producing electricity and biochar alone, although government assistance is needed initially to set up grower networks, annuity price schemes, and the first large-scale plants.

These factors present a great opportunity for Australian farmers, industry, and government to work together to establish a new industry that produces renewable energy and biochar. This chapter offers a detailed overview and example of a potential mallee biomass industry in the wheat and wool growing region of Western Australia (WA).

## THE AUSTRALIAN WHEAT AND WOOL GROWING REGIONS

### A Bare Landscape

The Australian dry land wheat and wool growing regions (known as the "wheat belt") comprise an extensive strip of land running through southern inland areas of four states: Western Australia, South Australia, New South Wales, and Queensland. The landscape is ancient, eroded and flat. Broad valley flats meander between low catchment divides 10–50 kilometers (km) distant, becoming more incised as they descend to coastal plains.

Viewed from a jet aircraft in late summer, the landscape is a bare patchwork of gray, brown, and light yellow, with a few thin dark lines of vegetation along the roads. Salt lakes, dry stream beds, and erosion gullies—scars of gray, white and red—accentuate the picture of desolation. Annual rainfall is 300 mm to 500 mm and occurs mainly in winter—just enough to grow a grain crop or graze sheep or cattle.

Before clearing began early in the 20th century, the land was covered by indigenous **mallee** eucalypt woodlands and scrublands of *Acacia* and *Casuarina*. This deep-rooted vegetation protected the soil and used up all of the rain that fell on it. Today, the land has been 95% cleared and planted with annual crops and pastures having root systems less than 20 cm deep. These annuals grow and **transpire** for only 4–5 months of the year in winter and spring and use only about 70% of annual rainfall. The rest of the rain is stored in the soil profile or percolates down to saline water tables, causing them to rise and discharge into valleys and flats, making once fertile lowlands saline. Over-clearing has also left sandy soil that is vulnerable to wind erosion during drought or over-stocking.

### The Missing Piece – A Viable Biomass Industry

Most farmers, government bureaucrats, and experts in soil and hydrology agree that in order to arrest salinity and improve the soil in Australia's wheat and wool regions, new agricultural systems are needed. Those systems would incorporate deep-rooted woody perennial crops such as "oil mallee."

Woody perennials grown in greenbelts can improve agricultural conditions in the land by utilizing excess water and arresting land salinization, and by protecting topsoil from winds and reducing erosive run-off. Moreover, the woody biomass could be used to produce biochar. Deployed as a soil amendment, biochar could further improve agricultural conditions by holding nutrients and water in the topsoil.

Experts say that to arrest soil salinity and erosion, 10–30% of the landscape should be covered by woody perennials. The only impediment to large-scale adoption has been the lack of economic returns for biomass. The remainder of this chapter addresses how those returns can be achieved, but first it is essential to have a basic understanding of oil mallee.

### What is "Mallee?"

Mallee is a term for trees with several stems growing from a single woody underground tuber. The term applies to many species of small- to medium-sized trees that are indigenous to dry Australian scrublands. In fact, Eucalyptus mallee species dominated the wheat and wool areas before they were cleared. The indigenous *Acacia*, *Hakea*, and *Grevillea* genera also include species with mallee form.

One remarkable trait of mallee eucalypts is their ability to **coppice**—grow rapidly from burned or cut stumps. This is how they survive the intense wildfires that occasionally ravage the dry Australian scrublands.

"Oil mallee" is a generic name given to several mallee eucalypt species that produce eucalyptus oil, which has long been valued for its utility as a solvent, disinfectant, medicine, and perfume.

Oil-producing mallees grow well in Mediterranean climates with wet winters and hot dry summers. They prefer deeper neutral to alkaline sands, loams, and duplex soils, which occur on about 50% of the Australian wheat and wool growing areas. Although oil mallee do not grow in the tropics, some tropical species of *Acacia*, *Grevillea*, and *Eucalyptus* have similar growth habits, which may be suitable for biomass industries in parts of Queensland that have been over-cleared for beef grazing.

## Integrating Mallee Belts on Farms

Dry land farms growing wheat and wool in Australia are 10 to 100 square kilometers (km), or 4 to 20 square miles, in area. Many grow grain crops such as wheat, barley, canola, and legumes for 4 years in 5 and carry no stock. These tracts are ideal for integrating mallee belts. Some farms running sheep in large paddocks are also suitable, but fields must be de-stocked while the mallee plantings become established.

Oil mallee trees grow faster in belts on cleared agricultural land because their deep, extensive roots utilize the excess water that infiltrates below the shallow roots of annual crops and pastures. In theory, belts of woody perennials could occupy up to 30% of the landscape, since the root systems extend about 12.5 m on each side of the belts. However, it is more realistic to assume that 10% of land could be changed over from grain to oil mallee, as grain growing is still a more profitable enterprise. This equates to 10 m-wide mallee belts about 100 m apart, but depending on the requirements of farm machinery, the belts may be spaced 60 m to 200 m apart.

Mallee belts are best planted across slopes to intercept the flow of soil water. They are generally of 10 m crown width, to satisfy Kyoto minimum width requirements for carbon sequestration. Belts can have three rows at 3.5-m spacings, four rows at 2.5 m, or two rows with a 7 m-wide laneway or fence between them (see Figures 20.1 through 20.3). Many farmers are also establishing "block plantings" of salt-resistant mallee and Australian tea tree species around the edges of saline flats on land that would otherwise become saline.

An ecologically sustainable wheat region, viewed from the air, would be less monotonous than the current bare tableau. While still mostly composed of cleared fields, an interlaced network of dark olive green—perennial mallee—binds the landscape together. Scrub corridors join scattered reserves of native vegetation. Thin, straight lines of mallee cross the slopes in the grain fields. Native vegetation surrounds saline flats; erosion scars are less evident; stream lines are mapped in dark green.

Fig. 20.1 Planting Mallee with Small Tractor-mounted Planter
(Photo: courtesy Carbon Neutral)

Fig. 20.2 Oil Mallee Belt

Background: 7-year old saplings.
Foreground: first coppice less than
12 months old.

Fig. 20.3 Four-row Oil Mallee Plantings
on Annual Pasture Land

Fig. 20.4 Prototype Oil Mallee Harvester

Harvester cuts trees at ground level, chops
biomass to size, and conveys it to windrows
or directly into mobile hoppers. (Photo:
courtesy John Bartle)

## Oil Mallee – Ideal Dry Land Crop for a Biomass Industry

Experience has proved that many native tree and shrub species can easily be re-established, and that vegetated belts effectively reduce erosion and land salinity. More than 12,000 hectares of plantings,[16] funded in part by past Australian Government Landcare programs, demonstrate that oil mallee and other tree species can produce sustainable yields.

Mallee eucalypts are very easy to grow. The only inputs are costs of initial cultivation: seedlings, planting, weed control, fertilizers and "pruning" of lateral roots by ripping to minimize competition with crops. Fertilizer applied to the surrounding crops should be sufficient to optimize mallee growth. Plantations are likely to be viable for 50 years or more; in fact, one eucalyptus oil plantation is reputed to be still producing 100 years after planting. About 80% of the costs and energy inputs are for harvest and transport at 7–10 year intervals. When tree deaths eventually make a plantation uneconomic, stumps are killed, the ground ripped, and new rows planted beside and between the old rows.

I worked for several years as a consultant to Carbon Neutral, a company in the State of Western Australia (WA) growing trees for carbon offsets. During that time I measured several belt and block plantings of 12–18 year-old mallee. Wood densities were 0.9–1.1 tons per cubic meter—among the densest hardwoods in the world. From the measured stem volumes I ran simulations using FullCAM software,[6] which showed dry biomass production was likely to be in the range of 2 tons of per hectare per year with 320 mm annual rainfall and 3.2 tons with 415 mm. The simulations also showed that 1–2.5 tons of $CO_2e$/ha per year (decreasing over time) are sequestered in the roots and soil.

Scientists from the State Department of Conservation and Environment have been researching the growth of mallee saplings and coppice for more than 10 years. They have found that 2 row coppiced belts of 5 m crown width yielded 5–10 tons of dry biomass per year per hectare of land under the crown width area.[13,23] The higher figures were obtained on deep loamy soil with higher rainfall or access to fresh ground water.

However, for the analysis in this chapter, I have assumed more conservative yields. Since most of the area receives less than 415 mm of rain annually, an average yield of 2.6 tons/ha/yr for the whole of the Australian wheat-growing region is assumed. The reasons for the conservative estimate are:

a.  The mallee belts are assumed to have at least 10 m crown width; tree roots in 10 m belts can have access to only 60% of the soil water available to 5 m belts, which are twice as long per unit of area, with twice the lateral area to draw water from.

b.  An additional 1.5 m outside the crown edges is removed from production due to competition effects—that is, a 10 m belt effectively occupies 13 m of cropland.

   c.    Most farmers would probably not sacrifice grain production to grow more, narrower mallee belts.

   d.    Some plantings will be in blocks, with still lower yields.[23]

When adjusted according to the above factors, a yield of 6 t/ha for 5 m belts correlates well with the conservative estimate of 2.6 t/ha for 10 m belts plus some block plantings; this also concurs with my simulated estimates from field measurements.

    By comparison, wheat—the main grain crop traditionally grown in the area— yields 1.2 to 2.5 tons of grain per hectare. Its value per ton is about three times higher than that projected for mallee biomass, but this is offset to a large extent by ever-increasing input costs. Each year, wheat requires tillage, planting, and fertilizing (all of which can be done in one operation with "minimum tillage" techniques). At least one application of herbicide is required before harvest. Inputs of nitrogen and phosphorus fertilizers, herbicides, and insecticides usually amount to about 40% of the value of the grain harvest. Based on conservative assumptions, the gross margins for wheat and oil mallee production compare favorably, as can be seen in Table 20.1. Growing mallee for biomass may be more profitable than sheep grazing, which generally has lower gross margins than grains.

Table 20.1 Comparing Gross Margin - Oil Mallee Versus Wheat (Assuming Average Yields and Costs) (NOTE: Dollar amounts in this chapter are in Australian dollars.)

| ITEM (Dollar amounts in Australian dollars.) | GROSS MARGIN FOR OIL MALLEE BIOMASS | GROSS MARGIN FOR WHEAT (www.dpi.nsw. gov.au, 2010) |
|---|---|---|
| Average Yield (dry tons per hectare/year) | 2.6 | 1.7 |
| Price ($ per dry ton) delivered to plant or bin | $80 | $240 |
| Transport and Handling Costs (per ton) | $20 | $35 |
| On farm price per dry ton (harvested product, excluding transport) | $60 | $205* |
| Harvest cost per hectare/year | $50 | $60 |
| Other variable costs per hectare/year (including sowing-planting, fertilizer and chemical inputs, harvest, insurance) | $30 | $155 |
| GROSS MARGIN (APPROX $ per ha) | $76 | $134 |
| *GROSS MARGIN* with establishment costs ($30) offset by sale of on-site C** | $106 | |

\* Wheat prices vary widely from about $130–270 per ton depending on world prices and exchange rates.
\*\*Carbon rights can be sold to carbon offset organizations such as Carbon Neutral who plant the trees at no cost to the farmer and provide up-front cash payment.

There are no significant technical, agricultural, or silvicultural (tree farming) impediments to growing mallee biomass. Harvesting and transporting machinery is being developed in Western Australia, based on that used for sugar cane (see Figure 20.4).

In summary, for the Australian wheat and wool growing regions—which have low rainfall, hot dry summers, short wet winters, and poor soils—indigenous mallee trees are clear winners in the biomass production stakes. Grown in 10 m-wide coppiced belts, mallee produces 50–100% more dry biomass than wheat crops. It will provide three revenue streams—energy, biochar, and on-site sequestered carbon—and potential for several other commercial products such as bio-oil, fuel pellets and eucalyptus oil.

Mallee grows year in, year out, provides at least fifteen harvests from a single planting with only one major cash outlay (at establishment), and presents   less climatic and price risks than grain crops.

## FINANCIAL INCENTIVES: VITAL TO BIOMASS PYROLYSIS INDUSTRY
### Nascent Industry Efforts and Obstacles
Several waste biomass plants operate in Australia, and others are planned. They are viable with tradable renewable energy certificates (RECs) alone without a carbon price because the feedstock is available free on or near the site. Bagasse-fired, conventional steam cycle thermal power plants with up to 50-megawatt (MW) capacity operate in the sugar cane belts of New South Wales and Queensland. At least 300 MW of biomass projects are proposed for the southwest of WA.[22]

There has been considerable interest in dedicated (grown specifically for industry) biomass in WA. In a pilot project at Narrogin, a one megawatt oil mallee pyrolysis plant produced eucalyptus oil and biochar and a 5-MW plant is planned.[20] A fuel pellet plant is planned near the port of Albany to process waste from wood chip plantations.[21]

The above underscores the proven potential for a commercial tree biomass industry in WA, but as of July 2010 it still does not exist. Why are dedicated biomass pyrolysis plants not already well established in developed nations such as the United States, Canada, and Australia?

The problem is that in the current energy market, such plants must have some form of subsidy to compete with coal. To date, governments have not provided direct subsidies for biomass energy, although they have done so for "clean coal." Several obstacles—political, cultural, and economic—stand in way of subsidies, including:

- General opposition to farm subsidies of any kind.

- Skepticism that biomass can provide significant energy.

- Opposition to growing trees for the sole purpose of creating feedstock to burn.

- Reluctance to jeopardize Australia's coal industry; coal is the nation's largest and most profitable export.

## Government Direct Subsidies for "Clean Coal"

Government carbon capture and storage (CCS) programs have been initiated in the United States, Canada, China, India, and Australia. These programs in effect represent a decision that coal should remain a major—if not the predominant—energy source. For example, Australia has allocated billions of dollars in research subsidies into CCS, an evolving technology that ultimately may not prove viable. Very little funding has been allocated to developing biomass pyrolysis capability, which seems misguided since it is a *proven* technology with the demonstrable potential to provide more than 15% of Australia's energy, and at the same time sequester more carbon than it emits.

However, governments have started undertaking fiscal intervention to promote the generation of renewable energy and reduce carbon emissions. Through this approach, biomass pyrolysis can become viable without direct subsidies.

## RET and RECs – An Evolving Financial Incentive

Australia has already provided a price mechanism that, combined with a carbon price, will make a biomass industry viable. Renewable Energy Target (RET) legislation, enacted in 2009, is intended to ensure that 20% of electricity is generated from renewable energy sources by 2020. The RET legislation creates tradable renewable energy certificates (RECs) which can be bought and sold to achieve an annual mandated percentage of electricity. This is a significant step forward, and will be markedly improved once the RET legislation is amended to achieve greater market stability for RECs.

## A Carbon Price – Yet to be Achieved in North America and Australia

Carbon trading has been operating in the European Union since 2005 and New Zealand has enacted a carbon-pricing scheme that became effective in July 2010. These schemes have, for the first time, applied an "externality cost" to greenhouse gas pollution. Carbon trading in effect subsidizes low carbon emitting technologies such as biomass energy, while taxing high carbon emitters such as coal. The other major developed nations are working toward implementing their own carbon pricing schemes, but have not yet succeeded.

At Copenhagen in 2009, attempts to create a world carbon market failed. In Australia, legislation that would offer financial incentives sufficient to give investors price certainty (the Carbon Pollution Reduction Scheme—CPRS) failed to pass the Australian Senate and similar legislation has likewise stalled in the United States. One of the main reasons for the failure in Australia was that the electorate considered the plan inequitable: it proposed to exempt large "trade exposed" polluters from paying for 65%–95% of their carbon emissions, thereby imposing a disproportionate burden on domestic taxpayers to meet reduction targets.

These failures notwithstanding, there is a logical, ready alternative to waiting for a worldwide carbon-pricing scheme. The governments of the United States, Canada, and Australia could set an interim carbon price of $10–$20 per ton on all fossil fuel carbon emissions (including those from trade exposed industries) with higher rates to be phased in. Simply amending emissions trading schemes to include agricultural production would provide even greater financial incentives for the biomass pyrolysis industry. This move would benefit both agriculture and the industry. More specifically, it would become more economic to use some agricultural land for biomass production (a carbon reducing enterprise) rather than the traditional sheep and cattle grazing.

### RECs and Carbon Price Combined – A Necessary Prerequisite

When both effective RECs *and* a price on carbon are in place, a commercial biomass pyrolysis industry in Australia will then be viable with only three products:

1. Renewable electricity, for which there is already a demand.
2. Carbon sequestered in tree plantations.
3. Biochar for agricultural or industrial uses, with its price increased to reflect its carbon offset value.

Viability, therefore, depends on government support. Demand for these products will escalate, and prices will increase, when government enacts carbon-trading legislation that includes agricultural emissions and sequestration, and amends the existing RET scheme to stabilize the market for RECs.

## POTENTIAL FOR TREE BIOMASS ENERGY AND BIOCHAR PRODUCTION IN AUSTRALIA

### Rural Renewal Based on Combined Biomass and Solar Energy

Belts of woody perennials will improve over-cleared agricultural land in Australia, with none of the downsides cited against grain-derived fuels (for example, increasing food prices) and palm oil cultivation (for example, clearing rain forest).

Moreover, the ratio of energy output to input of oil mallee pyrolysis for electricity and biochar is likely to be at least 5.3:1 if the process is optimized for biochar, or better than 7:1 if optimized for energy[12] (figures cited for switch grass). This is about twice as energy efficient as producing biodiesel and stock feed from canola (energy output : input 3.3:1).

In addition to being one of the most cost-effective renewable energy technologies,[24] biomass pyrolysis is ideally suited to supplement solar power stations. These industries in combination present the opportunity for much needed—and sustainable—economic revival for rural regions.

Solar generation is only possible while the sun is shining. By generating electricity with biomass at night, combined with daytime solar generation, it should theoretically be possible to produce double the amount of energy continuously. Such projects have already been proposed in Western Australia. Pyrolysis plants are ideal for this application, because syngas and bio-oil can be produced continuously, stored and used to fuel a gas turbine only when needed at night or in cloudy conditions, since these units can be quickly ramped up and down.

Australia's dry land agricultural areas are particularly well suited to this solar/biomass model, for four reasons:

1. The warm, sunny climates are ideal for solar power and suitable for biomass tree crops.

2. Much of the land lies 50–400 km (efficient transmission distance) inland from the populated coast areas and most of it is relatively cheap.

3. These areas are in economic decline due to worsening terms of trade for agricultural commodities, and urgently need new, sustainable industries.

4. Rail and road infrastructure is already in place for grain. Pyrolysis facilities could be located adjacent to grain-handling silos and heat they generate could be used for other industries, initially drying biomass, fuel pellets and grain.

## Potential for Biomass Energy in Australia

Five categories of biomass have potential for energy and biochar production in rural Australia:

1. Mallee eucalypt belts on dry land agricultural areas—the 40 million hectares of wheat and wool growing lands.

2. Belts of *Acacia* species (such as "brigalow" and "pindan") in more than 10 million hectares of cleared tropical and sub-tropical cattle grazing lands.

3. Waste wood from timber and woodchip plantations in high rainfall areas.

4. Bagasse waste from sugar cane.

5. Municipal and industrial organic waste (local and brought by rail from cities).

Saddler and colleagues (2004)[19] estimate that 26% of Australia's electricity requirements could be provided by 2040 if all biomass sources are used to generate renewable electricity. Over 50% of this figure (that is, about 15% of electricity generation), could be produced using the intermediate pyrolysis process described in this chapter to produce biochar for agricultural or industrial use (the reduction being due to the biomass energy retained in the biochar, and the extra energy needed to drive the pyrolysis).

## The Potential of 10% Mallee Tree Belts Alone

Mallee eucalypt belts can make a significant contribution to the biomass energy production estimated in the Saddler scenario. Table 20.2 below shows that if only 10% of the wheat and wool lands of Australia were used to grow mallee as feedstock for biochar-producing pyrolysis plants, this could provide at least 4% of Australia's electricity generation. The WA wheat and wool growing areas alone could provide about 18% of the capacity of the Western Australian South West electricity grid.

The Table 20.2 scenario avoids 9.9 million tons $CO_2e$ by displacing coal-fired electricity. In addition, it *further reduces* national greenhouse gas emissions by 12.5 million tons through (a) carbon sequestration by roots, tubers, and soil within the mallee belts, (b) potential carbon sequestration through application of biochar to soils, and (c) reduction of methane emissions by displacing some 8 million sheep. The total emissions avoided or removed are about 22 million tons, which represents 3.6% of Australia's total emissions of 576 million tons, or 24% of Australia's agricultural emissions of 88 million tons.[7]

These estimates are based on the following conservative assumptions:

- Ten percent of land (4 million ha) will be taken out of agricultural production to grow mallee biomass.

- The plantations are in belts or blocks of at least 10 m crown width.

- Dry biomass production averages 2.6 t/ha/year.

- Medium and fast pyrolysis plants producing electrical energy, biochar, and/or bio-oils.

The figures in Table 20.2 equate to 50 large-scale pyrolysis plants in the 40 million ha Australian dry-land agricultural region, each with the capacity to generate 190 GWh/yr of electricity. Eighteen of these would be located in WA. In locales with higher rainfall, the plants could be proportionally larger and the "grower cells" (described below) proportionally smaller.

## Huge Potential to Expand

It must be re-iterated that the scenario presented here represents only a small part of what could be achieved through a dedicated biomass industry in Australia. The renewable energy and carbon sequestration figures may be multiplied many-fold in the future. It is worth considering a plausible "higher end" vision:

1. Increase to 20% the area of the wheat/wool regions under biomass: add 100%

2. Additional 4 million hectares of dedicated biomass in tropical grazing areas: add 100%

3. Average biomass yield achieved is 3.9 t/ha/yr—50% higher than the conservative estimate in this analysis: add 50% to (2)

4. "Combined cycle" technology (utilizing hot turbine exhaust to fire auxiliary steam turbine) and/or cogeneration (using waste heat for industry) at most power stations: add 50% to electricity in (3)

This "higher end" scenario outlines a dedicated biomass industry that could produce a remarkable 29% of Australia's electricity generation and lock up 16% of carbon emissions. These increases could be achieved at a lower cost, because the plants and transmission lines would already be in place and would only need to be expanded.

Table 20.2 Potential Electricity Generation from Mallee Eucalypts in Australian Wheat and Wool Regions

| Mallee Biomass Energy and Yields | | |
|---|---|---|
| Dry biomass energy content | 19.5 | GJ/t |
| Dry biomass energy content | 5.4 | MWh/t |
| Assumed average dry biomass yield, mallee belts, 300–500 mm rainfall | 2.6 | t/ha |
| **Western Australia** | | |
| Dry biomass from 10% of WA grain belt (0.1 x 15 m ha x 2.6 t/ha/yr) | 3,900,000 | tons/yr |
| Annual energy content of mallee biomass | 21,125 | GWh |
| Energy from pyrolysis syngas and bio-oils (50% of energy) | 10,562 | GWh |
| Annual electricity generated @ 35% efficiency | 3696 | GWh |
| Total annual generation WA South West Grid | 20,679 | GWh |
| Oil mallee belts – potential % of above | 17.9% | |
| **Australia** | | |
| Dry biomass from 10% of Australian dry land grain belt (0.1*40m ha * 2.6 t/ha/yr) | 10,400,000 | tons/yr |
| Annual energy content of mallee biomass | 56,333 | GWh |
| Energy from pyrolysis syngas (50% of total) | 28,167 | GWh |
| Annual electricity generated @ 35% efficiency | 9,858 | GWh |
| % of total Australia generation (230,000 GWh in 2007) | 4.3% | |
| Biochar production @ 22% of dry biomass | 2,228,000 | tons/yr |
| $CO_2$e emissions reduction by displacement of coal @ 0.85 t/MWh | 8,379,300 | t $CO_2$e /yr |
| Biochar $CO_2$e sequestration potential @ 2.3 t$CO_2$e per ton biochar | 5,124,400 | t $CO_2$e /yr |
| Onsite $CO_2$e sequestration potential – roots and tubers of mallee trees: 4 million ha @ 1.5 t $CO_2$e /ha/yr | 6,000,000 | t $CO_2$e /yr |
| Methane emission avoided by displacing 8 million sheep @ 0.17 t$CO_2$e/ha[9] | 1,360,000 | t $CO_2$e /yr |

Non-dedicated biomass sources such as timber industry, municipal, and sugar cane wastes are beyond the scope of this chapter. If they were all utilized, there would be a further quantum increase in the production of renewable energy and emissions avoided through biochar and reduced landfill methane.

Combining solar with pyrolysis gas-fueled generation, as described previously, would multiply the production of renewable base-load electricity yet again.

## ATTRIBUTES OF A MALLEE BIOMASS INDUSTRY

Planning a biomass plant is a complex process involving myriad stakeholders at various levels, including scores of individual growers, farmers' groups, and product buyers; national, state, and local government agencies; and infrastructure providers such as electrical utilities, railroads, and road transport constituents. Optimizing location is the first step and a feasibility study would first address land use and infrastructure. The most important factors in locating a plant are:

- Available land for growing the feedstock within a viable transport radius

- Existing transport infrastructure and nodes

- Existing power lines

- Nearby industries that may use cogenerated heat

### Annuity Payments for Farmers

Growers within a "cell" of about 50 km radius must first be contracted to provide enough biomass to sustain the plant. As noted in Table 20.1, a one-time capital expenditure of about $1,500 per ha is required to establish the trees. This could be incurred by farmers who wish to fund their own mallee plantations, by carbon off-set organizations in return for carbon rights, or by industry or government, which could pay an annuity for leasehold over the land and ownership of the trees. Such annuities are already paid by woodchip companies to hundreds of farmers with blue gum plantations. Annuities of $50–100/ha or a standing-biomass price of about $40 per dry ton should be viable alternatives for farmers who do not wish to incur the costs of planting, harvest and transport. Farmers willing to have 100-year covenants on their plantations could obtain additional income from sequestered carbon.

Once farmers are offered an annuity, there should be no lack of growers; 12,000 ha of mallee eucalypts have already been planted without *any* annuity or income stream. An established tree nursery industry already produces mallee seedlings; it would need to expand to provide over 20 million seedlings per year (about 1,650 per ha[16]) over six years for each large pyrolysis plant.

After the production cells have been planned, tree planting should start immediately, regardless of the status of building the pyrolysis plant, since there is a lag of several years before the first harvest. Planting 80,000 ha of trees within a 50 km radius would need to be coordinated over 5–7 years. By the time the first mallee crops can be harvested, a carbon pricing scheme—or at least an interim scheme—will be in place.

## Optimal Plant Size and Type

The size of the pyrolysis plant will be determined by the amount of biomass that can be supplied and economies of scale. Operating costs per megawatt for a 30 MW plant have been cited as being less than 60% of those for a 10 MW plant.[10] A 20–35 MW plant would utilize 60–120,000 tons of dry biomass per year, the amount likely to be available within viable transport distance.[18]

Medium-scale on-farm pyrolysis units of about one megawatt capacity may be viable if the price of biochar is high enough. Although economies of scale would work against such operations, savings in transport may compensate for this.

Although combustion steam cycle power stations can generate more electricity per ton of biomass, they offer no biochar or fuel by-products. Furthermore, even when air cooling technology is used, steam generation requires significant amounts of fresh water. This alone makes them unsuitable for most dry land agricultural areas, where fresh water is scarce.

## Technologies Suitable for Dry Land Areas

Pyrolysis technologies are most suitable for dry land agricultural areas for the following reasons:[5]

- Unlike steam cycle generation, pyrolysis requires little water.

- Pyrolysis produces biochar, which has many uses and can potentially sequester carbon.

- Pyrolysis processes can produce a range of gaseous and liquid fuels, which can be stored or burned in efficient turbines or internal combustion engines.

- Pyrolysis can also be used with coal, offering the opportunities for carbon capture and storage via char.

The various pyrolysis technologies produce different proportions of electricity, biochar, and bio-oils.[12] With a potential for building more than 50 biomass plants, there will be scope to develop a variety of technologies depending on the desired products and prices obtainable, for example:

Slow and medium pyrolysis technologies produce the highest amounts of biochar and have the highest carbon sequestration potential, and would therefore be attractive to investors, particularly with higher carbon prices. Each ton of dry biomass produces 200–350 kg of biochar,[5, 12] enough to sequester over 0.5 to 0.9 tons $CO_2e$.

**Fast pyrolysis** produces smaller amounts of syngas and biochar and large amounts of bio-oil, a low-grade fuel, which can be used for heating, fueling turbines to generate electricity or refined for use in internal combustion engines. Commercial plants, with up to 65,000 tons per year capacity, are operating elsewhere in the world. A study commissioned by Avon Grow, a WA farmer group,[10] identified fast pyrolysis as one of the most viable uses for mallee biomass in WA, using current proven technology. Biochar production would be lower, at about 12% of dry biomass, and probably of poorer quality.[5]

## Carbon Sequestration in Roots, Tubers, and Soils

Regardless of what technology is chosen, significant amounts of carbon will be sequestered on site by the roots and tubers of the mallee trees and fixed in the soil from decayed roots and debris. For each ton of mallee biomass produced, an additional 600-800 kg of $CO_2$ is sequestered in the soil. Under carbon rights legislation, many farmers and plantation owners already receive payments from voluntary carbon offset companies for carbon sequestered by their trees.

With a carbon trading scheme that includes agriculture (as suggested above), this potential additional income stream will become even more attractive for growers.

## Industry Opportunity for Government in WA

Verve Energy, a state-owned electricity company,[20] has trial pyrolysis plants, but progress has been slow. Verve's 1 MW research plant at Narrogin is no longer operating and as noted they have received expressions of interest to construct a 5 MW plant to produce electricity, activated carbon, and distilled eucalyptus oil. Although this research has merit and should be continued, there is no need to wait for the outcome before commencing larger-scale operations. The current market for Renewable Energy Certificates (RECs) to subsidize operations, the existing high-value uses for biochar, and the inevitability of a carbon price make commercial production imminently viable.

Now is an opportune—if not ideal—time to construct large-scale (25 MW) pyrolysis plants in the WA wheat and wool region. The following financial analyses show that such plants will be profitable on the basis of producing electricity and biochar only. As higher-value biochar products such as carbon **reductants** (reducing agents), fertilizer amendments, and activated carbon are developed, pyrolysis is likely to become more economic than combustion. In the future, as technologies improve, fuels such as bio-diesels and ethanol reformed from syngas may also be produced.

Such projects will require upgrading the electricity grid, which is also operated by a government-owned company. Because the government owns both the grid and the major electricity generator, there is a compelling opportunity for the government to contribute to the construction of the first large-scale commercial pyrolysis plant.

## A Typical Large-Scale Mallee Pyrolysis Plant

Whether electricity production from biomass is by direct combustion to produce steam or pyrolysis to produce syngas or bio-oils, 10–15% of the energy contained in the feedstock is used or lost in the plant before the steam or gas arrives at the turbines. In this analysis, the conservative figure of 15% is used for both types of plants. In combustion power stations, this energy loss is accounted for in boiler house heat losses and in powering machinery such as dryers, grinders, and conveyors.[25] The remaining 85% of energy is contained in high-temperature steam that powers steam turbines, which drive alternators, which produce electricity. Steam turbines vary in efficiency from about 35–47% depending on their design and scale.

In pyrolysis plants, the assumed 15% energy loss is accounted for as heat taken to drive the pyrolysis reaction and energy used to power machinery.[14] The remaining energy is contained in pyrolysis products—varying proportions of syngas, bio-oil, and biochar depending on the particular pyrolysis technology used. Syngas and bio-oil products may be used to drive gas turbines, which vary in efficiency from about 35-45% and up to 60% for combined cycle set-ups where exhaust heat from the gas turbine is utilized to power a smaller steam turbine.

As the efficiency range for gas and steam turbines overlaps, the analyses in this chapter assume the same efficiency for both types of turbine.

Table 20.3 below illustrates a mass-energy balance for a hypothetical medium pyrolysis plant. Fifteen percent of the biomass energy is used to drive pyrolysis and other plant processes, 35% is contained in the biochar produced, and the remaining 50% is used to generate electricity.

Table 20.3   A Mass-energy Balance for Pyrolysis of One Ton Dry Mallee Biomass

| | Mass kg | Energy content MJ/kg* | Energy MJ | Energy kWh | % of total energy content | Electricity (MWh,35% efficiency) |
|---|---|---|---|---|---|---|
| Biochar | 220 | 31 | 6820 | 1894 | 35.0% | 0.66 (potential) |
| Bio-oil and syngas for electricity generation | 570 | 17 | 9740 | 2708 | 50.0% | 0.95 |
| Syngas and bio-oil for pyrolysis process | 210 | 14 | 2940 | 817 | 15.0%* | n/a |
| Mallee biomass (dried to 10% moisture) | 1000 | 19.5 | 19,500 | 5419 | 100.0% | n/a |

At an assumed stable carbon content of 63%, biochar could sequester 0.63*3.67 = 2.3 kg $CO_2$e per kg of biochar, if "stored" in soil (figure used by Quirk, et al. in the chapter of this book titled "Producing Biochar on Sugar Cane Farms: Industry Benefits, Local and Global Implications").

* Gaunt and Lehmann,[12] Wu et al,[26] Wisconsin Biorefining Initiative[24]

As Table 20.3 shows, pyrolysis of each ton of mallee biomass would produce:

- About 950 kWh of electricity from syngas, enough to power a typical Australian family home for two months.

- 220 kg of biochar, which could potentially sequester 220*2.3 = 506 kg $CO_2$e.

Table 20.4 summarizes statistics for a hypothetical oil mallee pyrolysis biomass plant in the Australian wheat and wool regions based on the assumptions and data presented above.

Table 20.4 Statistics for Hypothetical Mallee Biomass Power Plant in WA Wheat and Wool Region

| Component | Quantity | Measure |
|---|---|---|
| Land area of "production cell": 50 km radius of plant (ha) | 785,000 | Hectares |
| Area planted to mallee: 10% of 50 km radius area | 78,500 | Hectares |
| Tons dry biomass available @ 2.6 t/ha/yr | 204,100 | tons/yr |
| Tons dry biomass available per day | 559 | tons/day |
| Average generation capacity of power stations | 25 | MW |
| Price per dry ton delivered to plant | 80 | $/ton |
| Production cost of electricity from dedicated biomass crops (RIRDC, 2008) | 110 – 180 | $/MWh |
| Assumed wholesale price of electricity in Australia | 60 | $/MWh |
| Capital investment required for the plant (estimate)[18] | 90 million | $ |
| Capital investment in harvest and haulage equipment (rough estimate) | 10 million | $ |
| Capital investment in electricity grid | Probably in excess of $10 million | |

## BIOMASS PYROLYSIS– ECONOMICS 1.0

Commercial production of biochar and electricity from biomass will depend on costs of production, and the prices obtainable for the products, which in turn will depend on:

1. The price of renewable electricity (dependent on RECs price).
2. The price of sequestered carbon.
3. The value of the biochar product.

The cost of producing electricity from oil mallee biomass pyrolysis plants is higher than for combustion plants fired by coal or bagasse waste. RIRDC (2008) cites electricity generation costs of $110–180/MWh for biomass depending on feedstock haulage distance and technology used, compared to less than $60/MWh for coal.

The reasons for the higher cost are (a) oil mallee feedstock costs more than coal or bagasse, (b) more feedstock is required, and (c) capital and operating costs per MWh are higher.

Mallee feedstock is likely to cost about $80 per dry ton at the plant gate compared to about $40 per ton for coal used by Australian power stations.[15] Mallee also incurs a slight penalty in that its energy content (19.5 GJ/t) is slightly lower than black coal (19.9–22.5 GJ/t), although it is much higher than brown coal.[7]

Electricity generation efficiency is also a significant factor when comparing combustion and pyrolysis plant costs. As explained above, the analyses in this chapter assume that the efficiencies are the same for both types of plant.

For a pyrolysis technology that produces biochar, about 35% of the biomass energy is contained in the biochar and is not used to generate electricity. Hence about 70% more biomass is needed to produce each megawatt hour of electricity. Higher feedstock and operating costs are the main reasons for higher electricity generation cost. However, this cost may be offset by additional revenues from biochar.

Pyrolysis will be more economic than combustion when the biochar is worth more than the renewable electricity foregone; for example:

> If the renewable electricity price is $80/MWh, the biochar price would need to be at least 0.66*80/0.22 = $240 per ton. At 2.3 tons of sequesterable $CO_2$e per ton of biochar, this corresponds to a "carbon trading" price of $240/(2.3), that is, at least $100/ton $CO_2$e.

Biochar prices in excess of $240/ton should be obtainable if the biochar is processed for such higher-value uses as agricultural fertilizers or carbon reductants (the price of coke made from coal has already exceeded this level). However, since $CO_2$ prices will be nowhere near $100/ton (at least for decades), biochar production for carbon sequestration alone is not economically viable.

Table 20.5 below illustrates how an REC price of $38 per ton plus a carbon price of $30 per ton, and a biochar price of $240/ton, could make the viability of biomass power generation comparable to coal, at generation costs of around $115 and $170 per MWh for biomass combustion and pyrolysis, respectively. (These costs are well within the range cited by RIRDC, 2008.) It shows that, notwithstanding higher production costs, the existing RECs and imminent carbon price combined with sale of biochar should make biomass pyrolysis economic. However, removal of "perverse subsidies" for fossil fuels and amendment of the National Electricity Market[2] rules may also be necessary.

Table 20.5 Break-even Electricity Price per MWh in One Scenario of Coal Combustion vs. Biomass Combustion and Pyrolysis

| (Dollar amounts are in Australian dollars.) | COAL COMBUSTION POWER STATION | BIOMASS COMBUSTION POWER STATION | BIOMASS PYROLYSIS GAS POWER STATION* |
|---|---|---|---|
| Carbon emissions $tCO_2e$/MWh (Gaunt and Lehmann, 2007) | 1.0 | 0.1 | 0.15 |
| Biochar production, tons per MWh | 0 | 0 | 0.22 |
| Electricity generation cost, $/MWh | $50** | $115 | $168 |
| Minus RECs rebate at $38/MWh | $50 | $77 | $130 |
| Plus cost of $CO_2$ emitted at $30/t | $80 | $80 | $135 |
| Minus value of biochar at $240/t = Sales price of electricity | $80 | $80 | $80 |

* As detailed in Table 20.3.
**Average spot price of electricity in Australia 2007-8 was $ 52/MWh.[2]

## BIOCHAR IN AUSTRALIAN AGRICULTURE

This section briefly examines issues with biochar for carbon sequestration in agricultural soils and how biochar may be utilized in agriculture. Biochar will be worth more than its energy value (at least $240 per ton) when demand for high-value industrial carbon and fertilizer products made from it increases. **Slow pyrolysis** technologies optimized to produce up to 35% biochar may then become the norm.

### Biochar for Carbon Sequestration in Soils

The previous analyses assume that carbon from biochar will be 100% allowable as sequestered carbon under a trading scheme. In reality, this will depend on where and how the carbon is placed or stored. Biochar is a solid product that can be stored and there are various ways in which carbon can be buried and sequestered indefinitely. It is likely that biochar would be allowable as saleable sequestered carbon if it can be verified as having been produced and disposed of in such a way as to have a half-life in excess of 1,000 years. This could certainly be achieved if it is buried in anaerobic conditions conducive to mineralization, such as deep in suitable soil profiles or in mine voids. However, as explained previously it would not be economic to do this until carbon prices exceed $100/t $CO_2e$.

Although charcoal is generally accepted to have a half-life of at least 1,000 years, the actual longevity of any biochar in topsoil, and its precise actions and benefits, depends on the characteristics of both the biochar and the soil to which is applied. There are wide variations in qualities of biochars, soil chemistry, and the mobility of carbon in topsoil. (See the chapters of this book titled "What *Is* Biochar?;" "How Biochar Helps the Soil;" and "Characterizing Biochars: Attributes, Indicators, and At-Home Tests.") Over time, special rules may be devised that apply to sequestration of carbon in soils according to biochar quality, soil, and climate conditions. These rules or verification methods will be a necessary prerequisite for carbon in biochar applied to topsoil to be saleable under carbon trading schemes. When verification rules are in place and both its agronomic and carbon sequestration values can be realized, the value of biochar as a soil improver and fertilizer additive for commercial agriculture will increase.

However, this challenge should not defer biochar production. In the interim, there are many economic uses for biochars, including as fuels,[8] industrial reductants, and as described below for use in high-value horticultural cropping.

## Mallee Biochar Quality

Scant data is currently available to compare mallee biochars with those derived from more traditional feedstocks like corn stalks, switch grass, and straw. However, the Narrogin research facility has produced high-quality biochar from mallee eucalypt biomass. The stem wood is among the densest of all species and its energy content when dry is higher than most other biomass feedstocks. These factors and its high lignin content point to high yields of good quality biochar. The physical and chemical qualities of biochars vary depending on the production processes.[12] The range of pyrolysis technologies envisioned here provides a variety of options as to the quantity and quality of the biochar they produce.

## Biochar for Australian Dry Land Agricultural Soils?

There are two types of carbon in soils. *Biologically active carbon* is organic matter that can be rapidly oxidized. It improves the soil biologically, chemically, and physically but is rapidly lost by oxidation. It can be gradually built up over decades in the topsoil by good management techniques such as stubble retention, mulch crops, application of compost, and growing perennial pastures.

*Biologically inactive*, long-lived carbon such as biochar improves the soil mainly by improving retention of water and nutrients and providing better conditions for some soil organisms. Soils in most of the Australian dry land agricultural regions are low in both types of carbon, with levels generally below 0.5%.

Biochar trials elsewhere in the world have been encouraging. For example, in one un-replicated 1 hectare trial in Canada, about 3t/ha of fine biochar material containing 70% carbon was applied to a clay loam soil. The trial reported increased soybean yield by up to 19% and forage biomass by up to 100%.[8,17] It also highlighted the problem of biochar mobility: 30% simply blew away during application.

However, for dry-land Australian agriculture, biochar is unlikely to be used as a broad scale soil ameliorant for the following reasons:

- Annual applications of many tons of biochar over small areas of a few hundred hectares to produce *terra preta*-like soils are not likely to be cost effective in grain-growing regions. The low-yield, drought-tolerant crop varieties, designed for a short growing season, limited rainfall and high summer evaporation (1,500–2,000 mm) are unlikely to provide sufficient yield increase to justify the cost.

- It would take a lot of biochar to raise soil carbon from the typically near zero levels to that of a more fertile soil, say one percent. To raise carbon by one percentage point in the top 10 cm of the soil over the whole grain belt would require about 17 tons of biochar per hectare. Applied at 65 kg/ha/yr (the rate at which it could be produced), this would take more than 250 years (Table 20.6), or longer taking into consideration soil erosion and oxidation in the high soil temperatures.

Soil erosion in particular is an important factor to be considered in agricultural biochar applications. Many Australian agricultural soils have been poorly managed in the past, leading to severe erosion particularly during periods of drought, strong winds, and heavy rainfall. Carbon is the lightest fraction of soil and if the topsoil is left bare, most of it can be blown or washed away in a single extreme weather event. For this reason, good soil management practices such as minimum tillage cropping, stubble retention, de-stocking of grazed land during droughts, and windbreaks (a function provided by mallee belts) will be crucial to the effectiveness of any mode of biochar application.

Table 20.6  Biochar Yield and Application Calculations

| Component | Quantity | Measure |
|---|---|---|
| Biochar yield of mallee belts @ 2.6 t/ha biomass, 25% biochar | 0.65 | tons/ha |
| Biochar yield by weight, with 10% planted to mallee (estimated average for wheat/wool regions) | 0.065 | tons/ha |
| Mass top 10 cm of soil (assuming density of 1.2) | 1,200 | tons/ha |
| Mass of carbon required to raise soil C by 1% by weight | 12 | tons/ha |
| Mass of biochar @ 70% carbon required to raise soil C by 1% | 17 | tons/ha |
| Time required to raise soil C by 1% over the entire wheat/wool region | 264 | years |

There are other ways of using biochar that do show promise for Australian dry land agriculture. Initial trials banding biochar with wheat sown in wide-spaced rows in Western Australia[3] indicate significant yield increases, reduction in the rates of N, P and K required, and a reduction in nitrous oxide ($N_2O$) emissions, particularly from acid soils prone to waterlogging. These effects result in greenhouse gas emission reductions over and above the carbon sequestered in the biochar because not only is $N_2O$ a potent greenhouse gas,[5] but using less fertilizer means less emissions from fertilizer production.

Commercially produced biochar would need to be sold for well over its fuel value and a 2 t/ha application is likely to cost more than $800/ha. It would be impossible to recoup this cost in one wheat harvest. However, statistical trials may prove significant yield increases over a number of years, thus eventually exceeding the cost of biochar application.

However, applications of a few tons of biochar per hectare are likely to be viable for high-yielding irrigated crops, which are worth thousands of dollars per hectare. Biochar banded at these rates next to seedlings of high value vegetable crops may provide immediate yield increases by improving water retention and controlling nutrient release close to the roots.

A more exciting possibility for dry land agriculture is production of slow release **prilled** N/P/K/S fertilizers incorporating biochar. Used in this way, lower amounts of biochar may improve crop yields while at the same time reducing the amount of fertilizer nutrients required, in which case it may be cost effective when used at low rates. As yet, there is insufficient research data available to prove the practicability and viability of its use in prilled fertilizer.

### The Issue of Nutrient Removal

Some have resisted the idea of growing biomass for pyrolysis or combustion, arguing that this would deplete the nutrients in the topsoil. Granted, if biomass is removed from a site—particularly the leaf, bark and branch portions (which have the highest nutrient concentrations)—the soil can become depleted.[4] The scenario proposed here of 10% of cropping land being converted to mallee belts will not have this result because, unlike in block plantation situations:

- Mallee belts are only about 10 m in width.

- The narrow belts are surrounded by fertilized crops or pastures.

- Biochar and ash by-products can be applied to the belts and surrounding land, replacing the nutrients removed.

## KEY POINTS FROM THIS CHAPTER

- A dedicated biomass industry, using large-scale pyrolysis technologies to produce electricity and biochar will be economically viable in Australia with the existing RET and proposed carbon price schemes.

- Biomass from indigenous mallee eucalypts is ideal for pyrolysis industries and can produce high quality biochar.

- Woody perennials, such as mallee, make agriculture more sustainable by remediating and preventing the spread of salinity and reducing soil erosion.

- Carbon sequestered in the roots, tubers, and soils under mallee belts is an additional potential income stream for farmers.

- Biomass power plants can provide base load renewable electricity to supplement solar and wind.

- Power generation in gas turbines powered by large-scale slow or medium pyrolysis is ideal for regional Australia because it uses far less water than steam cycle plants powered by biomass combustion.

- One ton of dry mallee biomass could produce 950 kWh of renewable electricity (2 months energy use for a typical Australian family home) while at the same time potentially sequestering about 0.5 t $CO_2$e through biochar application to soils and 0.6 t $CO_2$e in the roots, tubers and organic matter in soils under mallee belts.

- A dedicated, large-scale commercial woody biomass pyrolysis industry utilizing 10% of the wheat and wool regions has the potential to:

   1. Provide at least 4% of Australia's electricity.
   2. Avoid or remove about 3.6% of Australia's current $CO_2$ emissions, or 24% of agricultural emissions.
   3. Remediate soils by applying biochar.

- Government assistance is needed initially in setting up grower networks, annuity price schemes, and the first of 50 or more large-scale pyrolysis plants.

# REFERENCES

1.  Australian Government, Department of Climate Change, December 2008. "Design of the Renewable Energy Target (RET) Scheme – Release of Exposure Draft Legislation." Fact sheet.

2.  Australian Energy Market Operator (AEMO), 2009. "An Introduction to Australia's Electricity Market."

3.  Blackwell, P., S. Shea, et al. 2007. "Improving Wheat Production with Deep Banded Oil Mallee Charcoal in Western Australia." Agrichar Initiative Conference Terrigal New South Wales.

4.  CRC for Temperate Hardwood Forestry, IUFRO Hobart. "New Pulping Technology and Eucalyptus Wood – The Role of Soil Fertility, Soil Fertility and Wood Ion Content."

5.  CSIRO, 2009. Sohi, S., E. Lopez-Capel, E. Krull, and E. Boll. "Biochar, Climate Change and Soil: A Review to Guide Future Research." CSIRO Land and Water Science Report.

6.  Australian Government, Department of Climate Change, 2001. "National Carbon Accounting Toolbox."

7.  Australian Government, Department of Climate Change, 2008. "National Greenhouse Accounts (NGA) Factors."

8.  Dynamotive, 2010. Dynamotive CQuest BioChar, Information Booklet 2009. http://www.dynamotive.com/assets/resources/PIB-BioChar.pdf.

9.  Eckard, R. University of Melbourne, 2010. "A Decision Support Framework for Greenhouse Accounting on Australian Dairy, Sheep, Beef or Grain Farms."

10. Enecon Pty. Ltd., 2007. "Bioenergy in the Avon." SEDO Project No. P588. Study Report for Avongro.

11. IEA, 2007. "IEA Energy Technology Essentials," 2007. http://www.energytech.at/pdf/iea_ete03.pdf.

12. Gaunt, J. and J. Lehmann. 2007. "Energy Balance and Emissions Associated with Biochar Sequestration and Pyrolysis Bioenergy Production."

13. Huxtable, D. and J. Bartle (Department of Environment and Conservation). February 2007. "Predicting Mallee Biomass Yield in the Western Australian Wheatbelt."

14. Laird, D.A., "The Charcoal Vision: A Win-Win-Win Scenario for Simultaneously Producing Bioenergy, Permanently Sequestering Carbon, while Improving Soil and Water Quality."

15. New Collie Coal, 2010. www.newcolliecoal.com.au/.

16. Oil Mallee Association, 2008. "Oil Mallee Industry Development Plan."

17. Pacific Pyrolysis, 2010. http://pacpyro.com/agrichar.html.

18. RIRDC, 2008. "Carbon Trading and Renewable Energy: A Discussion Paper on Carbon Credits and Bioenergy Developments for Forestry and Agriculture."

19. Saddler, H., M. Diesendorf, and R. Denniss. 2004. "A Clean Energy Future for Australia."

20. Verve Energy website, 2010. http://www.verveenergy.com.au/.

21. Parliament of Australia, Parliamentary Library. "Australian Agricultural Emissions." http://www.aph.gov.au/Library/pubs/ClimateChange/whyClimate/human/howMuch/agriculture.htm.

22. WA Office of Energy, 2007. "A Renewable Energy Target for Western Australia."

23. Wildy, D., J. Pate, and J. Bartle. 2003. "Silviculture and Water Use of Short Rotation Mallee Eucalypts." A report for the RIRDC/Land & Water Australia.

24. Wisconsin Biorefining Development Initiative, 2010. www.wisbiorefine.org.

25. N.H. Langton and Ellington, H.I. "The Physics of Power Stations." *Physics Education,* 1975:10:6, 448-452.

26. Wu, H., Q. Fu, R. Giles, and J. Bartle. "Energy Balance of Mallee Biomass Production in Western Australia." Bioenergy Australia 2005 conference: Biomass for Energy, the Environment and Society.

# GLOSSARY

**absorb**. "To soak up or drink in," like a sponge. Used when one substance takes into its volume another substance or radiation (ex. absorbs light). Compare to the more specialized word **adsorb**.

**Acacia**. A genus of shrubs and trees belonging to the subfamily *Mimosoideae* of the family *Fabaceae*. The plants tend to be thorny and pod-bearing, with sap and leaves typically bearing large amounts of tannins. An important form of **mallee**.

**acetic acid**. A colorless, pungent, water-soluble liquid, chemical formula $CH_3COOH$; the essential ingredient of vinegar, and the source of its sour taste and pungent smell.

**acid sulfate soils**. Soils rendered acidic through containing large amounts of dissolved sulfur in the form of sulfates, which in the presence of water give rise to sulfuric acid.

**activated carbon**. A very adsorbent (see **adsorb**) form of carbon, used in purifying water and gases.

**adsorb**. "To stick," similar to "adhere." A material adsorbs water when water sticks to it. Biochar is adsorbent, and since its structure is cellular with a lot of surface area for water to stick to, it can hold a lot of water. Compare **absorb**, **desorb**, **adsorption**, and **adsorption capacity**.

**adsorption**. The process of attraction of atoms or molecules from an adjacent gas or liquid to an exposed solid surface. Many chemical reactions can go a lot faster when the reacting molecules are adsorbed.

**adsorption capacity**. The capacity of a material to store liquid, especially water. The capacity is proportional to the material's surface area. See **adsorb**.

**agri-char**. Another name for biochar, emphasizing its role in fertilizing crops.

**agroecosystem**. A conceptual model consisting of (1) land used for crops, pasture, and livestock; (2) adjacent uncultivated land that supports other vegetation and wildlife; and (3) associated atmosphere, underlying soils, groundwater, and drainage networks.

**agroforestry**. The application of agricultural aims and principles to the management of woodlands. Tree farming. Also, a system of land use in which harvestable trees are grown, as a crop, among traditional crops or on pastureland.

**aliphatic**. A class of carbon compounds in which the carbon atoms form open chains.

**anion**. A negatively-charged ion (attracted to a positive-charged anode).

**anthropogenic**. Man-made.

**Anthrosols**. Soils formed or heavily modified through long-term human activity, such as from irrigation or adding organic waste. *Terra preta* is an Anthrosol.

**aromatic**. A class of carbon compounds containing an unsaturated ring of carbon atoms, and usually having an agreeable odor. Aromatic molecules are generally very stable and able to form planes or "sheets." Biochar contains many of these, and this trait is at the core of biochar's durability.

ash. The portion of moisture-free biochar that is not **organic**.

**ASTM**. The American Society for Testing and Materials.

**autopyrolysis**. Combustion (burning) that is self-initiated or self-sustained without input of energy.

**bagasse**. The dry, dusty, fibrous pulp that remains after sugar cane is crushed and its juice extracted.

**beetle, mountain pine or bark**. Beetle of western North America whose larvae feed on the inner bark of conifer trees.

**BET**. Brunauer-Emmett-Teller, the three scientists who published the most commonly used measure of surface area; the BET method measures the adsorption (see **adsorb**) of nitrogen vapor in a partial vacuum at liquid nitrogen temperatures (minus 196°C).

**biodiesel**. Diesel fuel derived from plant materials (often soybeans), not from a fossil source.

**biofuels**. Fuels derived from renewable plant materials, not fossil sources; examples include grain and switchgrass ethanol and **biodiesel**.

**biomass**. Biological material derived from living, or recently living, plants.

**bio-oils**. Oils derived from plant materials, not from fossil sources.

**bokashi** (Japanese, "fermented organic matter"). Fermented wheat bran used to pickle kitchen waste, in order to hasten decomposition and reduce odors by preventing putrefaction.

**bokashi system**. A composting system that uses a mixture of microorganisms to inoculate compost and hasten decomposition.

**carbonize**. Conversion of an organic substance to a residue richer in carbon by heating, partial burning (that is by **pyrolysis**)

**carbon to nitrogen ratio (C:N)**. The ratio of carbon atoms to nitrogen atoms in a given material.

*Casuarina*. Genus of 17 species of evergreen shrubs and trees in the family Casuarinaceae; native to Australasia, southeastern Asia, and islands of the western Pacific Ocean. An important **mallee** genus.

**cation**. A positively charged ion (attracted to a cathode or negative pole)

**Cation Exchange Capacity (CEC)**. A measure of a material's capacity to retain positive ions, such as ammonium and potassium, in an exchangeable form that is available to plants.

**cellulose**. An inert carbohydrate, the chief constituent of plant cell walls.

**Chernozems**. (Ukrainian, "black soil"). A type of very fertile, naturally occurring soil that contains high percentages of humus, phosphoric acids, phosphorous, and ammonia and produces a high agricultural yield.

**cogeneration**. Simultaneous generation of two or more forms of usable energy, such as electricity and heat.

**communities-mentoring-communities (CMC) program**. A development program whose governing principle is that communities learn a practice from another community that has successful adopted the practice.

**compost tea**. A nutrient-containing liquid made by steeping compost in water. Used as fertilizer and to help prevent plant diseases.

**collier**. A miner or seller of coal. Also a maker of charcoal.

**coppice**. The ability to grow rapidly from burned or cut stumps. As a verb, the practice of **coppicing**.

**coppicing**. Forest management practice in which trees are harvested without removing the stumps, so that the cut trees re-grow, enabling further wood harvests from the same stump.

**$CO_2e$. Equivalent of carbon dioxide** ($CO_2$). To compare the expected greenhouse effect of a given gas with carbon dioxide, its greenhouse potential may be expressed in $CO_2$ equivalents.

**db**. Abbreviation of **dry basis**.

**desorb**. To release a substance that has previously soaked into or stuck to a material. Opposite of **absorb** and **adsorb**.

**dry basis**. The dry-basis moisture content of a material expresses the ratio of the moisture mass present in the material to the mass of the dry matter. A standardized dry basis is determined by weighing a volume of the material after heating to some standard temperature high enough and for long enough to drive most moisture off the material (see also **wet basis**).

**dunder**. The yeast-rich foam leftovers from one batch of rum that is used to start the yeast culture of a second batch. Also, the lees from boiled sugarcane juice, used in the distillation of rum.

**ecosystem**. A community consisting of all organisms living in that particular area and the nonliving, physical components of the environment the organisms interact with, such as air, soil, water, and sunlight.

**ecotone**. A transition area between two adjacent but different plant communities, such as forest and grassland. Coined from a combination of eco(logy) plus -tone, from the Greek *tonos* or tension—in other words, a place where ecologies are in tension.

**endothermic**. Heat-absorbing. Refers to processes or reactions that consume more energy than they release.

**exothermic**. Heat-releasing. Refers to processes or reactions that release more energy than they consume.

**eutrophication**. The natural or artificial addition of nutrients to bodies of water and the effects of the added nutrient, which can include dense growth and decay of aquatic plant life, resulting in increased demand for oxygen, contributing to death of other organisms.

**fast pyrolysis**. A process in which organic materials are very rapidly heated (in a few seconds) to 450–600°C in absence of air. Under these conditions, the organic vapors produced have too little time to condense in the solid char also produced, and are emitted. The vapors are condensed externally into pyrolysis oil. Typically, 50–75% of the feedstock weight is converted into pyrolysis oil. See **pyrolysis, slow pyrolysis**.

**feedstock/feedstock material**. Raw material. In the case of biochar, the raw material for producing biochar is some form of **biomass**.

**fermentation**. Conversion of sugar to alcohol brought about by enzymes secreted by certain yeasts, molds, and bacteria. The basis of many commercial fermentation offerings such as the **bokashi system**.

**forage rape** (*Brassica napus*). A quick-growing short-season, leafy member of the *Brassicaceae* (mustard or cabbage) family. It is tolerant of cold, drought and heat, and is used to feed grazing deer and livestock.

**gasify, gasifier**. To convert a material into gas is to gasify. Any apparatus designed to gasify is a gasifier.

**gasification**. See **gasify**.

**global warming**. Sustained increase in average temperature of the earth. Popular alternative to term "climate change."

**graphene**. Graphite's major structural element, it is an isolated sheet of joined, hexagonal, carbon rings. Graphite consists of many graphene sheets stacked together.

**graphite**. One of the forms of elemental carbon; used for pencil leads.

**graphitic**. All substances that consist of carbon in its form as graphite.

**green cane harvesting (GCH)**. The practice of harvesting sugar cane without previously burning the crop (to remove its foliage).

**greenhouse effect**. The capacity of certain atmospheric gases to trap heat, after the manner of a greenhouse.

**greenhouse gas (GHG)**. A gas believed to contribute to the **greenhouse effect**.

**greenwaste**. Biodegradable waste.

**heat treatment temperature (HTT)**. The highest temperature that a biomass experiences while being modified by heat. HTT dictates char properties.

**hectare (ha)**. A unit of surface area equal to 10,000 square meters. One hectare equals 2.471 acres.

**hemicellulose**. Any of a group of gummy polysaccharides intermediate in complexity between sugar and **cellulose**.

**humose**. The usually dark brown or black fraction of soil organic matter that forms as a result biological decomposition of organic material.

**hydrophilic**. "Water-loving." Describes any material that dissolves easily in water. An example is alcohol.

**hydrophobic**. "Water-fearing." Having little or no ability to mix with water or water-soluble liquids; the most well-known example is oil.

**hygroscopic**. Having the ability readily to attract and hold moisture from the environment, by absorption or adsorption. Most biochars are hygroscopic. See **absorb** and **adsorb**.

**hypha** (plural, **hyphae**). The thread-like processes of a fungal mycelium, through which a fungus absorbs nutrients. In layman's terms, tiny fungus roots.

**infective**. Able to cause infections; able to spread disease.

**inoculation**. In the context of biochar applications, the addition of living organisms and nutrients to biochar in order to generate a conditioned biochar, which will get a better response from the crop.

**inorganic**. Not derived from living organisms; in chemistry, not composed of hydrocarbons.

**intercalated**. In chemistry, the reversible inclusion of a molecule (or group) between two other molecules (or groups). Examples include DNA intercalations and "graphite intercalation compounds" where molecules are inserted between graphite layers.

**ironmonger**. Originally, referred to a person who made tools from iron, as well as the place where his wares were sold. The term is still widely used in the UK, and is the US equivalent of a hardware store.

**joule**. A unit of energy equal to the work done when a current of 1 ampere passes through a resistance of 1 ohm for 1 second. In laymen's terms, 1 joule is the energy required to lift a small apple one meter against the Earth's gravity.

**Kyoto requirements**. The restrictions on carbon emissions and carbon sequestration targets set in the Kyoto accords.

**labile**. Unstable.

**labile matter**. See **mobile matter**.

**leach**. To remove soluble constituents from soil, char, or other material with water.

**leachable**. Susceptible to being leached.

**lignin**. An **organic** substance that, with **cellulose**, forms the chief part of wood.

**lignocellulosic**. Comprised of **lignin** and **cellulose**, the two primary substances that make up wood.

**lodgepole pine**. Conifer of western North America. Lodgepole pine is the common name for *Pinus contorta*.

**mallee**. Scrubland vegetation found in southern Australia, composed primarily of woody shrubs and trees of the genus *Eucalyptus*; more broadly, any short tree with a large underground stem fused with the main root, called a lignotuber.

**methanol**. Colorless, toxic, flammable alcohol, formula $CH_3OH$; also known as wood alcohol.

**microbes**. Microorganisms, especially bacteria.

**micro-gasification**. This simply denotes gasification on a small, but not microscopic, scale. See **gasify**.

**mineralization**. The process that converts an organic substance into an inorganic substance.

**mobile matter**. The organic portion of biochar that disperses into the soil and becomes food for soil microbes. Sometimes called "**labile matter**."

**moisture**. Wetness. The water content of biochar.

**mountain pine beetle**. *Dendroctonus ponderosae*, is native to the forests of western North America. Outbreaks of the insect, also called the bark beetle, the Rocky Mountain pine beetle, or the Black Hills beetle, can result in losses of millions of trees.

**mycorrhiza**. A symbiotic association of a fungus with the roots of certain plants, in which the **hyphae** form a woven mass around the plants roots or penetrate the cells of the roots; the colonization of fungus on or in plant roots. See **hypha**.

**N₂O**. Nitrous oxide (laughing gas). A greenhouse gas with global warming potential about 300 times carbon dioxide, and a long residence time in the atmosphere of 150 years. Agriculture is the main contributor to increasing N₂O in the atmosphere through widespread use of nitrogen-based fertilizers.

**NGO**. Non-governmental organization. A voluntary association, pursuing a particular cause or interest, which is not created by a government, but may work cooperatively with government.

**oil mallee**. **Mallee** grown as a crop, for its oil.

**open burn**. Burning that is open to the air—an ordinary fire.

**organic**. Derived from living organisms; in chemistry, composed of hydrocarbons.

**PAHs**. See **polycyclic aromatic hydrocarbons**.

**pathogen**. A disease-producing agent, especially a virus or bacterium or other microorganism.

**pathogenic**. Disease-causing.

**photovoltaic (PV)**. Converting solar energy to electric energy.

**pH**. Potential hydrogen. A measure of the concentration of hydrogen in a solution, which is a standard measurement of acidity or alkalinity (basicity). The pH scale runs from 0 to 14, with lower numbers indicating increasing acidity and higher numbers indicating increasing alkalinity. The neutral pH, that of distilled water, is 7. Plants are very sensitive to soil pH.

**pit burn**. A method of charcoal production in which biomass is set alight in a pit, then covered with dirt to smolder into char.

**Plaggen**. A type of soil created in the Middle Ages in northern Europe as a result of intentional "plaggen cultivation." **Turves** of peat were collected from areas with low agricultural productivity and used as cattle bedding. The bedding material, together with manure, was later applied to agricultural fields, creating rich top-soils on top of sandy soils. Like *terra preta* soils, Plaggen have thick man-made surface horizons.

**polycyclic aromatic hydrocarbons**. Hydrocarbon compounds that consist of linked **aromatic** rings. They are a by-product of fuel (fossil or biomass) combustion, but also occur naturally and are linked to numerous ill health effects.

**prill**. To aggregate material from a molten state into small spheres, granules or pellets. Solid fertilizers are commonly manufactured and applied as prills.

**proximate analysis**. Test used to gauge the heating value of coal. The test measures moisture content, volatile content, fixed and free carbon remaining after heating, and ash (mineral) content. An adaptation of the same test can be used to assess biochar.

**putrefaction**. Decomposition of **organic** matter by bacteria and fungi, resulting in strongly odorous products; rotting. Putrefaction provides nutrients for plants, but also creates a **pathogenic** condition within the soil.

**pyroligneous**. Produced by the distillation of wood.

**pyroligneous acids**. Also referred to as **smoke water** or **wood vinegar**. A by-product of producing biochar through pyrolysis, made by condensing smoke emitted by kilns. Long used in China and Japan as a bio-pesticide and to increase seed germination rates.

**pyrolysis**. Use of heat to break down complex chemical substances into simpler substances.

**pyrophoric**. Prone to self-heating and combustion—spontaneous combustion.

**recalcitrant**. Term applied to organic matter or nutrients that are stable and not subject to release into soluble form. Strong resistance against mineralization. See **resident matter**.

**reductant**. Reducing agent, a substance that brings about reduction in another substance, being itself oxidized. The class of reactions known as oxidation is familiar to most people; examples include fire and rust. Reduction may be conceptualized as the chemical opposite of oxidation. Among its older and easier to grasp definitions is that reduction is the loss of oxygen or the gain of hydrogen. Modern chemists, however, define reduction more precisely.

**refractory**. Heat-resistant; used especially to describe materials that have the ability to retain their shape and chemical identity when subjected to high temperatures and that are used for lining furnaces.

**resident matter**. The **organic** portion of biochar that remains stable in the soil for a very long time. Also known as **recalcitrant** matter.

**residence time**. The average amount of time that a representative particle spends within a particular space or system. Residence time is a function of the speed with which material is fed into the system and speed at which the system processes material. Any given particle may exit the system faster or slower than average, but the overall average is the residence time for that system.

**retort**. A closed vessel with an outlet tube used for distilling, separating, or decomposing substances that are placed inside and subjected to heat.

**rhizome**. A root-like, horizontal stem, commonly horizontal in position, which usually sends shoots upward and roots downward along its length. Also called creeping rootstalks, or rootstocks.

**rhizosphere**. The few centimeters (sometimes meters) of soil that immediately surround the plant roots and are affected by chemical secretions from them.

**rick**. A stack or pile, usually of wood or straw. In the southern United States, a unit of firewood (half a cord, or a cube measuring 4 feet on a side).

**sesquiterpenes**. A common group of plant poisons found naturally in plants and insects, and act as defensive agents.

**slow pyrolysis**. Characterized by gradual heating, which produces a purer and more uniform char product than **fast pyrolysis**. See also **pyrolysis**.

**silviculture**. The cultivation and management of woodlands.

**smoke water**. Also known as **wood vinegar**. See **pyroligneous** acids.

**sustainable.** Maintainable. Among environmentalists, describes any activity depending only on non-exhaustible or naturally renewable resources.

**syngas.** Abbreviation for "synthesis gas;" loosely, any artificially created gas that contains mostly hydrogen and carbon monoxide.

***terra preta de Indio*** (Portuguese, "black earth of the Indian"). Fertile, black, biochar-rich soil found in scattered tracts throughout the Amazon basin; also, the pre-Columbian civilization responsible for creating that soil.

**thermo-gravimetric analyzer (TGA).** Custom-built, modified apparatus used for chemical analysis of a material. Only ten such machines exist in the world.

**thinly distributed.** Describing crop residue, manure, or other **biomass**, indicates that the volume of biomass is not concentrated in any single place.

**TLUD ("TEE-lud"), top-lit updraft.** A gasifier stove in which the fuel burns from the top down in a self-sustained burn, while air flows through from the bottom up. Efficiently produces biochar.

**top-lit updraft.** This denotes the combination of two **pyrolysis** technologies: The fire of pyrolysis is lit at the top of the fuel column and burns downward. The fire is fed by an updraft of air, moved by the heat of pyrolysis, through the fuel column.

**torrefied, torrified.** Scorched, charred, **carbonized**.

**torrefy, torrify.** To subject to fire or intense heat; roast or scorch.

**total dissolved solids (TDS).** A measure of the combined content of all substances contained in water apart from the water itself; what remains of a water sample after all $H_2O$ has evaporated or been distilled away. An indicator of water quality.

**transpire.** To emit or give off gases, or water vapor, through the surface, as for example leaves give off water vapor and oxygen.

**trench burn.** See **pit burn**.

**vermicomposting.** Composting using worms. Vermicelli is pasta that looks like worms.

**vinasse.** The residue left in a still after distillation. In the sugar industry, the residue left after molasses is fermented.

**wb.** Abbreviation of **wet basis**.

**wet basis.** The wet basis is simply the mass of the material before drying. The wet-basis moisture content expresses the ratio of the moisture mass present in the material to the mass of the wet matter. The moisture content is the difference between wet basis and the mass of the dried material (see also **dry basis**).

**wood vinegar.** Also known as **smoke water**. See **pyroligneous acids**.

# DEDICATION

Portrait: Martyn Fox

I went to the forest where your body fell.
There I saw the giant red gum,
felled one hundred years before you.
I stood before that ancestor of the forest you helped save.
I cut a piece from that decaying elder of your forest.
I made it into biochar - that charcoal you made
that gives fertiliser or fuel and captures carbon from our atmosphere.
I have drawn you using your favoured material – Biochar.
Made from willow, bamboo and the red gum near where you lay.
Your ashes have been returned near that gum.
May you rest in peace, two sleeping beings of the forest.

With love,
Martyn Fox

# GEOFF MOXHAM
## 1950-2009

On Thursday, 27th August 2009, Geoff was tragically killed in a freak accident in the forest on his community at Terania Creek, Australia. While cutting pole trees for the new kiln roof rafters, some vines that were entangled in a nearby tree behind him pulled down the top of that tree which fell where he was standing.

Biochar is a funny combination of science and nature but this was also a description of Geoff as well - his passion for magic, alchemy and the deep mysteries of science; his now ironic love for the forest and trees, nature and the planet; his delicate Buddhist awareness to 'the benefit all sentient beings', that ranged from his family, community, and alternative culture, even through to compassion for the inherently destructive nature of the business world that so disgusted him.

Even on a micro level: Geoff wrote to me once and listed the multiplicity of beings that live in just one square metre of topsoil: "10 trillion bacteria, 10 billion protozoa, 5 million nematodes, 100,000 mites, 50,000 springtails, 10,000 creatures called rotifers and tardigrades, 5,000 insects and arachnids, 3,000 worms and 100 snails and slugs". As you can see on one of his videos on BodgersHovel.com he describes the addition of Biochar to the soil as providing "5-star high-rise apartment living conditions" for the whole range of biota to live in.

When he first approached me to create BodgerHovel.com I had no idea what Biochar was and could see no real point to creating a 'pyrolysis kiln' nor could I see what was so special about a pyrolysed charcoal fan-forced stove. Of course when I videoed him doing his 'pyrolysis drum' demonstrations and saw how a 'charcoal stove' could be used to super-heat metal enough for welding, I finally got it. It was good for 'carbon-neutral' coffee as well! The sequestering of carbon into Biochar along with soil improvement were the perfect icing on the cake.

'Bodgers' were nomadic woodworkers who travelled from village to village building household items from local timbers and received food and board in return. This concept fascinated Geoff and he also loved the idea that stemmed from that about 'bodgey' being something 'knocked up' or 'half done' because that is just how charcoal should be pyrolysed - half done. Geoff took that 'bodger' idea a step further into the 'barefoot doctor' concept - where a nomadic doctor roams villages (in China) offering to heal with Chinese medicines in return for food and shelter. He wanted to merge that concept with the Bodger idea and Biochar. He envisaged 'nomadic Biochar practitioners' working their way around initiating landholders into the benefits of pyrolysis, biochar for the soil and sequestering carbon: www. BarefootBioChar.com.

Passion for one's principles is such an admirable trait and Geoff was always an Eco-warrior right from the start, now fallen in battle - anti-apartheid, anti-Vietnam, saving Terania forest-action and more. He wanted to save the planet, create his perfect 'seed-world' and propagate that to all who may listen. He happily enjoyed the fruits of his life's labour, but left us too soon, in the end.

Jay

# CONTRIBUTING EDITORS

### Paul Taylor PhD:

With an enduring interest in environmental issues and solutions Paul has intensely researched biochar, global warming and climate since 2006. He developed presentations on these subjects, which have been lauded for not just raising the problems but bringing solutions. Paul gradated with the University medal in physics from University of NSW, received a PhD from University of Colorado, and worked at Harvard Smithsonian Astrophysical Observatory and MIT.

### Gary Levi:

Gary has 25+ years of experience as a business/real estate lawyer, executive, and independent writer/consultant. His eclectic pursuits flow from an intellectual curiosity that often eludes neat categories. Gary has been interested in writing ever since he could hold a crayon. He's written and edited books and articles on myriad subjects for diverse constituents: from solar water heaters to IP-based call centers to investing in European real estate to health care…and now biochar. Gary can be contacted at getloc@comcast.net.

### John Lierman PhD, B.A. in Biology:

John earned his bachelor's degree in biology at Rice University, Houston, Texas, with an emphasis in estuarine biology and a Ph.D. in early Christianity from the University of Cambridge. Prior to this project he published a monograph of his own as well as numerous articles, and edited a collection of scholarly essays. He is now studying law at the University of Arizona, specializing in water and environmental law.

### Ron Taylor:

Ron had 30 years' experience in engineering design and manufacture, including motorcycle racing frames and motors, before moving into Brand Protection using DNA codes. He ran the "Most Counterfeit Free Games Ever" for the Sydney 2000 Olympics and his company currently protects all sporting codes in Australia and New Zealand. He also has a number of property interests and is involved in residential developments.

# CONTRIBUTING AUTHORS

**Paul Anderson PhD:** psanders@ilstu.edu

Paul S. Anderson, PhD, ("Dr. TLUD" (Tee-lud)) heads the international and improved cookstove activities of Chip Energy Inc, supporting NGOs and agencies interested in the advantages of micro-gasifiers and biochar. He is a retired university professor working on Top-Lit UpDraft (TLUD) pyrolytic gasifiers since 2001. His current interests are biochar production systems under US$50,000, and cooking and heating devices for residential and small business in developing countries.

**Albert Bates:** biochar@thefarm.org

Albert Bates is author of *The Biochar Solution (2010), The Post Petroleum Survival Guide (2006)* and *Climate in Crisis (1990)*. A former environmental rights lawyer, paramedic, brick mason, flour miller, and horse farmer, he co-founded the Global Ecovillage Network and the Ecovillage Network of the Americas.

**Karl Frogner PhD:** pattamo_kop@yahoo.com

Karl Frogner is President & Project Development Head, UB International; Member, Advisory Committee, International Biochar Initiative; Project Development Head, Mongolian Biochar Initiative; and Project Development Consultant, Thai Biochar Initiative. His dissertation in Population Biology at the University of Chicago dealt with population regulation through resource competition's effect on time to first reproduction.

**Peter Hirst:** peter@keziahsforge.com

Master Collier and Principal at New England *Biochar*. Barnstable/Yarmouth, Massachusetts.

Master Smith at Keziah's Forge.

**Stephen Joseph PhD:** joey.stephen@gmail.com

Stephen is vice chairman of the IBI and co-editor with Dr Johannes Lehmann of the first major publication on biochar. He is a visiting professor at the University of NSW, director of a number of companies involved in bioenergy and biosequestration, and Chairman of Anthroterra Pty Ltd a company set up to develop the next generation of organic biochar based fertilizers. He holds a B.Sc. in Engineering and a Ph.D. in Architecture and Applied Anthropology and is a Fellow of the Australian Institute of Energy.

# CONTRIBUTING AUTHORS

## James Joyce BE Chem (Hons) MBA PhD:

james@bigchar.com.au

James has 2 decades of research and operational experience in sugarcane processing, bio-energy, alternative energy and coal production. He is the principle of JA Process Engineering, Director of Black is Green P/L and of KLIM Australia (a process equipment manufacturer and technology developer linked to KLIM of China.

## Jonah Levin: Jonah@biocharengineering.com

Jonah Levine is the Vice President of Technical Sales for Biochar Engineering Corporation and a coordinating co-founder of the United States Biochar Initiative. Jonah holds degrees in Applied Ecology (B.S.) and Utility Engineering (M.S.). Jonah's interest in biochar stems from a background in ecology and engineering bringing biological solutions into an engineered human existence.

## Julie Major PhD: Julie@biochar-international.org

Julie is the Agricultural Extension director for the International Biochar Initiative. Julie studied weed dynamics on Terra Preta de Indio soils of the Brazilian Amazon for her M.S. degree, sparking her interest in biochar as a soil amendment. Her Ph.D. from Cornell University studied the effect of biochar on soil fertility and its fate after soil application.

## Jim Mason: Jim@alpowerlabs.com

Jim Mason is a General Specialist working at the intersection of engineering, anthropology, information science. He is a graduate of Stanford University, with degrees in Anthropology and Philosophy, after a long tour of Mechanical Engineering. Jim is the Founder of ALL Power Labs, an incubator for open source energy experiments and distributed manufacturing solutions. Current projects include: the BEK (Biochar Experimenters Kit) and the GEK (Gasifier Experimenters Kit).

## Hugh McLaughlin, PhD, PE:

hmclaughlin@alternabiocarbon.com

Hugh is a Director of Biocarbon Research at Alterna Biocarbon, has performed fundamental research on char and activated carbon production and properties for decades. Dr. McLaughlin is an expert in characterization of biochar and understanding the relationship between starting biomass characteristics and carbonization conditions on resulting biochar properties.

# CONTRIBUTING AUTHORS

**Daniel Mulqueen:** Daniel@biocharengineering.com

Daniel is the Vice President of Research Engineering for Biochar Engineering Corporation. He holds a B.S. with honors in Engineering Physics focusing in nanoscale surface engineering. He was mentored by Dr. Tom Reed where he learned the fundamentals of biomass thermal conversion. Daniel has designed, built and operated numerous machines producing tens of thousands of pounds of char.

**Robert Quirk:** rgquirk@bigpond.com

Robert is a Farmer and agricultural scientist. He has been growing sugar cane in northern New South Wales, Australia for 50 years. Robert's involvement in scientific research started about 17 years ago and has been published widely on sustainable farming, including acid sulfate soils and biochar. He was the inaugural chair, and is a member of the board of the Better Sugar Initiative.

**Ben Rose:** BSc (Env) Dip. Ed: biroses@westnet.com.au

Ben has worked 14 years in natural resource management for the Department of Agriculture and Food WA, 3 years as a secondary science teacher and several years in agricultural technical work. The past 5 years he has consulted to Carbon Neutral estimating the growth and C sequestration of native tree species, conducted energy & emissions audits for mining and housing companies, conducted land management workshops and developed a carbon calculator and website.

**Karen Siepen:** Website: www.rcra.com.au

Karen is the director of Renewable Carbon Resources Australia, a dedicated manufacturer of biochar for the past 6 years. Karen brings hands on experience and valuable knowledge to provide biochar to the public and speaks regularly at associations and trade/garden shows. Most recently she has combined efforts with Black is Green Pty Ltd to bring the mobile BiGchar unit to the marketplace for commercial biomass conversion to biochar.

**Christoph Steiner, PhD:** christoph.steiner@biochar.org

Christoph works on biochar project development and consults for governmental and non-governmental organizations. From 2001 to 2006 he coordinated a project on nutrient and carbon management in the central Amazon for the German Federal Ministry of Education and Research, University of Bayreuth and the Austrian Academy of Science. He worked on recreation of Terra Preta soil, focusing on use of biochar as soil amendment.

## CONTRIBUTING AUTHORS

**Paul Taylor PhD:** potaylor@bigpond.com

With an enduring interest in environmental issues and solutions Paul has intensely researched biochar, global warming and climate since 2006. He developed presentations on these subjects, which have been lauded for not just raising the problems but bringing solutions. Paul gradated with the University medal in physics from University of NSW, received a PhD from University of Colorado, and worked at Harvard Smithsonian Astrophysical Observatory and MIT.

**Bob Wells:** robertorson@aol.com

Bob has a background in mechanical technology, conventional and organic farming, business and sales management. He has owned and operated businesses in electronics, metalworking, marine sales and service, commercial fishing, and organic farming. His latest venture, New England Biochar, with business partner Peter Hirst, is promising to bring all this experience to bear on the challenge of providing biochar and biochar technology.

**Kelpie Wilson:** Kelpie@biochar-international.org

Kelpie is a writer, and communications editor for IBI. Prior to that she was environmental editor and columnist for Truthout.org. In the 1990s, she was executive director of the Siskiyou Regional Education Project. After her B.S. in mechanical engineering, she worked for a small R&D firm designing Stirling cycle engines

## RESOURCE ACCESS

# RESOURCES: COMPANIES & ORGANIZATIONS

| Energy Pellet | Bioenergy | Biochar | Absorbent Biocarbon |

**Alterna Biocarbon** is a biocarbon manufacturer, and Alterna Biocarbon builds, owns and operates biocarbon facilities.

Our head office is in Prince George, BC. The leading-edge carbonization technology for transforming biomass and other organic waste into biocarbon was developed in South Africa, earlier this decade. The state-of-the-art technology was purchased by Alterna Biocarbon in 2005. The company subsequently built a small industrial facility in South Africa.

Alterna Biocarbon's "Van Aardt process" is a platform technology that transforms biomass feedstock into a variety of carbon-based energy products; this is a pyrolysis-based system using Alterna's patent-pending thermochemical biorefining design. The fundamental aspect of the technology is carbonization.

Alterna Biocarbon's Van Aardt process is the leading biocarbon technology. The technology has unmatched process economics and efficiencies, exemplified by high product yields, with very little external input energy, and a short cycle time.

The exceptional features of the technology are:

- Efficient conversion of biomass into high energy density product
- "Clean" (not overly complicated) design reducing capital and maintenance costs, and improving reliability
- Low energy input
- Very low fossil fuel footprint
- Low operating costs
- Variable biomass type input flexibility
- Variable biomass quality input flexibility
- Modular design flexibility to match plant capacity to biomass availability

Contact Us: P: 1-250-649-2460  E: info@alternaenergy.ca  W: www.alternabiocarbon.com

# CHIP ENERGY
## CLEAN RENEWABLE FUEL
401 W. Martin Dr.   PO BOX 85
GOODFIELD, IL 61742
PH 309-965-2005  Fax 309-965-2905

**www.chipenergy.com**

Chip Energy Inc is a biomass energy company dealing with all the issues: biomass collection, processing, storage, fuels handling, gasifiers for conversion to heat, biochar production, and heat transfer into buildings and other applications.

Chip Energy developed a virtually smokeless boiler that uses diverse biomass fuels in chip or pellet form, combining a small footprint micro-gasifier with a flash boiler to create an efficient, easy to operate heating system, which produces high quality Biochar as a by-product.

The Chip Energy Biomass Furnace has been tested for computer control logic, safety, fuel feed compatibility, char removal consistency, and low emissions. In 24 hours of continual automatic operation 500 pounds of wood chips or pellets are converted into nearly 100 pounds of biochar while supplying 180,000 Btu/hr (60 kWthermal). Built and shipped in a 20 ft container, for turnkey operation.

A basic unit for Developing Countries is shipped in a 10 ft container or on a 4 x 8 ft steel platform, ready for connection and operation.

Chip Energy considers requests to handle special fuels such as fruit pits or husks (rice, coffee, etc.) and special applications or adaptations to existing heat-using installations, such as cacao drying.

Multiple units deliver correspondingly greater amounts of biochar and heat or combustible gases, controlled by one PLC. Biochar characteristics can be significantly controlled by the user via the PLC with digital display and touch-screen settings.

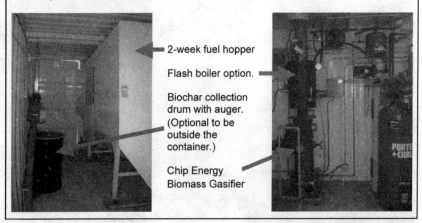

2-week fuel hopper

Flash boiler option.

Biochar collection drum with auger. (Optional to be outside the container.)

Chip Energy Biomass Gasifier

**Biochar Engineering Corporation (BEC)** is based in Golden Colorado. We design and build biochar production equipment; sell and broker biochar; and offer research, networking, and consulting services. Our biochar production equipment processes waste biomass, such as agricultural or forestry residue, to produce biochar. BEC is currently producing first-generation field-scale beta units for research in agricultural soil fertility, mine tailings reclamation and forest management. BEC technology mimics nature's intelligence, creating valuable co-products including biochar and process heat. Future developments will include modules to produce electricity or liquid fuels.

We are constantly scaling-up and broadening our abilities, so please continue to see our progress online at www.biocharengineering.com, or visit us in person in Golden, Colorado.

*Jonah Levine, VP Technical Sales, Biochar Engineering Corp 303.621.5491*

**Biocharproject.org** is a living evolving resource with the sole purpose of enlightening people to the exciting future of biochar and its beneficial environmental potential. It is one family's journey to discover themselves and the beautiful land they were born in with the soul intention of sharing this wonderful discovery that is biochar. Their passion for this ancient technology will see them gain many new friends who all have the common good of the planet as a special bond with each other as we teach learn and do many new things.

Charmaster Dolph Cooke
Author of
www.biocharproject.org

This journey is about living and as a reader of the website you will learn so many things about biochar, Man and nature. You will feel excited and will want to be part of the action. I implore you to look us up now and become part of our journey, send us your questions and answers and help us help the world with Biochar.

# NOTES